Progress
in
Mathematics

1 GENERAL

GW00320191

Les Murray BA

Senior Teacher and Head of Mathematics, Garstang County High School

Stanley Thornes (Publishers) Ltd

First published in 1984 by Stanley Thornes (Publishers) Ltd, Educa House, Old Station Drive, Leckhampton, Cheltenham GL53 0DN, UK

Reprinted 1985

British Library Cataloguing in Publication Data

Murray, L.
  Progress in mathematics.
  Book 1 G
  1. Mathematics–1961
  I. Title
  510 QA37.2

  ISBN 0-85950-171-X

Acknowledgements

Hodder & Stoughton, for the excerpt from *Campanus Euclid* on p. 279, as reproduced from *The Story of Mathematics*.

Ronald Sheridan's Photo-Library for the photograph of the Cheops Pyramid on p. 300.

To PJB

Typeset by Grafikon Ltd, Oostkamp, Belgium.
Printed and bound in Great Britain at The Bath Press, Avon

Preface

This book is versatile, so pupils are not expected to work through it from cover to cover.

Although the order of contents is a suitable one to follow, the discretion of the teacher will determine the order of work and whether or not one chapter should be completed before another is attempted. The starting point for a pupil or class will not necessarily be at the beginning of a chapter. Numerous carefully graded questions have been provided to allow plenty of freedom — again the teacher must be selective. Few worked examples are given, thus allowing for alternative methods of introducing topics.

The material has been carefully planned to allow for the use of a calculator, but total dependence on calculator use is not encouraged.

Exercises where photocopy masters are available to the teacher are marked **M**

I hope this brief description will give some understanding of my primary aim, which is to provide a comprehensive and enjoyable graded mathematics scheme.

The completion of these books has been dependent on the valued help and advice given to me by many people, in particular Mrs Alice Dickson of Garstang High School, Mr Roger Wilson, Head of Mathematics at Parklands High School, Chorley, and Mr J. Britton, Head of Mathematics at Copthall School, London. My thanks also go to staff and pupils of Garstang High School, for their interest and co-operation while writing has been in progress; to the Department of Egyptology at the British Museum, for the invaluable information provided; to Mr M. J. Stewart of the Royal Lancaster Hospital; to Mr P. Larsson of the Department of Environmental Sciences, University of Lancaster; and in particular to Mr Martin Beadle of the Meteorological Centre and Field Station, University of Lancaster.

Les Murray
1984

Contents

sequences; dot patterns; rectangular numbers; square numbers; triangular numbers; number patterns; anagrams

1 Introducing Numbers

Copy these number names:

0 = zero	16 = sixteen
1 = one	17 = seventeen
2 = two	18 = eighteen
3 = three	19 = nineteen
4 = four	20 = twenty
5 = five	21 = twenty-one
6 = six	30 = thirty
7 = seven	40 = forty
8 = eight	50 = fifty
9 = nine	60 = sixty
10 = ten	70 = seventy
11 = eleven	80 = eighty
12 = twelve	90 = ninety
13 = thirteen	100 = one hundred
14 = fourteen	1000 = one thousand
15 = fifteen	1 000 000 = one million

Exercise 2

A Copy each of the following.
Write the correct digit in place of each box.

1. 539 = ? hundreds + ? tens + ? units

2. 846 = ? hundreds + ? tens + ? units

3. 2137 = ? thousands + ? hundreds + ? tens + ? units

4. 6208 = ? thousands + ? hundreds + ? tens + ? units

5. 7492 = ? thousands + ? hundreds + ? tens + ? units

B Copy each of these. Write each answer in figures in the normal way:

1. 4 hundreds + 5 tens + 6 units = ☐?

2. 7 hundreds + 2 tens + 9 units = ☐?

3. 8 thousands + 4 hundreds + 3 tens + 5 units = ☐?

4. 2 thousands + 0 hundreds + 7 tens + 8 units = ☐?

5. 5 thousands + 3 hundreds + 1 ten + 2 units = ☐?

C
1. 600 + 40 + 7
2. 200 + 90 + 3
3. 100 + 50 + 7
4. 7000 + 300 + 20 + 6
5. 9000 + 800 + 40 + 5
6. 6000 + 900 + 10 + 4
7. 400 + 2000 + 3 + 80
8. 30 + 8000 + 500 + 1
9. 2 + 90 + 700 + 4000
10. 2000 + 8 + 60 + 500

D *e.g.* 247 = 200 + 40 + 7

1. 829
2. 386
3. 2418
4. 72
5. 25
6. 563
7. 4637
8. 6594
9. 1328

E
1. four hundred + 80 + seven
2. eight + forty + 500
3. 70 + nine hundred + 3
4. nine + eight hundred
5. 5000 + seventy + 600 + two
6. three + twenty + 7000 + 400
7. four thousand + 9 + five hundred + thirty
8. ninety + 4 + 600 + eight thousand

Exercise 3

A Write, in words, the value of each underlined digit:

e.g. 624$\underline{7}$5 seventy

1. 4$\underline{5}$2
2. $\underline{5}$86
3. 29$\underline{7}$
4. $\underline{3}$09
5. $\underline{7}$2
6. $\underline{7}$28
7. 3$\underline{4}$91
8. 261$\underline{8}$
9. $\underline{5}$419
10. 3$\underline{6}$ 547
11. 18 9$\underline{4}$3
12. $\underline{2}$9 365
13. 41 89$\underline{3}$
14. $\underline{7}$0 024
15. 9$\underline{4}$ 316

B Copy these sentences, writing the given numbers in words:

1. Light from the Sun takes just over 8 minutes to reach the Earth.
2. Mercury takes 88 days to orbit the Sun.
3. Earth takes about 365 days to orbit the Sun.
4. Jupiter takes about 4333 days to orbit the Sun.
5. Pluto takes about 90 472 days to orbit the Sun.

C Write these numbers using figures:

1. four
2. forty-three
3. seventy-nine
4. nine hundred
5. six hundred and twelve
6. two thousand and eighty-four
7. one thousand, five hundred and six
8. three thousand, two hundred and fifty-seven
9. ninety-eight thousand, three hundred and fourteen
10. five million, one hundred and eighty-two thousand, seven hundred and thirty-six

D Write these numbers in words:

1. 2	**6.** 93	**11.** 3700	**16.** 32 501
2. 8	**7.** 500	**12.** 4250	**17.** 483 900
3. 14	**8.** 708	**13.** 6186	**18.** 3 400 000
4. 28	**9.** 960	**14.** 7023	**19.** 6 324 085
5. 49	**10.** 1000	**15.** 12 047	**20.** 74 506 000

Exercise 4

1. Write these numbers in order. Put the smallest first.

   (a) 19, 46, 21, 7, 13, 54, 83, 45
   (b) 321, 97, 208, 14, 512, 73, 400, 162
   (c) 246, 630, 1042, 999, 3255, 98, 257

2. Write these numbers in order. Put the largest first.

   (a) 41, 12, 84, 23, 62, 5, 14, 78
   (b) 76, 3, 185, 502, 90, 800, 19, 228
   (c) 651, 1023, 284, 5116, 78, 2917, 48, 590

3. Which is the smaller number:

(a) 9 or 4?	(e) 124 or 99?	(i) 5670 or 5607?
(b) 14 or 17?	(f) 307 or 703?	(j) 14 671 or 9883?
(c) 36 or 29?	(g) 761 or 679?	(k) 38 006 or 29 978?
(d) 48 or 71?	(h) 2085 or 2508?	(l) 52 069 or 51 996?

4. Which is the larger (or greater) number:

(a) 7 or 2?	(e) 419 or 287?	(i) 4630 or 4619?
(b) 15 or 12?	(f) 376 or 637?	(j) 12 086 or 12 102?
(c) 49 or 73?	(g) 904 or 789?	(k) 47 009 or 38 947?
(d) 68 or 42?	(h) 1937 or 1973?	(l) 84 028 or 84 208?

5. Which is the smallest number:

(a) 76, 43, 81, 28, 65, 30, or 51?

(b) 487, 308, 912, 77, 59, 107, 62, or 218?

(c) 1463, 3416, 2500, 1390, 7600, 2108, or 1802?

(d) 5984, 10 080, 9097, 31 400, 10 008, 5098, 9970, or 27 463?

(e) 17 547, 23 049, 23 409, 17 507, 17 570, 17 057, or 17 075?

6. Which is the largest number:

(a) 83, 47, 98, 18, 36, 65, 59, 92, or 79?

(b) 209, 316, 290, 93, 184, 361, 49, 306, or 360?

(c) 6300, 6030, 3600, 3060, 6003, 3006, 6295, or 6098?

(d) 4734, 1963, 4743, 4473, 4702, 4207, 4773, or 4737?

(e) 12 079, 12 097, 10 297, 10 972, 12 709, 12 790, 12 097, or 12 099?

Exercise 5

A Answer these:

1. Is 8 less than 5?	**6.** Is 518 greater than 476?
2. Is 14 less than 18?	**7.** Is 826 larger than 697?
3. Is 25 greater than 19?	**8.** Is 473 smaller than 288?
4. Is 92 less than 79?	**9.** Is 2406 greater than 3299?
5. Is 127 greater than 172?	**10.** Is 1768 less than 1902?

B Copy each sentence and fill in the missing word 'greater' or 'less'?

1. 6 is ? than 4.	**4.** 86 is ? than 68.
2. 23 is ? than 19.	**5.** 207 is ? than 199.
3. 78 is ? than 87.	**6.** 452 is ? than 504.

7. 760 is [?] than 706.   **9.** 3164 is [?] than 3416.

8. 893 is [?] than 938.   **10.** 7096 is [?] than 7609.

Note   < means 'is less than'

         > means 'is greater than'

C   Write these sentences using the correct sign < or > :

   1. 17 is less than 42   **4.** 709 is larger than 486

   2. 36 is greater than 25   **5.** 647 is bigger than 375

   3. 184 is smaller than 248   **6.** 2831 is less than 3109

D   Write using words instead of the sign < or > :

   1. $9 < 17$ **3.** $91 > 89$ **5.** $765 < 908$

   2. $52 > 36$ **4.** $117 < 263$ **6.** $6170 > 6071$

E   Copy these, but fill in the correct sign < or > :

   1.   7 [?] 5   **6.**   438 [?] 427   **11.**   9182 [?] 9028

   2.   26 [?] 42   **· 7.**   615 [?] 561   **12.**   14 607 [?] 14 076

   3.   71 [?] 54   **8.**   764 [?] 823   **13.**   40 266 [?] 42 006

   4.   98 [?] 69   **9.**   1209 [?] 1216   **14.**   71 084 [?] 70 841

   5. 217 [?] 208   **10.** 3006 [?] 3060   **15.** 98 999 [?] 99 899

Exercise 6

1. Using each of the digits 2, 5 and 9 once only in each number:

   (*a*) Write as many different 3-digit numbers as you can.

   (*b*) Which is the smallest of these 3-digit numbers?

2. Using each of the figures 0, 3, 7 once only in each number, write as many different 3-digit numbers as you can. (Your numbers must not begin with 0.)

3. Using each of the digits 2, 7 and 8 once only in each number, write, in order of size (smallest first), as many different 3-digit numbers as you can.

4. Write, in order of size, largest first, all the 2-digit numbers that can be formed using the digits 4, 6 and 9.

   A digit may only be used once in each number.

5

5. Write all possible numbers between 4000 and 7000 that can be formed using each of the digits 2, 4, 5 and 7 once only in each number.

6. Using any of the digits 3, 4, 6, 8 and 9 once only in each number, write:
   (*a*) the largest number that can be made,
   (*b*) the smallest 3-digit number that can be made,
   (*c*) the smallest 4-digit even number that can be made,
   (*d*) the smallest 3-digit even number that can be made,
   (*e*) the largest 3-digit odd number that can be made,
   (*f*) all the 2-digit even numbers that can be made (write them in order of size, largest first),
   (*g*) all the 3-digit odd numbers that can be made (give them in order of size, smallest first).

7. Use all eight figures 1, 2, 3, 4, 5, 6, 7, 8 to form two 4-digit numbers. Add these two 4-digit numbers together. What is the largest total that can be obtained by doing this?

2 Addition and Subtraction

Exercise 1

Copy and carry out these calculations:

1. 62
      + 27

3. 2073
      + 912

5. 123
        43
     + 211

7. 4004
       1651
     + 204

2. 362
      + 410

4. 5154
      + 2342

6. 361
        205
     + 332

8.   23
        2410
      + 125

9. 24 + 5

10. 37 + 20

11. 41 + 46

12. 402 + 82

13. 461 + 207

14. 5028 + 2621

15. 432 + 3247

16. 31 + 26 + 42

17. 114 + 51 + 213

18. 520 + 3147 + 231

19. 43 + 8214 + 632

20. 7003 + 430 + 1001 + 54

Exercise 2

Copy and carry out these calculations:

1. 45
      + 7

3. 68
      + 17

5. 35
      + 48

7. 516
      + 248

2. 32
      + 9

4. 49
      + 32

6. 62
      + 19

8. 763
      + 119

9.

$$\begin{array}{r} 476 \\ + 258 \\ \hline \end{array}$$

11.

$$\begin{array}{r} 84 \\ + 47 \\ \hline \end{array}$$

13.

$$\begin{array}{r} 5982 \\ + 2409 \\ \hline \end{array}$$

15.

$$\begin{array}{r} 418 \\ 327 \\ + 124 \\ \hline \end{array}$$

10.

$$\begin{array}{r} 397 \\ + 446 \\ \hline \end{array}$$

12.

$$\begin{array}{r} 372 \\ + 821 \\ \hline \end{array}$$

14.

$$\begin{array}{r} 3765 \\ + 2473 \\ \hline \end{array}$$

16.

$$\begin{array}{r} 347 \\ 259 \\ + 144 \\ \hline \end{array}$$

17. 284 + 165
18. 239 + 407
19. 146 + 82
20. 78 + 641
21. 628 + 175
22. 496 + 129
23. 5107 + 2658
24. 1482 + 3298
25. 47 + 263 + 105

26. 451 + 84 + 296
27. 2076 + 49 + 763
28. 74 + 2961 + 548
29. 648 + 32 + 99
30. 506 + 17 + 2315
31. 47 + 9306 + 284
32. 5231 + 446 + 323
33. 464 + 2929 + 76
34. 4102 + 749 + 3064

Exercise 3

A Copy and carry out these additions:

1.

$$\begin{array}{r} 6415 \\ 28 \\ + 207 \\ \hline \end{array}$$

3.

$$\begin{array}{r} 76 \\ 320 \\ + 5182 \\ \hline \end{array}$$

5.

$$\begin{array}{r} 706 \\ 1995 \\ + 513 \\ \hline \end{array}$$

7.

$$\begin{array}{r} 358 \\ 39 \\ 9 \\ + 3604 \\ \hline \end{array}$$

9.

$$\begin{array}{r} 81 \\ 8064 \\ 410 \\ + 26 \\ \hline \end{array}$$

2.

$$\begin{array}{r} 9 \\ 2436 \\ + 727 \\ \hline \end{array}$$

4.

$$\begin{array}{r} 694 \\ 52 \\ + 421 \\ \hline \end{array}$$

6.

$$\begin{array}{r} 45 \\ 8 \\ 713 \\ + 4087 \\ \hline \end{array}$$

8.

$$\begin{array}{r} 7250 \\ 581 \\ 43 \\ + 1162 \\ \hline \end{array}$$

10.

$$\begin{array}{r} 549 \\ 3215 \\ 91 \\ + 6124 \\ \hline \end{array}$$

B Set out these additions in columns before adding:

1. 52 + 7613 + 478
2. 407 + 3190 + 64
3. 2938 + 76 + 511
4. 202 + 9 + 9137
5. 5163 + 121 + 4265

6. 8362 + 156 + 70 + 317
7. 683 + 88 + 215 + 5840
8. 99 + 9184 + 17 + 472
9. 7306 + 1208 + 43 + 650
10. 6951 + 39 + 5 + 764

Exercise 4

A Add 10 to each of these numbers:

1. 53　　　2. 76　　　3. 548　　　4. 207　　　5. 3164

B Add 100 to each of these numbers:

1. 281　　　2. 607　　　3. 5826　　　4. 2384　　　5. 56

C Add 39 to each of these numbers:

1. 50　　　2. 240　　　3. 41　　　4. 76　　　5. 385

D Copy and complete these mapping diagrams:

1.

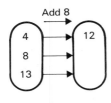

3.

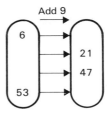

2.

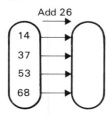

4.

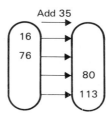

E Copy and complete:

e.g. 5, 9 $\xrightarrow{+}$ 14

1. 6, 8 $\xrightarrow{+}$ ⬚?   **3.** 41, 27 $\xrightarrow{+}$?   **5.** 59, 36 $\xrightarrow{+}$?

2. 23, 38 $\xrightarrow{+}$?   **4.** 52, 48 $\xrightarrow{+}$?   **6.** 84, 77 $\xrightarrow{+}$?

Exercise 5

A Copy these and fill in the missing numbers:

1. 14 + 25 = ?   **6.** 72 + 84 = ?

2. 36 + ? = 79   **7.** ? + 51 = 119

3. 48 + 32 = ?   **8.** 39 + ? = 138

4. ? + 29 = 91   **9.** 216 + 783 = ?

5. 54 + ? = 100   **10.** ? + 462 = 999

B Copy these and fill in the missing digits:

1.
```
   5 2
 + 2 ?
   ? 8
```
4.
```
   3 ? 6
 + ? 5 ?
   8 2 5
```
7.
```
   3 5 8
 + ? ? ?
   8 4 6
```
10.
```
   2 ? 9 7
 + 3 5 ? 9
   ? 0 8 ?
```

2.
```
   ? 6
 + 2 ?
   7 3
```
5.
```
   ? 2 9
 + 1 4 ?
   7 ? 6
```
8.
```
   ? ? ?
 + 4 5 9
   9 0 8
```
11.
```
   4 ? 4 0
 + ? 5 8 ?
   9 1 ? 7
```

3.
```
   3 4
 + ? ?
   8 2
```
6.
```
   6 5 ?
 + ? ? 7
   9 1 1
```
9.
```
   ? 5 ?
 + 4 4 8
   7 ? 6
```
12.
```
   2 6 8 9
 + ? ? ? ?
   9 0 8 5
```

10

Exercise 6 ▬▬▬▬▬▬▬▬▬▬▬▬▬▬ M

Copy and complete these addition squares:

1.

+	5	8	13	15	23
7					
9					
14					
19					
36					

4.

+	11		23	46	52	
					66	
18		35				
				74		
35						97
43						
						121

2.

+	12	29	16	47	35
27					
41					
64					
36					
59					

5.

+	65		32	26	
17		46			
74					
			73		
16				54	
		87			

3.

+	16		47	65
18		41		
34				
			99	
76				

6.

+	44	25		9		37	
32							114
58							
						85	
14							
79		100					
				61			
67				86			

Across

1. 39 plus 57.
3. 283 + 475.
6. The sum of 19 and 68.
8. Increase 98 by 32.
9. The total of 86, 218, and 235.
12. 42 added to 24.
13. Twenty-eight plus thirty-seven.
16. 29 more than 57.
17. 56 increased by 25.
19. Twenty-three plus 7-down.
21. 14 increased by 69.
22. This number is the same when read backwards.
23. 3-across added to 18-down.
25. 286 more than the sum of 367 and 325.
28. Four hundred and ninety-six plus one hundred and ninety.
30. The sum of the digits of 22-down.
32. 547 + 316.
34. 39 plus 54.
36. 3-across increased by 19.
38. 132 more than 33-down.
40. 352 + 409 + 186.
41. The sum of the digits of 3-across.
42. 590 more than 35-down.

Down

2. 26 more than 35.
3. 420 added to 296.
4. 44 + 9.
5. 454 added to 352.
6. 42 add 43.
7. Increase 59 by 14.
10. 351 + 167 + 428.
11. Seven more than nineteen.
14. 28 plus 24.
15. The total of 76 and 23.
16. Add together 47 and 36.
17. 18 more than 12-across.
18. 60 added to 15-down.
20. 16 plus 17 plus 36.
21. 632 add 246.
22. See 30-across.
24. 2-down reversed.
26. 108 + 216 + 463.
27. Equal to 16-across.
29. 23 + 23 + 23.
31. 377 increased by 97.
33. See 38-across.
35. The units digit is 7.
37. 32 + 64 is 19 more than this.
39. The sum of the digits of 736 426.

Exercise 8

Answer these. Look for quick methods.

1. (a) 6 + 2
   (b) 2 + 6

2. (a) 7 + 4
   (b) 4 + 7

3. (a) 8 + 0
   (b) 0 + 8

4. (a) 9 + 6
   (b) 6 + 9

5. (a) 12 + 5
   (b) 5 + 12

6. (a) 24 + 15
   (b) 15 + 24

7. (a) 37 + 23
   (b) 23 + 37

8. (a) 59 + 38
   (b) 38 + 59

9. (a) 84 + 63
   (b) 63 + 84

10. (a) 72 + 60
    (b) 60 + 72

11. (a) 120 + 74
    (b)   74 + 120

12. (a) 258 + 122
    (b) 122 + 258

13. (a) 419 + 265
    (b) 265 + 419

14. (a) 650 + 328
    (b) 328 + 650

15. (a) 847 + 298
    (b) 298 + 847

Exercise 9

1. (a) 3 + 6 + 7
   (b) 3 + 7 + 6
   (c) 7 + 3 + 6
   (d) 7 + 6 + 3
   (e) 6 + 7 + 3
   (f) 6 + 3 + 7

2. (a) 4 + 8 + 9
   (b) 4 + 9 + 8
   (c) 9 + 4 + 8
   (d) 9 + 8 + 4
   (e) 8 + 9 + 4
   (f) 8 + 4 + 9

3. (a) 14 + 6 + 9
   (b) 14 + 9 + 6

4. (a) 22 + 38 + 27
   (b) 22 + 27 + 38

5. (a) 51 + 39 + 64
   (b) 39 + 51 + 64

6. (a) 63 + 37 + 85
   (b) 63 + 85 + 37

7. (a) 75 + 25 + 64
   (b) 75 + 64 + 25

8. (a) 249 + 151 + 186
   (b) 249 + 186 + 151

Exercise 10

Answer these. Look for quick methods. Use brackets to show the order of your calculations.

A *e.g. 1* 17 + 8 + 2
    = 17 + (8 + 2)
    = 17 + 10
    = <u>27</u>

e.g. 2 36 + 27 + 24
    = 36 + 24 + 27
    = (36 + 24) + 27
    = 60 + 27
    = <u>87</u>

1. 9 + 4 + 6	**8.** 38 + 24 + 46	**15.** 39 + 68 + 21
2. 14 + 7 + 3	**9.** 49 + 65 + 35	**16.** 17 + 40 + 33
3. 11 + 9 + 8	**10.** 45 + 38 + 25	**17.** 52 + 38 + 58
4. 8 + 12 + 9	**11.** 62 + 57 + 38	**18.** 76 + 29 + 14
5. 15 + 15 + 12	**12.** 13 + 55 + 57	**19.** 83 + 75 + 25
6. 29 + 11 + 18	**13.** 41 + 74 + 39	**20.** 93 + 80 + 57
7. 16 + 13 + 27	**14.** 54 + 91 + 46	

B *e.g.* 3 + 4 + 7 + 6
  = (3 + 7) + (4 + 6)
  = 10 + 10
  = <u>20</u>

1. 2 + 9 + 8 + 1	**5.** 34 + 2 + 8 + 6	**9.** 53 + 67 + 89 + 11
2. 5 + 6 + 4 + 5	**6.** 11 + 3 + 9 + 7	**10.** 24 + 71 + 26 + 19
3. 7 + 9 + 1 + 3	**7.** 45 + 29 + 15 + 31	**11.** 52 + 60 + 48 + 40
4. 48 + 5 + 2 + 15	**8.** 88 + 37 + 42 + 43	**12.** 95 + 56 + 44 + 85

Exercise 11

Write the answers to these additions. Use quick methods if you can. You need not show your working.

1. 7 + 9	**8.** 37 + 23 + 34	**15.** 49 + 69 + 51
2. 8 + 2 + 7	**9.** 37 + 28 + 23	**16.** 51 + 33 + 49
3. 6 + 9 + 4	**10.** 23 + 39 + 37	**17.** 62 + 47 + 38
4. 8 + 15 + 2	**11.** 49 + 51	**18.** 81 + 76 + 19
5. 9 + 17 + 1	**12.** 49 + 51 + 63	**19.** 25 + 57 + 75
6. 4 + 29 + 6	**13.** 49 + 51 + 76	**20.** 38 + 47 + 32
7. 18 + 12 + 13	**14.** 49 + 58 + 51	**21.** 63 + 38 + 62

22. 41 + 53 + 47	25. 23 + 48 + 77	28. 29 + 46 + 31
23. 77 + 23 + 84	26. 16 + 84 + 35	29. 83 + 17 + 38
24. 77 + 69 + 23	27. 46 + 24 + 66	30. 39 + 48 + 51

Exercise 12 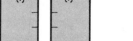 M

Make an addition slide rule using two pieces of card:

Use your slide rule to answer the following:

1. 10 + 15

2. 12 + 8

3. 4 + 17

4. 9 + 9

5. 20 + 11

6. 11 + 8

7. 8 + 11

8. 15 + 17

9. 17 + 15

10. 15 + 15

11. 10 + 18

12. 4 + 16

13. 7 + 19

14. 25 + 3

15. 18 + 13

16. 21 + 9

17. 26 + 7

18. 31 + 2

19. 20 + 12

20. 14 + 11

Magic Squares

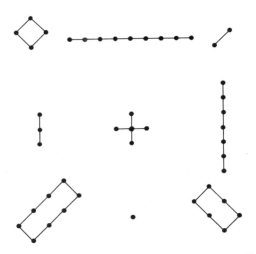

Chinese legend About 4000 years ago, Emperor Yu stood on the banks of the Yellow River and saw a divine tortoise come out of the river. It had two mysterious signs on its back. One was the magic square above.

Albrecht Dürer's engraving called 'Melencolia' has a magic square on it (Germany 1471–1528). It shows the sullen mood of the thinker unable to make decisions.

It is a symmetrical
4 × 4 magic square.

The date of the
engraving is 1514.

16	3	2	13
5	10	11	8
9	6	7	12
4	**15**	**14**	1

Find the missing numbers in the following magic squares:

1.

8		4
1	5	
6	7	

2.

3	8	7
		2

3.

		6
7		11
		10

4.

5		9
	6	
		7

5.

	27	
	15	
18	3	

6.

		9
	8	
7		5

7.

	13		14
		11	4
15		12	3
	10		17

8.

13			16
		10	5
	7	6	
1	14		4

9.

3			16
		4	13
12	5	18	7
		11	

10.

	12		8
			11
16	13	4	9
	10	15	

11.

16		3	13
5			
9		6	12
4			1

12.

18			6
	16		
8	15	11	
21		14	9

13.

3	20			
	8		12	4
9	21	13	5	17
22	14		18	10
			6	

14.

			17	10
25			6	
2	20		8	26
9	22		15	3
	11		24	12

Here is a 'totally magic' magic square!

Magic number = 34

1	12	7	14
8	13	2	11
10	3	16	5
15	6	9	4

1. Check any block of four.

2. Cut off any number of columns then place them at the other side of the square. It is still magic!

3. Carry out step 2 with rows.

4. Test other magic squares in the same way.

Swiss mathematician Leonhard Euler (1707–83) discovered this magic square:

1	48	31	50	33	16	63	18
30	51	46	3	62	19	14	35
47	2	49	32	15	34	17	64
52	29	4	45	20	61	36	13
5	44	25	56	9	40	21	60
28	53	8	41	24	57	12	37
43	6	55	26	39	10	59	22
54	27	42	7	58	23	38	11

Magic constant = 260

Stop halfway, the total = 130

A chess knight can move from square 1 to square 64 in numerical order by following the normal knight's moves.

Exercise 15

Copy and complete these magic squares:

1.

	8	
11		9

2.

10		
	7	
	9	

3.

	10	
	14	7

4.

	23	20
14		

5.

16		8
6		

6.

	25	4
	13	

7.

15		
		6
9		

8.

26	12	
		14

9.

5	9	
15		

10.

17			
		12	9
9		8	13
5	16		2

11.

15	10		
4		16	
14		2	7
	8		12

12.

		16	5
	15	11	18
7		10	
20	9		

19

Exercise 16   Magic Triangles

M

Copy and complete these triangles so that the numbers along each side give the same total.

Questions 1 and 2 use the digits 1, 2, 3, 4, 5 and 6 once only in each answer.

1.
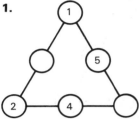

2.
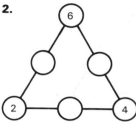

Questions 3 to 6 use the digits 1, 2, 3, 4, 5, 6, 7, 8 and 9 once only in each answer.

3.
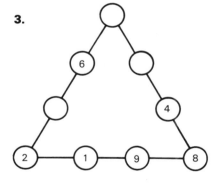

4.
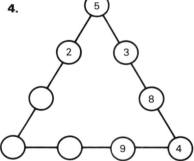

5.
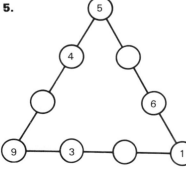

6.
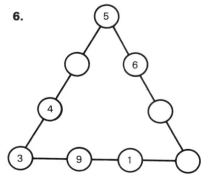

Copy and complete these triangles so that the numbers along each side give the same total.

Questions 1 and 2 use the digits 1, 2, 3, 4, 5 and 6 once only in each answer.

1.

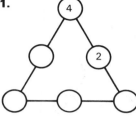

2.

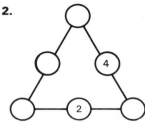

Questions 3 to 6 use the digits 1, 2, 3, 4, 5, 6, 7, 8 and 9.

3.

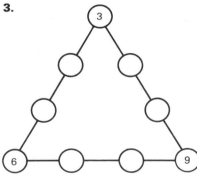

4.

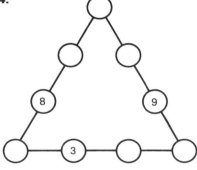

5.

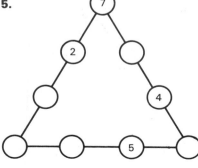

6.

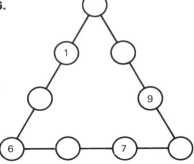

Exercise 18

1. Find the value of 38 plus 45.
2. Add two thousand to 3461.
3. What is the sum of 84, 136 and 27?
4. Increase 179 by 48.
5. Find a number that is 86 more than 97.
6. Which is greater, 79 + 84 or 108 + 54?
7. Find the sum of the digits of the number 24 897.
8. A boy had saved 1832 stamps. If he was given a further 1329 stamps, how many would he have altogether?
9. On a school trip, three coaches were used. Forty-six pupils travelled on the first coach, thirty-nine on the second, and forty-eight on the third. How many pupils were there on this school trip?
10. The table gives the number of pupils in each form of a certain school:

Form	1A	1B	2A	2B	3A	3B	4A	4B	5A	5B
Number in the form	29	31	32	28	27	28	31	30	28	29

   (a) How many pupils were there in the third year?
   (b) How many pupils were there altogether?

11. The total age of Dawn, aged 15 years, Edward, aged 18 years, and their sister Fiona, is 52 years. What will their total age be in twelve years' time?

12. Gina is 16 years old and her brother Harry is 19 years old. How old is their father if he is 13 years older than their combined ages?

13. Find the sum of 128, 296 and 72.

14. Find the sum of the digits of the answer obtained when 26 546 is added to 41 875.

Exercise 19 Addition Puzzles

1. Add this list of numbers.
Now look at the list upside down
and add it up again.

What do you notice about both answers?

```
  196
  688
  809
  918
+ 861
▨▨▨
```

2. Using the digits from 1 to 9 once only in each sum, write down as many addition sums as you can where the two numbers add up to 18. (Note that 11 + 7 is not allowed since the digit 1 is used twice, but 12 + 6 is allowed.)

3. Find a route through this rectangle to obtain a total of 43. Start with the number 5 and finish with the number 6. You must move either straight across or straight down and cross edges. You are not allowed to move diagonally and cross corners.

Start

5	2	1	7	4	6
3	4	6	3	3	1
2	7	1	4	5	4
4	4	4	6	3	5
7	3	5	2	2	7
6	2	5	1	4	1
2	6	5	2	3	6

End

(*e.g.* 5 + 2 + 1 + 6 + 1 + 4 etc. is allowed, while 5 + 2 + 4 + 1 is not allowed.)

4. (*a*) Find 3 + 4 + 5 + 6 + 7 + 8 + 9.
(*b*) Find 13 + 14 + 15 + 16 + 17 + 18 + 19.
(*c*) Find 43 + 44 + 45 + 46 + 47 + 48 + 49.
(*d*) Find 49 + 50 + 51 + 52 + 53 + 54 + 55.

5. Using all the digits from 1 to 9, in that order, once only, write down an addition that totals 144.

6. In every event of a competition it is possible to obtain 1, 2, 3 or 4 points. After 6 events, a certain team has a total of 14 points. Write down the various ways in which that team could obtain 14. (4 + 3 + 3 + 2 + 1 + 1 is one of the possible ways.) Two ways are said to be the same if the points are the same regardless of order. Note that 4 + 3 + 3 + 2 + 1 + 1 is the same as 4 + 3 + 3 + 1 + 2 + 1.

1.

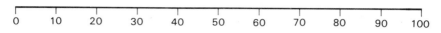

Carefully copy the line above and mark on the line the positions of the numbers:

(a) 35   (c) 95   (e) 77   (g) 23   (i) 67
(b) 55   (d) 45   (f) 18   (h) 82   (j) 5

2.

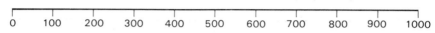

Carefully copy the line above and mark on the line the positions of the numbers:

(a) 250   (c) 450   (e) 525   (g) 380   (i) 120
(b) 850   (d) 775   (f) 630   (h) 970   (j) 50

3.

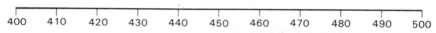

Carefully copy this line and mark the positions of:

(a) 425   (c) 495   (e) 413   (g) 458   (i) 442
(b) 435   (d) 465   (f) 487   (h) 473   (j) 405

4.

Carefully copy this line and mark the positions of:

(a) 280   (c) 340   (e) 200   (g) 255   (i) 175
(b) 160   (d) 240   (f) 220   (h) 305   (j) 325

5.

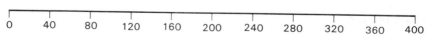

Carefully copy this line and mark the positions of:

(a) 140   (c) 20   (e) 180   (g) 50   (i) 370
(b) 100   (d) 340   (f) 300   (h) 270   (j) 230

Exercise 21

1.

(*a*) Is 48 closer to 40 or to 50? So 48 should be rounded to ⌐?⌐

(*b*) Is 74 closer to 70 or to 80? So 74 should be rounded to ⌐?⌐

(*c*) Is 56 closer to 50 or to 60? So 56 should be rounded to ⌐?⌐

(*d*) Is 94 closer to 90 or to 100? So 94 should be rounded to ⌐?⌐

(*e*) Is 35 closer to 30 or to 40?
It is halfway, so we shall round it *up* to 40.
We shall agree to round *upwards* anything that is halfway.

2.

(*a*) Is 520 closer to 500 or to 600?
So 520 should be rounded to ⌐?⌐

(*b*) Is 780 closer to 700 or to 800?
So 780 should be rounded to ⌐?⌐

(*c*) 360 should be rounded to ⌐?⌐

(*d*) 655 should be rounded to ⌐?⌐

(*e*) 450 should be rounded to ⌐?⌐

3.

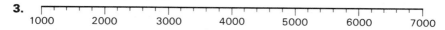

(*a*) Is 4700 closer to 4000 or to 5000?
So 4700 should be rounded to ⌐?⌐

(*b*) 6400 should be rounded to ⌐?⌐

(*c*) 2650 should be rounded to ⌐?⌐

(*d*) 5420 should be rounded to ⌐?⌐

(*e*) 1873 should be rounded to ⌐?⌐

(*f*) 4500 should be rounded to ⌐?⌐

Exercise 22

1. Round these numbers to the nearest ten:

(*a*) 37	(*c*) 23	(*e*) 16	(*g*) 46	(*i*) 55
(*b*) 84	(*d*) 68	(*f*) 92	(*h*) 25	(*j*) 75

2. Round these numbers to the nearest hundred:

(a) 640	(d) 920	(g) 169	(j) 777	(m) 750
(b) 280	(e) 374	(h) 855	(k) 351	(n) 350
(c) 460	(f) 541	(i) 249	(l) 649	(o) 550

3. Round these numbers to the nearest thousand:

(a) 5600	(d) 3750	(g) 6293	(j) 2584	(m) 2499
(b) 9400	(e) 6480	(h) 4527	(k) 4064	(n) 7500
(c) 1800	(f) 1920	(i) 8672	(l) 8496	(o) 3500

Exercise 23

1.

(a) Is 564 closer to 560 or 570?
So we round 564 to ⬚ ?
564 has been rounded to the nearest ten. (If we round 564 to the nearest hundred it becomes 600.)

(b) Is 526 closer to 520 or 530?
So we round 526 to ⬚ ?

(c) Is 613 closer to 610 or 620?
So 613 should be rounded to ⬚ ?

2.

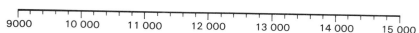

(a) Is 10 584 closer to 10 000 or 11 000?
So 10 584 should be rounded to ⬚ ?

(b) Is 13 652 closer to 13 000 or 14 000?
So 13 652 should be rounded to ⬚ ?

3.

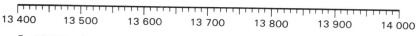

Is 13 652 closer to 13 600 or 13 700?
So 13 652 should be rounded to ⬚ ?

4.

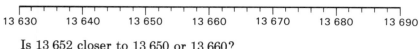

13 630   13 640   13 650   13 660   13 670   13 680   13 690

Is 13 652 closer to 13 650 or 13 660?

So 13 652 should be rounded to ?

5. (a) What is 8761 rounded to the nearest thousand?

(b) What is 8761 rounded to the nearest hundred?

(c) What is 8761 rounded to the nearest ten?

Exercise 24

1. (a) Round 637 to the nearest hundred.

(b) Round 637 to the nearest ten.

2. (a) Round 4754 to the nearest thousand.

(b) Round 4754 to the nearest hundred.

(c) Round 4754 to the nearest ten.

3. (a) Round 347 to the nearest hundred.

(b) Round 347 to the nearest ten.

(c) Round 350 to the nearest hundred.

4. (a) Round 14 453 to the nearest thousand.

(b) Round 14 453 to the nearest hundred.

(c) Round 14 453 to the nearest ten.

(d) Round 14 453 to the nearest ten thousand.

(e) Round 14 500 to the nearest thousand.

Exercise 25

To estimate the answer to 78 + 54 we 'round' the numbers 78 and 54.
78 is nearly 80, so we call it 80. 54 is closer to 50 than to 60, so we call
it 50.

e.g. 1   78 + 54   Note the sign $\approx$.

      $\approx$ 80 + 50   It means 'almost equal to'

      = 130   or 'approximately equal to'.

The answer reads '78 + 54 is approximately equal to 80 + 50, which is
equal to 130'.

e.g. 2 $835 + 671$
           $\approx 800 + 700$
           $= \underline{\underline{1500}}$

When we round numbers, as in the examples, so that only the first digit is not zero but all the other digits are always zeros, we are rounding to *one significant figure*.

Estimate the answers to these. Work with one significant figure as shown in the examples.

1. $37 + 52$
2. $71 + 24$
3. $68 + 46$
4. $19 + 83$
5. $90 + 47$
6. $214 + 576$
7. $391 + 825$

8. $652 + 903$
9. $189 + 741$
10. $236 + 164$
11. $475 + 318$
12. $763 + 252$
13. $9371 + 5067$
14. $3723 + 8214$

15. $73 + 48 + 36$
16. $62 + 19 + 94$
17. $549 + 114 + 389$
18. $174 + 632 + 503$
19. $731 + 329 + 120$
20. $208 + 976 + 485$

Exercise 26

Use a calculator to find an answer to each of these:

1. $7 + 8$
2. $39 + 52$
3. $68 + 59$
4. $207 + 354$
5. $682 + 729$

6. $72 + 684$
7. $926 + 64$
8. $2165 + 847$
9. $3096 + 4168$
10. $374 + 5907$

11. $829 + 7065 + 78$
12. $2196 + 658 + 2990$
13. $7160 + 47 + 899$
14. $4007 + 992 + 2107 + 74$
15. $9 + 8062 + 98 + 354$

Exercise 27

Use a calculator to show that these statements are true:

1. $9 + 4 = 4 + 9$
2. $28 + 59 = 59 + 28$
3. $42 + 58 = 58 + 42$
4. $296 + 175 = 175 + 296$
5. $1280 + 397 = 397 + 1280$
6. $6159 + 3897 = 3897 + 6159$
7. $7263 + 0 = 7263$
8. $0 + 2845 = 2845$

9. $326 + 0 + 297 = 326 + 297$
10. $19 + 48 + 81 = 19 + 81 + 48$
11. $72 + 69 + 28 = 69 + 72 + 28$
12. $215 + 427 + 605 = 215 + 605 + 427$
13. $196 + 734 + 471 = 471 + 734 + 196$
14. $83 + 62 + 97 + 38 = 83 + 97 + 62 + 38$
15. $726 + 325 + 174 = 900 + 325$

Exercise 28

Find out which of these are wrong. (Use quick methods.)
If a sum is wrong, find its correct answer with a calculator.

1. $4 + 9 = 13$
2. $27 + 65 = 96$
3. $48 + 72 = 110$
4. $129 + 514 = 642$
5. $420 + 630 = 1005$

6. $7216 + 1047 = 8262$
7. $907 + 107 = 1014$
8. $49 + 73 = 1112$
9. $357 + 2186 = 5756$
10. $923 + 284 = 1207$

11. $756 + 324 = 432$
12. $604 + 406 = 1010$
13. $824 + 428 = 1212$
14. $492 + 3780 = 4400$
15. $5068 + 963 = 14\,031$

Exercise 29

Use a calculator to help you to solve these problems:

1. Find the sum of 296 and 385.

2. Add three thousand to the sum of 5162 and 894.

3. Find the sum of the digits of the answer to $39\,681 + 41\,908$.

4. There were 398 girls and 465 boys in a school. How many was that altogether?

5. A firm made lamps as shown. How many did they make in a week?

Day	Mon	Tues	Wed	Thurs	Fri
Number of lamps	869	754	928	1230	709

Exercise 30　Calculator Puzzles

1. Use *only* the keys $\boxed{3}$, $\boxed{5}$, $\boxed{+}$ and $\boxed{=}$ (as many times as you wish).
Try to obtain these answers. Show your methods.

e.g. 1 $\quad 5 + 5 + 3 + 3 = 16$
e.g. 2 $\quad 35 + 3 + 3 = 41$

(*a*) 29
(*b*) 46

(*c*) 44
(*d*) 31

(*e*) 14
(*f*) 26

(*g*) 77
(*h*) 37

(*i*) 52
(*j*) 98

2. Use only the keys $\boxed{4}$, $\boxed{9}$, $\boxed{+}$ and $\boxed{=}$ (as many times as you wish). Try to obtain these answers. Show your methods.

(a) 17   (c) 21   (e) 28   (g) 23   (i) 29
(b) 25   (d) 19   (f) 31   (h) 34   (j) 50

3. Use only the keys $\boxed{3}$, $\boxed{9}$, $\boxed{+}$ and $\boxed{=}$ (as many times as you wish). List all possible answers up to 50 that can be obtained by using only these four given keys.

4. Use only the keys $\boxed{4}$, $\boxed{6}$, $\boxed{+}$ and $\boxed{=}$ (as many times as you wish). Try to obtain these answers. Show your methods.

(a) 16   (c) 54   (e) 39   (g) 86   (i) 91
(b) 48   (d) 100   (f) 57   (h) 90   (j) 92

5. You may use the keys $\boxed{3}$, $\boxed{7}$, $\boxed{+}$ and $\boxed{=}$ as many times as you need, but only those four keys may be used. Try to obtain the answer 47 by using only 7 depressions. (The number of depressions refers to the number of times the keys are pressed.)

6. Use any number key except $\boxed{9}$. Use $\boxed{+}$ and $\boxed{=}$ as many times as you wish. No other keys should be used. Key in a sum that gives the same answer on the display as $397 + 489$. Show your method.

Exercise 31

Copy and carry out these subtractions:

1.   56
          $-\ 6$

2.   18
          -11

3.   76
          -24

4.   75
          -30

5.   583
          -142

6.   659
          -316

7.   798
          -222

8.   4165
          -2031

9.   5927
          -2504

10.   8746
          -3544

11.   7285
          -1263

12.   9403
          -5102

Exercise 32

Carry out these subtractions without using your calculator:

1. $7 - 3$	**6.** $59 - 36$	**11.** $567 - 145$	**16.** $805 - 502$
2. $16 - 5$	**7.** $64 - 41$	**12.** $439 - 217$	**17.** $731 - 410$
3. $57 - 4$	**8.** $73 - 22$	**13.** $878 - 536$	**18.** $599 - 386$
4. $19 - 13$	**9.** $85 - 40$	**14.** $937 - 204$	**19.** $7648 - 3432$
5. $26 - 12$	**10.** $97 - 35$	**15.** $754 - 613$	**20.** $8597 - 4564$

Exercise 33

A

	(a)	(b)	(c)
1.	$8 - 5$	$18 - 15$	$48 - 45$
2.	$9 - 3$	$13 - 7$	$23 - 17$
3.	$31 - 17$	$41 - 27$	$44 - 30$
4.	$83 - 39$	$84 - 40$	$94 - 50$
5.	$78 - 44$	$74 - 40$	$84 - 50$
6.	$128 - 76$	$228 - 176$	$138 - 86$
7.	$154 - 93$	$160 - 99$	$161 - 100$
8.	$287 - 194$	$293 - 200$	$290 - 197$
9.	$311 - 176$	$321 - 186$	$315 - 180$
10.	$372 - 214$	$400 - 242$	$458 - 300$
11.	$769 - 447$	$770 - 448$	$772 - 450$
12.	$687 - 391$	$696 - 400$	$690 - 394$

B For each question, find the number that goes in the box to make the calculation correct:

1. $9 - 4 = 15 - \boxed{?}$		**9.** $81 - 47 = \boxed{?} - 147$
2. $12 - 3 = \boxed{?} - 13$		**10.** $437 - 194 = 537 - \boxed{?}$
3. $8 - 2 = 18 - \boxed{?}$		**11.** $285 - 176 = 295 - \boxed{?}$
4. $13 - 5 = 23 - \boxed{?}$		**12.** $93 - 56 = 97 - \boxed{?}$
5. $15 - 6 = \boxed{?} - 16$		**13.** $82 - 38 = \boxed{?} - 40$
6. $14 - 8 = 114 - \boxed{?}$		**14.** $3652 - 1765 = \boxed{?} - 2000$
7. $18 - 13 = \boxed{?} - 23$		**15.** $7084 - 3819 = \boxed{?} - 4000$
8. $64 - 39 = 164 - \boxed{?}$		

Exercise 34

Carry out each of the following calculations by first adding the same number to each of the numbers given to obtain an easier subtraction.

e.g. 1 $847 - 385 = 862 - 400 = \underline{\underline{462}}$.

(Note that 15 was added. $847 + 15 = 862$ and $385 + 15 = 400$.)

e.g. 2 $847 - 385 = 852 - 390 = \underline{\underline{462}}$.

(5 could have been added in the first example, as in this instance, instead of 15.)

1.	$57 - 29$	**9.**	$872 - 782$
2.	$83 - 68$	**10.**	$401 - 294$
3.	$458 - 277$	**11.**	$654 - 428$
4.	$826 - 451$	**12.**	$513 - 107$
5.	$324 - 193$	**13.**	$181 - 143$
6.	$678 - 282$	**14.**	$6208 - 4823$
7.	$740 - 556$	**15.**	$3487 - 1769$
8.	$908 - 568$		

Exercise 35

Copy and carry out these subtractions:

1.	$\begin{array}{r} 13 \\ -\ 7 \\ \hline \end{array}$	**4.**	$\begin{array}{r} 60 \\ -23 \\ \hline \end{array}$	**7.**	$\begin{array}{r} 526 \\ -296 \\ \hline \end{array}$	**10.**	$\begin{array}{r} 807 \\ -264 \\ \hline \end{array}$	**13.**	$\begin{array}{r} 864 \\ -367 \\ \hline \end{array}$
2.	$\begin{array}{r} 20 \\ -\ 6 \\ \hline \end{array}$	**5.**	$\begin{array}{r} 462 \\ -147 \\ \hline \end{array}$	**8.**	$\begin{array}{r} 642 \\ -337 \\ \hline \end{array}$	**11.**	$\begin{array}{r} 762 \\ -178 \\ \hline \end{array}$	**14.**	$\begin{array}{r} 501 \\ -247 \\ \hline \end{array}$
3.	$\begin{array}{r} 56 \\ -28 \\ \hline \end{array}$	**6.**	$\begin{array}{r} 527 \\ -263 \\ \hline \end{array}$	**9.**	$\begin{array}{r} 560 \\ -215 \\ \hline \end{array}$	**12.**	$\begin{array}{r} 940 \\ -273 \\ \hline \end{array}$	**15.**	$\begin{array}{r} 706 \\ -108 \\ \hline \end{array}$

Exercise 36

Copy and carry out these subtractions:

1.	7352 − 4210	**5.**	7065 − 2515	**9.**	9421 − 4756	**13.**	7032 − 2957
2.	7486 − 2138	**6.**	7384 − 2537	**10.**	8532 − 3536	**14.**	8030 − 4256
3.	6590 − 1427	**7.**	4072 − 1643	**11.**	7603 − 4278	**15.**	7004 − 3056
4.	9726 − 4371	**8.**	6721 − 2476	**12.**	6058 − 1473	**16.**	9006 − 2408

Exercise 37

$9 - 5 = 4$ is a subtraction question.

We can use this question to write two addition questions:
$4 + 5 = 9$ or $5 + 4 = 9$

Answer each of these subtraction questions and check them by doing an addition question:

```
e.g.    692         Check    347
      − 347                + 345
       ─────               ─────
        345                 692
       ═════               ═════
```

1. 16 − 11		**6.** 243 − 115		**11.** 832 − 337		**16.** 7604 − 1462	
2. 36 − 14		**7.** 396 − 143		**12.** 491 − 146		**17.** 9012 − 5143	
3. 53 − 29		**8.** 572 − 218		**13.** 942 − 243		**18.** 6003 − 2106	
4. 67 − 48		**9.** 604 − 215		**14.** 668 − 229		**19.** 7900 − 5432	
5. 72 − 39		**10.** 756 − 288		**15.** 5137 − 2043		**20.** 8042 − 7057	

Exercise 38

A Copy each question and fill in the missing numbers:

1. $15 - \boxed{?} = 8$ **5.** $61 - \boxed{?} = 19$ **9.** $100 - \boxed{?} = 33$

2. $\boxed{?} - 9 = 12$ **6.** $72 - \boxed{?} = 34$ **10.** $146 - \boxed{?} = 107$

3. $\boxed{?} - 14 = 15$ **7.** $\boxed{?} - 35 = 49$ **11.** $256 - \boxed{?} = 128$

4. $\boxed{?} - 14 = 28$ **8.** $\boxed{?} - 52 = 48$ **12.** $\boxed{?} - 249 = 457$

B Copy each question and fill in the missing digits:

1.
```
    6 ?
  - ? 3
  ─────
    4 4
```

4.
```
  ? ? ?
  - 2 4 1
  ───────
    5 3 7
```

7.
```
    7 5 ?
  - ? 6 7
  ───────
    4 ? 3
```

10.
```
  ? 8 4 0
  - 1 ? 7 ?
  ─────────
    5 3 ? 6
```

2.
```
    8 3 ?
  - ? 1 4
  ───────
    3 ? 1
```

5.
```
    ? 4 5
  - 3 ? 8
  ───────
    4 1 ?
```

8.
```
    6 2 1
  - ? ? ?
  ───────
    1 9 3
```

11.
```
    4 ? 5 2
  - ? 9 ? 5
  ─────────
    2 4 0 ?
```

3.
```
    9 5 6
  - ? ? ?
  ───────
    2 3 5
```

6.
```
    ? 3 ?
  - 3 ? 2
  ───────
    5 6 2
```

9.
```
    ? ? ? ?
  - 2 5 8 7
  ─────────
    2 4 4 5
```

12.
```
    8 6 6 1
  - ? ? ? ?
  ─────────
    4 7 8 6
```

C For each question, write down the calculation that gives the larger answer:

1. $83 - 57$ or $83 - 47$ **6.** $937 - 284$ or $947 - 284$

2. $61 - 23$ or $61 - 33$ **7.** $62 - 45$ or $92 - 65$

3. $128 - 84$ or $128 - 74$ **8.** $671 - 425$ or $641 - 405$

4. $546 - 392$ or $546 - 402$ **9.** $683 - 196$ or $653 - 176$

5. $74 - 39$ or $64 - 39$ **10.** $415 - 238$ or $445 - 258$

D Copy and complete this table:

Crisps Sales

Day	Number of packets of crisps in stock	Number sold	Number left
Mon	487	258	
Tues	373	196	
Wed	405		156
Thurs	432	297	
Fri		175	248
Mon	536	317	
Tues	363		118
Wed		197	257
Thurs	329	191	
Fri	462		293

Exercise 39 Shopkeepers' Addition

Answer these:

A
1. 328 – 49
2. 541 – 284
3. 619 – 155
4. 483 – 291
5. 705 – 437
6. 219 – 179
7. 820 – 508
8. 928 – 749
9. 376 – 158
10. 650 – 287

B How much change would you get from £1 if you spent:
1. 28 p?
2. 76 p?
3. 49 p?
4. 92 p?
5. 81 p?
6. 54 p?
7. 18 p?
8. 37 p?
9. 65 p?
10. 83 p?

Exercise 40

Answer these. Use quick methods.

e.g. 1   63 − 28
          = 65 − 30
          = 35

e.g. 2   846 − 329
          = 847 − 330
          = 517

1. 54 − 36
2. 71 − 22
3. 86 − 39
4. 92 − 54
5. 63 − 25
6. 74 − 47

7. 90 − 41
8. 85 − 38
9. 72 − 33
10. 562 − 217
11. 728 − 319
12. 687 − 108

13. 851 − 523
14. 975 − 438
15. 690 − 271
16. 463 − 254
17. 746 − 119
18. 874 − 536

Exercise 41

Copy these. Write the correct number in place of each box.

1. 90 + $\boxed{?}$ = 100
2. 74 + $\boxed{?}$ = 100
3. $\boxed{?}$ + 87 = 100
4. 88 + 12 = $\boxed{?}$
5. 37 + 63 = $\boxed{?}$
6. $\boxed{?}$ + 55 = 100
7. $\boxed{?}$ + 55 = 100
8. 93 + $\boxed{?}$ = 100

9. 61 + $\boxed{?}$ = 100
10. $\boxed{?}$ + 31 = 100
11. 100 = 94 + $\boxed{?}$
12. $\boxed{?}$ = 59 + 41
13. 14 + $\boxed{?}$ = 100
14. 100 = $\boxed{?}$ + 48
15. $\boxed{?}$ + 26 = 100

Exercise 42

1. From 19 take 8.
2. Take 12 from 25.
3. Take 40 from 70.
4. From 31 take 22.
5. Subtract 27 from 52.
6. Take 28 from 66.
7. From 50 take 33.

8. 100 take 74.
9. 47 take 25.
10. Take 36 from 91.
11. Take 59 from 83.
12. Subtract 24 from 72.
13. From 125 take 65.
14. Take 147 from 261.

15. From 502 take 276.

16. From 615 take 308.

17. Take 469 from 572.

18. Take 3974 from 8003.

19. Subtract 7068 from 9100.

20. From 6610 take 2899.

Exercise 43

1. Subtract 26 from 87.

2. Find the difference between 47 and 72.

3. Take 39 from 81.

4. From 65 take 27.

5. 93 minus 56.

6. Reduce 86 by 48.

7. By how many is 32 less than 61?

8. What number, when added to 64, gives 82?

9. By how many is 105 greater than 76?

10. How many more than 58 is 131?

11. The sum of two numbers is 165. If the smaller of these numbers is 78, find the larger number.

12. The difference between two numbers is 94. If the larger number is 147, find the smaller number.

13. If Mike has a mass of 54 kg and Mary has a mass of 38 kg, how much lighter is Mary than Mike?

14. In a canteen, 417 dinners have been made. How many dinners are left after 348 have been served?

15. Janet is 145 cm tall, while Sally measures 162 cm. Find the difference in their heights.

16. Tom has 287 stamps less than Sam. If Sam has 1403 stamps, how many has Tom?

17. In a cricket match A. Batt scored 148 runs. If his team scored 315 runs altogether, what total did the rest of the team score?

18. In an election there were two candidates. If 42 346 voters voted and if Mr Topping got 25 491 votes, how many votes did the loser, Mr Unwin, get?
By how many votes did Mr Topping win (i.e. what was his majority)? (Assume that there were no spoilt votes.)

19. A newsagent sold 492 papers out of a total of 564. How many did she have left?

20. A boy guessed that there were 2656 peas in a jar. If the actual number was 3422 peas, by how many was he wrong?

Exercise 44

Use a calculator to answer these:

1. $62 - 49$	**8.** $3410 - 2090$	**15.** $7903 - 1792$
2. $146 - 98$	**9.** $7006 - 1992$	**16.** $29\,384 - 12\,476$
3. $763 - 144$	**10.** $7841 - 38$	**17.** $38\,472 - 10\,243$
4. $507 - 392$	**11.** $6412 - 1349$	**18.** $5816 - 2997$
5. $860 - 145$	**12.** $8051 - 967$	**19.** $74\,203 - 9148$
6. $5621 - 2193$	**13.** $9999 - 6789$	**20.** $80\,920 - 79\,284$
7. $4807 - 986$	**14.** $6005 - 1448$	

Exercise 45

Use a calculator to show that these are true:

1. $15 - 6 = 14 - 5$	**7.** $281 - 153 = 288 - 160$
2. $29 - 12 = 30 - 13$	**8.** $323 - 156 = 300 - 133$
3. $84 - 38 = 86 - 40$	**9.** $392 - 84 = 400 - 92$
4. $79 - 42 = 80 - 43$	**10.** $456 - 175 = 481 - 200$
5. $99 - 27 = 100 - 28$	**11.** $658 - 426 = 662 - 430$
6. $146 - 97 = 149 - 100$	**12.** $1213 - 936 = 1277 - 1000$

13. $1087 - 815 = 1100 - 828$
14. $2356 - 1296 = 2360 - 1300$
15. $8147 - 4286 = 8161 - 4300$
16. $5006 - 2199 = 5000 - 2193$
17. $7832 - 4087 = 7845 - 4100$
18. $14\,765 - 9738 = 15\,000 - 9973$
19. $82\,320 - 49\,388 = 82\,932 - 50\,000$
20. $76\,594 - 26\,999 = 76\,595 - 27\,000$

Exercise 46

Find out which of these are wrong.
If an answer is wrong, find the correct answer with a calculator.

1. $17 - 4 = 21$

2. $73 - 25 = 58$

3. $84 - 36 = 48$

4. $160 - 72 = 92$

5. $148 - 74 = 74$

6. $542 - 266 = 275$

7. $875 - 397 = 478$

8. $761 - 284 = 477$

9. $903 - 576 = 317$

10. $886 - 199 = 687$

11. $1356 - 973 = 483$

12. $2107 - 1928 = 169$

13. $8264 - 5836 = 2428$

14. $7391 - 2778 = 4613$

15. $9065 - 5809 = 3156$

Exercise 47

Use a calculator to help you with these problems:

1. From 761 take 385.

2. Take 139 from 482.

3. I have £278. How much more do I need to make £507?

4. There were 837 pupils in a school. If 459 were girls, how many were boys?

5. A library had 2469 books. How many more must it buy to have a total of 3182 books?

6. There were 28 763 spectators at a football match. How many more would make 40 000?

7. A newsagent sold 9238 newspapers in a month. How many more must he sell to have a total sale of 12 093 papers?

Exercise 48

Answer these. Where possible, use quick methods.

1. $6 + 8 - 8$

2. $14 + 7 - 7$

3. $12 - 12 + 16$

4. $10 + 13 - 10$

5. $29 + 32 - 29$

6. $83 + 41 - 41$

7. $34 - 34 + 92$

8. $43 + 66 - 43$

9. $38 + 87 - 87$

10. $26 - 15 + 15$

11. $59 - 26 + 26$

12. $75 + 48 - 75$

13. $81 - 43 + 43$

14. $20 + 16 + 35 - 16 - 20$

15. $82 - 82 + 18 - 18 + 57$

16. $29 + 14 - 14 + 41 - 29$

17. $73 + 84 + 61 - 73 - 61$

18. $52 + 70 - 25 - 70 + 25$

19. $153 + 106 + 729 - 153 - 106$

20. $374 + 281 + 870 - 374 - 870$

21. $57 - 38 + 62 + 38 - 62$

22. $29 + 23 - 54 - 29 + 54$

23. $98 - 46 - 23 + 23 + 46$

24. $91 - 87 - 91 + 87 + 200$

25. $182 + 265 + 154 - 265 - 182$

Exercise 49

1. Given that $29 + 34 = 63$, find $34 + 29$.

2. Given that $307 + 468 = 775$, find $468 + 307$.

3. If $629 + 182 = 811$, find $182 + 629$.

4. If $79 + 97 = 176$, find $176 - 97$.

5. Given that $381 + 268 = 649$, find $649 - 381$.

6. If $572 + 248 = 820$, find $820 - 572$.

7. Given that $493 + 288 = 781$, find $288 + 493$.

8. If $4404 - 3462 = 942$, find $4404 - 942$.

9. If $8497 - 2621 = 5876$, find $2621 + 5876$.

10. Given that $782 + 6136 = 6918$, find $6136 + 782$.

11. Given that $1002 - 138 = 864$, find $864 + 138$.

12. Given that $594 + 285 = 879$, find $879 - 285$.

Copy and complete this table:

Day	1A	1B	2A	2B	3A	3B	4A	4B	5A	5B	Total number of pupils present each day
Mon	30	29	31	32	28	28	29	33	31	28	
Tues	28	30	29	30	30	27	29	31	32	26	
Wed	28	31	30	31	31	28	28	32		26	296
Thurs	30	31	30	29	31	29		32	33	27	
Fri	29	31	28		28	27	29		33	28	295
Total number of attendances per class in a week			153			143					

The table above shows how many pupils were at school each day during a certain week.

Now answer these:

1. How many pupils attended school on Monday?
2. How many pupils attended school on Tuesday?
3. How many from Class 4A attended school on Thursday?
4. How many pupils attended school on Thursday?
5. On which day were the greatest number of attendances?
6. How many attendances were there in a week for Class 2A?
7. How many attendances were there in a week for Class 3B?
8. How many attendances were there in a week for Class 4B?
9. Which class had the fewest number of attendances for the week?
10. Find the total of Monday's, Tuesday's and Wednesday's attendances.
11. What was the total weekly attendance?
12. Find the difference between the weekly attendances for Class 1B and Class 5B.

Exercise 51

1. 6 cm more string will give me a length that is 13 cm shorter than 51 cm. How long is the string I have got?

2. The sum of two numbers is 107. If one of the numbers is 39 more than the other, find them both.

3. Alan had 69 marbles and Pat had 54. If Alan gave Pat 27 of his marbles, how many more than Alan did Pat then have?

4. Janet and Colin each had 43 sweets. If Janet gave Colin 19 of her sweets, how many more than Janet did Colin then have?

5. Mark and Ann together have 584 stamps, while Ann and Norman have a total of 545 stamps. How many stamps do they each have if Mark has 222 stamps?

Exercise 52 M

| 0 | 1 | 2 | 3 | 4 | 5 | 6 |

| 7 | 8 | 9 | + | − | = |

Copy the squares above. Cut out your squares.

Use them to *try to* make all the numbers from 1 to 50.

e.g.

| 3 | 0 | − | 2 | 9 | = | 1 |

Set the above answer out as $30 - 29 = 1$.

(*Note* $12 - 6 = 6$ is not allowed since 2 sixes are needed.)

42

Exercise 53   Some Puzzles

1. Write down a 3-digit number.   *e.g.*   723
Reverse the digits.   327

Subtract the smaller number from   723
the larger number. $-\ 327$

                                                   396

Reverse the digits of your answer.   693
Add these last two numbers.   693

                                        $+\ \ 396$

                                         1089

Now, repeat the steps above for these numbers:
(*a*) 612   (*c*) 921   (*e*) 715   (*g*) 447   (*i*) 914
(*b*) 846   (*d*) 503   (*f*) 286   (*h*) 158   (*j*) 653

What do you notice about all your answers?
Repeat the steps above again using your own 3-digit numbers (make up four of your own).
Try to find a 3-digit number that does not work.

2. Using all the digits 9, 8, 7, 6, 5, 4, 3, 2, 1, in that order, and using + and $-$, try to obtain a question that has an answer of 100. (e.g. $98 + 7 - 6 - 54 + 32 + 1 = \underline{78}$, but 100 is needed.)

3. Use the digits 1, 2, 3, 4, 5, 6, 7, 8, 9, in that order, and use + and $-$ to obtain a question that has an answer of 100.

4. Use the digits 9, 8, 7, 6, 5, 4, 3, 2, 1, in that order, and use + and $-$ to obtain a question that has an answer of 1000.

5. Ann, Bob, Sally and John played a game using some special cards. They shared the cards equally between themselves at the beginning of the game. At the end of the game, Ann had 29 cards, Bob had 83, Sally had 54, and John had 26.
How many cards did they each win or lose?

3 Multiplication and Division

Compare the answers to both parts of each of the following questions:

1. (*a*) $5 + 5 + 5 + 5 =$ $\boxed{?}$
   (*b*) $4 \times 5 =$ $\boxed{?}$

2. (*a*) $8 + 8 =$ $\boxed{?}$
   (*b*) $2 \times 8 =$ $\boxed{?}$

3. (*a*) $7 + 7 + 7 =$ $\boxed{?}$
   (*b*) $3 \times 7 =$ $\boxed{?}$

4. (*a*) $6 + 6 + 6 + 6 + 6 =$ $\boxed{?}$
   (*b*) $5 \times 6 =$ $\boxed{?}$

5. (*a*) $2 + 2 + 2 + 2 + 2 + 2 + 2 + 2 =$ $\boxed{?}$
   (*b*) $8 \times 2 =$ $\boxed{?}$

6. (*a*) $4 + 4 + 4 + 4 + 4 + 4 =$ $\boxed{?}$
   (*b*) $6 \times 4 =$ $\boxed{?}$

7. (*a*) $3 + 3 + 3 + 3 + 3 + 3 + 3 =$ $\boxed{?}$
   (*b*) $7 \times 3 =$ $\boxed{?}$

8. (*a*) $9 + 9 + 9 + 9 + 9 =$ $\boxed{?}$
   (*b*) $5 \times 9 =$ $\boxed{?}$

9. (*a*) $8 + 8 + 8 + 8 + 8 + 8 =$ $\boxed{?}$
   (*b*) $6 \times 8 =$ $\boxed{?}$

10. (*a*) $6 + 6 + 6 + 6 =$ $\boxed{?}$
   (*b*) $4 \times 6 =$ $\boxed{?}$

A Copy and complete this multiplication square:

×	0	1	2	3	4	5	6	7	8	9	10
0				0							
1							6				
2									16		
3								21			
4			8								
5				20							
6		6									
7											70
8					40						
9	0										
10										90	

B The following arrangements of squares are parts of the multiplication square above. Copy them and fill in the missing numbers:

1.   **3.**   **5.**   **7.**   **9.**

2.   **4.**   **6.**   **8.**   **10.**

45

11.

		45
49		

12.

		24
	28	

13.

50		

14.

	27	
20		

15.

	49

Exercise 3

Copy and complete these multiplication squares:

1.

×	3	6	9
4			
6			
8			

4.

×	2	4	6	8
2				
4				
6				
8				

2.

×	4	7	2	9
3				
9				
8				
6				

5.

×	9	3	8	
4				
			48	
7				
5				35

3.

×	3	5	7	9
3				
5				
7				
9				

6.

×	8	10	7		4
5					
3					
	32				
7			63		
2					

Exercise 4   The 9-times Table

You can do the 9-times table on your fingers.

1. Hold out your hands as shown, palms towards you.

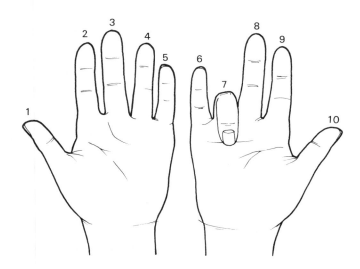

2. Number your fingers from 1 to 10 starting at the left.

3. Bend the finger that represents the number that is to be multiplied by 9. (In the drawing above we are finding 7×9, so finger number 7 is bent over.)

4. Count the fingers to the left of the finger that is bent. These are the tens. (In the example, it is 60.)

5. The fingers to the right of the bent finger show the units. (In the example, there are 3.)

6. So $7 \times 9 = 63$.

7. Try this method for other numbers that you want to multiply by 9.

Exercise 5

For each of the given numbers (answers), write down a question from your multiplication tables to give that answer.

e.g. 1 12; 3 × 4 = 12 (Note that 2 × 6 = 12 is also a correct answer.)

e.g. 2 70; 7 × 10 = 70

The numbers you use in your question must not be bigger than 10. (For the second example, 2 × 35 is not an acceptable answer.)

1. 42	**5.** 24	**9.** 36	**13.** 81	**17.** 54
2. 80	**6.** 30	**10.** 49	**14.** 27	**18.** 60
3. 32	**7.** 56	**11.** 40	**15.** 63	**19.** 28
4. 15	**8.** 21	**12.** 18	**16.** 48	**20.** 72

Exercise 6 M

Copy and complete:

1.

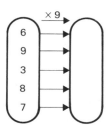

3.

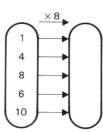

5.

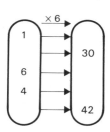

2.

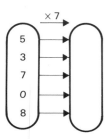

4.

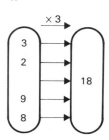

6.

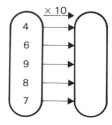

Exercise 7

To estimate the answer to 5×68, we need to 'round' the number 68. It is nearly 70, so we call it 70.

We set out our work like this:

e.g. 1 $\quad 5 \times 68 \approx 5 \times 70 = \underline{\underline{350}}$

The answer reads '5×68 is approximately equal to 5×70, which is equal to 350'.

e.g. 2 $\quad 6823 \times 8 \approx 7000 \times 8 = \underline{\underline{56\,000}}$

Estimate the answers to these:

1. 2×19	**5.** 316×8	**9.** 3×582	**13.** 8067×9
2. 42×5	**6.** 9×853	**10.** 3553×6	**14.** 3×4512
3. 6×27	**7.** 2×980	**11.** 8×2735	**15.** 7×9741
4. 4×93	**8.** 5×407	**12.** 1689×7	**16.** 7296×8

Exercise 8

A Copy and carry out these calculations:

1. $\begin{array}{r} 13 \\ \times\ 3 \\ \hline \end{array}$	**5.** $\begin{array}{r} 50 \\ \times\ 9 \\ \hline \end{array}$	**9.** $\begin{array}{r} 300 \\ \times\ 5 \\ \hline \end{array}$	**13.** $\begin{array}{r} 129 \\ \times\ 3 \\ \hline \end{array}$	**17.** $\begin{array}{r} 628 \\ \times\ 6 \\ \hline \end{array}$
2. $\begin{array}{r} 20 \\ \times\ 4 \\ \hline \end{array}$	**6.** $\begin{array}{r} 57 \\ \times\ 7 \\ \hline \end{array}$	**10.** $\begin{array}{r} 501 \\ \times\ 7 \\ \hline \end{array}$	**14.** $\begin{array}{r} 180 \\ \times\ 4 \\ \hline \end{array}$	**18.** $\begin{array}{r} 9152 \\ \times\ 9 \\ \hline \end{array}$
3. $\begin{array}{r} 19 \\ \times\ 3 \\ \hline \end{array}$	**7.** $\begin{array}{r} 68 \\ \times\ 7 \\ \hline \end{array}$	**11.** $\begin{array}{r} 521 \\ \times\ 4 \\ \hline \end{array}$	**15.** $\begin{array}{r} 312 \\ \times\ 8 \\ \hline \end{array}$	**19.** $\begin{array}{r} 6085 \\ \times\ 8 \\ \hline \end{array}$
4. $\begin{array}{r} 16 \\ \times\ 5 \\ \hline \end{array}$	**8.** $\begin{array}{r} 402 \\ \times\ 2 \\ \hline \end{array}$	**12.** $\begin{array}{r} 208 \\ \times\ 7 \\ \hline \end{array}$	**16.** $\begin{array}{r} 576 \\ \times\ 0 \\ \hline \end{array}$	**20.** $\begin{array}{r} 6305 \\ \times\ 6 \\ \hline \end{array}$

B Carry out these calculations. Set them out in columns:

1. 31 × 2	**11.** 8 × 847	**21.** 4 × 3578
2. 83 × 3	**12.** 659 × 2	**22.** 1496 × 6
3. 19 × 4	**13.** 754 × 5	**23.** 8734 × 8
4. 41 × 7	**14.** 9 × 486	**24.** 9 × 7846
5. 92 × 6	**15.** 6 × 531	**25.** 2 × 8507
6. 58 × 5	**16.** 8 × 568	**26.** 5 × 4785
7. 901 × 8	**17.** 7 × 639	**27.** 8 × 1609
8. 397 × 7	**18.** 234 × 9	**28.** 7 × 4265
9. 9 × 819	**19.** 5 × 9236	**29.** 3159 × 9
10. 6 × 780	**20.** 7054 × 3	**30.** 6 × 8457

Exercise 9 M

Copy and complete:

1.

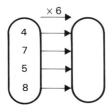

2.

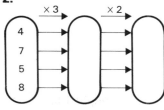

3.

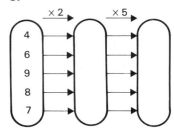

4.

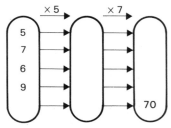

5.

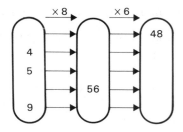

50

Exercise 10

A	B	C	D	E	F	G	H	I	J	K	L	M	N	O	P	Q	R	S	T	U	V	W	X	Y	Z
48	54	91	27	85	63	24	32	72	87	52	96	18	84	60	49	26	42	36	56	35	44	90	81	45	28

For each of the following questions carry out the given calculations. Look up each answer in the table above to obtain a letter. Re-arrange the letters obtained in each question to spell the name of a town or city in the United Kingdom.

1. 8 × 12, 6 × 10, 9 × 6, 4 × 9, 7 × 8, 12 × 6, 6 × 7
2. 12 × 3, 6 × 8, 10 × 9, 6 × 16, 5 × 12, 3 × 8, 4 × 6
3. 21 × 3, 3 × 24, 2 × 21, 9 × 3, 9 × 7, 3 × 16, 7 × 13
4. 14 × 4, 2 × 18, 2 × 27, 24 × 4, 5 × 17, 12 × 4, 7 × 9
5. 2 × 9, 24 × 2, 2 × 12, 14 × 6, 4 × 18, 6 × 3, 3 × 14, 8 × 4,
   8 × 9, 18 × 3

Exercise 11

1. Find 5 times 9.

2. Multiply 37 by 4.

3. Find the product of 72 and 8.

4. What is the product of 69 and 7?

5. Multiply 6 by 49.

6. How many days are there in 5 weeks?

7. Eggs are packed in boxes of 12. How many eggs would I have if I had 7 boxes?

8. How many hours are there in 9 days?

9. A greengrocer sold 58 bags of potatoes in a day. If each bag contained 3 kg, how many kilograms were sold altogether?

10. On average, there are 9 words on a line in my book. There are 38 lines on a page. About how many words are there on each page?

11. Sound travels 1120 ft in one second. If there are 6 seconds between seeing a flash of lightning and hearing the thunder, how many feet must I be from the flash?

12. A car travelled for 3 hours at a steady 96 km per hour. How far did it travel?

13. I have five boxes of matches and there are forty-eight matches in each box. How many matches have I got altogether?

14. James has 3 boxes of marbles and there are 137 marbles in each box. How many is that altogether?

15. A jar contained 249 sweets. How many sweets would eight of those jars contain?

Exercise 12

Use your calculator to answer these. Try to say how many zeros there will be in your answer before you use your calculator.

1. 20×30	11. 300×1000	21. 6300×2400
2. 40×60	12. 200×700	22. 3180×5200
3. 70×50	13. 800×600	23. 9030×7100
4. 500×90	14. 5000×3000	24. 20×50
5. 100×40	15. $700 \times 80\,000$	25. 60×500
6. 80×200	16. 240×300	26. 5000×8000
7. 600×70	17. 90×4300	27. 2500×400
8. 90×300	18. 630×8000	28. $800 \times 75\,000$
9. 9×4000	19. 7200×3100	29. 2400×5000
10. 8000×7	20. $41\,000 \times 1400$	30. 3250×2400

Exercise 13

A Are these statements true or false? (Check them on your calculator.)

1. $72 \times 9 = 9 \times 72$
2. $98 \times 37 = 37 \times 98$
3. $364 \times 28 = 28 \times 364$
4. $36 \times 42 = 63 \times 24$
5. $52 \times 28 = 25 \times 82$
6. $932 \times 167 = 167 \times 932$
7. $284 \times 536 = 482 \times 635$
8. $43 \times 68 = 34 \times 86$
9. $42 \times 68 = 24 \times 86$
10. $108 \times 503 = 801 \times 305$

B Work these out on your calculator:

1. How many seconds are there in a year (365 days)?

2. If light travels 299 792 km in a second, how far does it travel in 13 s?

3. What will be the total mass of 148 people if each person has a mass of about 76 kg?

4. Seventeen coaches each carry 53 passengers. How many people is that altogether?

5. A shop sold 29 gross of pencils. How many was that?

Exercise 14

e.g. 1 760×237
        $\approx 800 \times 200$
        $= \underline{160\ 000}$

e.g. 2 5189×470
        $\approx 5000 \times 500$
        $= \underline{2\ 500\ 000}$

Estimate the answers to these:

1. 28×64	**8.** 50×77	**15.** 392×491
2. 41×79	**9.** 68×214	**16.** 7436×3860
3. 57×62	**10.** 562×91	**17.** 8613×5195
4. 19×93	**11.** 185×433	**18.** 6271×7059
5. 84×35	**12.** 647×826	**19.** 4924×984
6. 97×45	**13.** 779×358	**20.** 3548×9482
7. 48×39	**14.** 98×294	

Exercise 15

Find the answers to these multiplications:

A

1. 5×10	**5.** 10×60	**9.** 150×10	**13.** 10×290
2. 10×8	**6.** 80×10	**10.** 10×163	**14.** 10×378
3. 24×10	**7.** 10×100	**11.** 10×200	**15.** 10×694
4. 10×39	**8.** 10×120	**12.** 250×10	**16.** 961×10

B

1. 6×100	**4.** 70×100	**7.** 100×180	**10.** 100×692
2. 32×100	**5.** 100×69	**8.** 100×300	**11.** 706×100
3. 46×100	**6.** 100×100	**9.** 470×100	**12.** 100×984

C	**1.** 4×20	**5.** 50×17	**9.** 40×75	**13.** 30×758
	2. 6×30	**6.** 34×60	**10.** 90×82	**14.** 206×70
	3. 80×5	**7.** 51×70	**11.** 46×80	**15.** 50×560
	4. 40×13	**8.** 63×90	**12.** 70×89	**16.** 419×90

D	**1.** 2×300	**5.** 19×800	**9.** 900×51	**13.** 600×98
	2. 400×6	**6.** 600×57	**10.** 25×200	**14.** 800×512
	3. 9×900	**7.** 500×40	**11.** 82×600	**15.** 307×900
	4. 200×14	**8.** 49×400	**12.** 74×700	**16.** 230×700

E	**1.** 18×13	**6.** 28×47	**11.** 52×69	**16.** 314×16
	2. 23×23	**7.** 16×56	**12.** 74×35	**17.** 829×61
	3. 21×34	**8.** 78×14	**13.** 207×19	**18.** 184×750
	4. 29×24	**9.** 25×58	**14.** 570×73	**19.** 106×891
	5. 37×26	**10.** 31×49	**15.** 203×56	**20.** 302×805

Exercise 16

Answer these. Look for quick methods.

A	**1.** (a) 2×3	**4.** (a) 9×8	**7.** (a) 6×1	**10.** (a) 7×29
	(b) 3×2	(b) 8×9	(b) 1×6	(b) 29×7
	2. (a) 5×6	**5.** (a) 7×0	**8.** (a) 10×4	**11.** (a) 46×8
	(b) 6×5	(b) 0×7	(b) 4×10	(b) 8×46
	3. (a) 4×7	**6.** (a) 8×3	**9.** (a) 5×11	**12.** (a) 15×24
	(b) 7×4	(b) 3×8	(b) 11×5	(b) 24×15

B	**1.** (a) $2 \times 4 \times 5$	(c) $5 \times 2 \times 4$	(e) $4 \times 5 \times 2$
	(b) $2 \times 5 \times 4$	(d) $5 \times 4 \times 2$	(f) $4 \times 2 \times 5$
	2. (a) $5 \times 6 \times 3$	(c) $3 \times 5 \times 6$	(e) $6 \times 3 \times 5$
	(b) $5 \times 3 \times 6$	(d) $3 \times 6 \times 5$	(f) $6 \times 5 \times 3$
	3. (a) $5 \times 7 \times 8$	(b) $5 \times 8 \times 7$	
	4. (a) $3 \times 20 \times 9$	(b) $3 \times 9 \times 20$	
	5. (a) $9 \times 2 \times 17$	(b) $9 \times 17 \times 2$	

Exercise 17

Answer these. Look for quick methods. Use brackets to show the order of your calculations.

e.g. 1	$4 \times 10 \times 7$	*e.g. 2*	$7 \times 5 \times 4$	*e.g. 3*	$6 \times 9 \times 5$
	$= (4 \times 10) \times 7$		$= 7 \times (5 \times 4)$		$= 6 \times 5 \times 9$
	$= 40 \times 7$		$= 7 \times 20$		$= (6 \times 5) \times 9$
	$= \underline{\underline{280}}$		$= \underline{\underline{140}}$		$= 30 \times 9$
					$= \underline{\underline{270}}$

1. $8 \times 5 \times 9$ **5.** $4 \times 7 \times 5$ **9.** $15 \times 21 \times 6$

2. $7 \times 2 \times 15$ **6.** $2 \times 19 \times 5$ **10.** $4 \times 29 \times 15$

3. $25 \times 4 \times 8$ **7.** $20 \times 13 \times 5$ **11.** $7 \times 5 \times 10 \times 4$

4. $13 \times 5 \times 20$ **8.** $25 \times 17 \times 4$ **12.** $4 \times 9 \times 25 \times 7$

Exercise 18

Copy and complete:

1. $3 \times 7 = \boxed{?} \times 3$ **6.** $\boxed{?} \times 7 = 7 \times 11$

2. $8 \times 4 = 4 \times \boxed{?}$ **7.** $6 \times 19 = \boxed{?} \times 6$

3. $5 \times 10 = \boxed{?} \times 5$ **8.** $21 \times 9 = 9 \times \boxed{?}$

4. $9 \times \boxed{?} = 6 \times 9$ **9.** $15 \times \boxed{?} = 26 \times 15$

5. $2 \times \boxed{?} = 13 \times 2$ **10.** $37 \times 54 = \boxed{?} \times 37$

Exercise 19

Copy, then answer these. Use quick methods where possible.

1. $3 \times 4 \times 5$ **11.** $7 \times 2 \times 15$ **21.** $45 \times 63 \times 2$

2. $3 \times 5 \times 4$ **12.** $15 \times 8 \times 2$ **22.** $2 \times 78 \times 35$

3. $5 \times 3 \times 4$ **13.** $15 \times 9 \times 4$ **23.** $58 \times 2 \times 45$

4. $5 \times 4 \times 3$ **14.** $2 \times 7 \times 25$ **24.** $2 \times 39 \times 50$

5. $4 \times 5 \times 3$ **15.** $25 \times 5 \times 4$ **25.** $35 \times 84 \times 2$

6. $4 \times 3 \times 5$ **16.** $9 \times 25 \times 4$ **26.** $75 \times 61 \times 4$

7. $9 \times 2 \times 5$ **17.** $25 \times 13 \times 2$ **27.** $77 \times 75 \times 4$

8. $2 \times 5 \times 9$ **18.** $19 \times 25 \times 2$ **28.** $4 \times 46 \times 125$

9. $2 \times 15 \times 6$ **19.** $25 \times 37 \times 4$ **29.** $125 \times 92 \times 4$

10. $15 \times 6 \times 2$ **20.** $35 \times 26 \times 2$ **30.** $8 \times 89 \times 125$

Exercise 20

Use quick methods, as shown in the examples:

e.g. 1 35×58
$= 70 \times 29$
$= \underline{\underline{2030}}$

e.g. 4 31×18
$= 93 \times 6$
$= \underline{\underline{558}}$

e.g. 2 35×58
$= 7 \times 290$
$= \underline{\underline{2030}}$

e.g. 5 42×37
$= 21 \times 74$
$= 7 \times 222$
$= \underline{\underline{1554}}$

e.g. 3 31×18
$= 62 \times 9$
$= \underline{\underline{558}}$

1. 45×46
2. 45×39
3. 25×48
4. 25×17
5. 19×15

6. 15×18
7. 16×23
8. 18×29
9. 14×24
10. 21×31

11. 24×24
12. 43×28
13. 75×51
14. 62×105
15. 63×87

Exercise 21

e.g. 63×27

Look at this method:

$$
\begin{array}{r}
63 \\
\times 27 \\
\hline
20 \times 63 = 1260 \\
7 \times 63 = 441 \\
\hline
1701 \\
\end{array}
$$

Now try the same method for these:

1. 17×15
2. 29×13
3. 48×26
4. 64×31

5. 79×42
6. 53×38
7. 96×57
8. 107×83

9. 490×68
10. 84×590
11. 70×132
12. 62×256

John Napier (1550–1617) was the son of a Scottish nobleman. He invented ways of calculating. One of the calculating aids he invented is known as Napier's Bones (or rods). They were used not only in Europe but also in China and Japan.

Copy these 'bones' on squared paper or on card.

Index	0	1	2	3	4	5	6	7	8	9
1	0/0	0/1	0/2	0/3	0/4	0/5	0/6	0/7	0/8	0/9
2	0/0	0/2	0/4	0/6	0/8	1/0	1/2	1/4	1/6	1/8
3	0/0	0/3	0/6	0/9	1/2	1/5	1/8	2/1	2/4	2/7
4	0/0	0/4	0/8	1/2	1/6	2/0	2/4	2/8	3/2	3/6
5	0/0	0/5	1/0	1/5	2/0	2/5	3/0	3/5	4/0	4/5
6	0/0	0/6	1/2	1/8	2/4	3/0	3/6	4/2	4/8	5/4
7	0/0	0/7	1/4	2/1	2/8	3/5	4/2	4/9	5/6	6/3
8	0/0	0/8	1/6	2/4	3/2	4/0	4/8	5/6	6/4	7/2
9	0/0	0/9	1/8	2/7	3/6	4/5	5/4	6/3	7/2	8/1

Now cut out each 'bone' (or rod) from your numbered set (as in the example)

You should finish with 11 strips (strips 0 to 9 plus an index strip).

Exercise 23

Use your 'bones' to try these examples:

e.g. 1 43×2

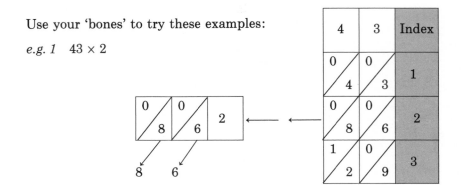

e.g. 2   96 × 4

9	6	Index
0 / 9	0 / 6	1
1 / 8	1 / 2	2
2 / 7	1 / 8	3
3 / 6	+ 2 / 4	4

3   8   4   (6 + 2 = 8)

Now use your 'bones' to work these out:

A
1. 21 × 4
2. 32 × 3
3. 24 × 2
4. 3 × 23
5. 3 × 20
6. 60 × 4
7. 7 × 50
8. 28 × 2
9. 23 × 4
10. 3 × 19
11. 6 × 71
12. 83 × 3
13. 76 × 6
14. 9 × 47
15. 8 × 69
16. 58 × 4
17. 71 × 8
18. 84 × 2
19. 7 × 39
20. 8 × 53

B
1. 203 × 3
2. 413 × 2
3. 3 × 312
4. 4 × 201
5. 5 × 107
6. 302 × 4
7. 157 × 6
8. 298 × 3
9. 4 × 176
10. 8 × 491
11. 832 × 7
12. 796 × 5
13. 6 × 405
14. 9 × 750
15. 293 × 8

Exercise 24

1. There were 28 classes in our school. Each class had 32 pupils in it. How many pupils attended our school?

2. In a cinema there were 36 seats in each row. If there were 19 rows, how many people could the cinema seat?

3. I cut 84 pieces of string from one long length. If each piece was 145 mm long, find the length of string I started with.

4. My car will travel 17 km on 1 litre of petrol. How far will it travel on 59 litres?

5. If each of your lessons was 45 minutes long and you had 35 lessons per week, how many minutes would that be?

6. My book has 172 pages. There are, on average, 39 lines on each page and 11 words on each line. How many words is that altogether?

Division

Exercise 25

Write down division statements for these:

e.g. • • • • | • • • • shows $8 \div 2 = 4$

1. • • • | • • • | • • • | • • • | • • •
2. • • • | • • • | • • •
3. • • • • • | • • • • •
4. • • • • | • • • • | • • • •
5. • • • • • • | • • • • • • | • • • • • • | • • • • • •
6. • • • • | • • • • | • • • • | • • • •
7. • • | • • | • • | • • | • • | • • | • •
8. • • • • • • • • • • | • • • • • • • • • •

Exercise 26

Answer these:

e.g. 1 $6 = 2 + 2 + 2$ 3 twos make 6 $6 \div 3 = 2$
e.g. 2 $20 = 4 + 4 + 4 + 4 + 4$ 5 fours make 20 $20 \div 5 = 4$

1. $6 = 3 + 3$ ⟦?⟧ threes make 6 $6 \div$ ⟦?⟧ $= 3$

2. $12 = 2 + 2 + 2 + 2 + 2 + 2$ ⟦?⟧ twos make 12 $12 \div$ ⟦?⟧ $= 2$

3. $25 = 5 + 5 + 5 + 5 + 5$ ⟦?⟧ fives make 25 $25 \div 5 =$ ⟦?⟧

4. $16 = 2 + 2 + 2 + 2 + 2 + 2$ ⟦?⟧ twos make 16 $16 \div$ ⟦?⟧ $= 2$
            $+ 2 + 2$

5. $27 = 9 + 9 + 9$ ⟦?⟧ nines make 27 $27 \div 3 =$ ⟦?⟧

6. $28 = 7 + 7 + 7 + 7$ ⟦?⟧ sevens make 28 $28 \div 4 =$ ⟦?⟧

7. $35 = 5 + 5 + 5 + 5 + 5 + 5 + 5$ $\boxed{?}$ fives make 35 $35 \div \boxed{?} = 5$

8. $32 = 8 + 8 + 8 + 8$ $\boxed{?}$ eights make 32 $32 \div \boxed{?} = 8$

9. $30 = 6 + 6 + 6 + 6 + 6$ $\boxed{?}$ sixes make 30 $30 \div 5 = \boxed{?}$

10. $36 = 4 + 4 + 4 + 4 + 4 + 4 + 4 + 4 + 4$ $\boxed{?}$ fours make 36 $36 \div \boxed{?} = 4$

When 6 marbles are shared equally between 3 children they get 2 marbles each.

     We can write $6 \div 3 = 2$

If each of the 3 children put their 2 marbles together again, there will be 6 marbles.

     We can write $3 \times 2 = 6$

So $6 \div 3 = 2$ and $3 \times 2 = 6$

To check division we can multiply.

Exercise 27

Copy and complete:

1. (a) $2 \times 10 = \boxed{?}$ (b) $20 \div 2 = \boxed{?}$ (c) $20 \div 10 = \boxed{?}$

2. (a) $6 \times \boxed{?} = 18$ (b) $18 \div 6 = \boxed{?}$ (c) $18 \div 3 = \boxed{?}$

3. (a) $\boxed{?} \times 8 = 24$ (b) $24 \div \boxed{?} = 8$ (c) $24 \div 8 = \boxed{?}$

4. (a) $3 \times 10 = \boxed{?}$ (b) $\boxed{?} \div 3 = 10$ (c) $\boxed{?} \div 10 = 3$

5. (a) $8 \times \boxed{?} = 40$ (b) $40 \div 5 = \boxed{?}$ (c) $\boxed{?} \div 8 = 5$

6. (a) $7 \times \boxed{?} = 42$ (b) $42 \div 7 = \boxed{?}$ (c) $42 \div \boxed{?} = 7$

7. (a) $\boxed{?} \times 9 = 45$ (b) $45 \div \boxed{?} = 9$ (c) $\boxed{?} \div 9 = 5$

8. (a) $6 \times \boxed{?} = 48$ (b) $48 \div \boxed{?} = 6$ (c) $48 \div 6 = \boxed{?}$

Exercise 28

Carry out each division. Check it by multiplication.

e.g. $10 \div 2 = 5$ *Check* $5 \times 2 = 10$

1. $40 \div 10$	**10.** $100 \div 10$	**19.** $42 \div 6$
2. $14 \div 2$	**11.** $18 \div 9$	**20.** $63 \div 9$
3. $16 \div 4$	**12.** $50 \div 5$	**21.** $72 \div 8$
4. $21 \div 3$	**13.** $63 \div 7$	**22.** $72 \div 9$
5. $24 \div 8$	**14.** $40 \div 8$	**23.** $56 \div 8$
6. $30 \div 6$	**15.** $28 \div 7$	**24.** $56 \div 7$
7. $35 \div 7$	**16.** $36 \div 4$	**25.** $54 \div 9$
8. $32 \div 8$	**17.** $54 \div 6$	**26.** $40 \div 5$
9. $45 \div 5$	**18.** $48 \div 6$	**27.** $56 \div 7$

Exercise 29

1. 2 boys share 12 coins. How many does each get?

2. 15 sweets are shared by 3 girls. How many does each get?

3. How many boxes of 4 cakes can be made up out of 12 cakes?

4. A half dozen girls share 24 sheets of paper. How many sheets does each girl get?

5. At a party 27 balloons are shared by 9 boys. How many does each boy get?

6. If I cut a piece of string, 27 m long, into 3 m lengths, how many lengths will I have?

7. How many people can share 32 straws if they are given 4 each?

8. How many packs of screws must I buy if I need 35 screws and they are sold in packs of 5?

9. A piece of wood, 81 cm long, is cut into 9 small lengths of equal size? How long is each piece?

10. How many people can share 25 marbles so that they get the same number each?

Exercise 30

You can use a multiplication square to help you with division.

The marked squares show:

$$6 \times 5 = 30$$

or $30 \div 6 = 5$

or $30 \div 5 = 6$

or $5 \times 6 = 30$

Use the multiplication square to help you to answer these:

×	1	2	3	4	5	6	7	8	9
1	1	2	3	4	5	6	7	8	9
2	2	4	6	8	10	12	14	16	18
3	3	6	9	12	15	18	21	24	27
4	4	8	12	16	20	24	28	32	36
5	5	10	15	20	25	30	35	40	45
6	6	12	18	24	30	36	42	48	54
7	7	14	21	28	35	42	49	56	63
8	8	16	24	32	40	48	56	64	72
9	9	18	27	36	45	54	63	72	81

1. $25 \div 5$

2. $15 \div 3$

3. $24 \div 4$

4. $24 \div 6$

5. $21 \div 7$

6. $28 \div 4$

7. $35 \div 5$

8. $64 \div 8$

9. $90 \div 9$

10. $70 \div 10$

11. $42 \div 7$

12. $18 \div 2$

13. $36 \div 6$

14. $24 \div 3$

15. $45 \div 9$

16. $60 \div 6$

17. $49 \div 7$

18. $36 \div 9$

19. $48 \div 8$

20. $32 \div 4$

Exercise 31   M

A Copy and complete:

e.g. 4 $\xrightarrow{\times 6}$ 24
$\xleftarrow{\div 6}$

1. 5 $\xrightarrow{\times 4}$?
$\xleftarrow{\div 4}$

4. ? $\xrightarrow{\times 3}$ 21
$\xleftarrow{\div 3}$

2. 8 $\xrightarrow{\times 2}$?
$\xleftarrow{\div 2}$

5. 3 $\xrightarrow{\times ?}$ 21
$\xleftarrow{\div ?}$

3. ? $\xrightarrow{\times 10}$ 40
$\xleftarrow{\div 10}$

6. 6 $\xrightarrow{\times ?}$ 36
$\xleftarrow{\div ?}$

7.

$$7 \xrightarrow{\times 5} \boxed{?}$$
$$\xleftarrow{\div \boxed{?}}$$

10.

$$\boxed{?} \xrightarrow{\times 6} 54$$
$$\xleftarrow{\div \boxed{?}}$$

8.

$$\boxed{?} \xrightarrow{\times 3} 18$$
$$\xleftarrow{\div \boxed{?}}$$

11.

$$8 \xrightarrow{\times 7} \boxed{?}$$
$$\xleftarrow{\div \boxed{?}}$$

9.

$$\boxed{?} \xrightarrow{\times \boxed{?}} 40$$
$$\xleftarrow{\div 5}$$

12.

$$9 \xrightarrow{\times \boxed{?}} \boxed{?}$$
$$\xleftarrow{\div 8}$$

B Now complete these:

e.g.

$$12 \diagup \begin{matrix} 4 \\ 4 \\ 4 \end{matrix}$$

1.

8

5.

21

9.

15

2.

14

6.

36

10.

12

3.

30

7.

30

11.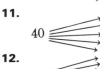

40

4.

40

8.

18

12.

63

Exercise 32

Estimate the answers to these. Work with one significant figure.

1. $87 \div 2$
2. $76 \div 4$
3. $92 \div 6$
4. $59 \div 3$
5. $178 \div 5$
6. $880 \div 9$
7. $375 \div 8$

8. $715 \div 7$
9. $288 \div 3$
10. $637 \div 4$
11. $350 \div 8$
12. $2915 \div 6$
13. $7403 \div 5$
14. $8792 \div 2$

15. $9032 \div 9$
16. $5565 \div 5$
17. $8650 \div 4$
18. $6917 \div 7$
19. $4734 \div 8$
20. $8500 \div 6$

Exercise 33

These are all division questions:

$15 \div 3$, $\frac{15}{3}$, $3\,\overline{)15}$, $3\,\lceil\overline{15}$, $3\,)15$ $3\,\lfloor 15$

They all say the same thing.
You may set these out in any of the ways shown above:

1. $2\,\overline{)80}$ **7.** $4\,\lfloor 48$ **13.** $4\,\overline{)804}$ **19.** $3\,\lceil\overline{699}$

2. $2\,)46$ **8.** $3\,\overline{)96}$ **14.** $6\,\overline{)660}$ **20.** $3\,\overline{)690}$

3. $82 \div 2$ **9.** $3\,\overline{)60}$ **15.** $2\,\overline{)648}$ **21.** $2\,\lfloor 608$

4. $3\,\lceil\overline{69}$ **10.** $3\,\overline{)900}$ **16.** $264 \div 2$ **22.** $2\,)486$

5. $4\,\overline{)80}$ **11.** $3\,\overline{)963}$ **17.** $3\,\lceil\overline{936}$ **23.** $3\,\overline{)906}$

6. $4\,\overline{)84}$ **12.** $4\,\lfloor 800$ **18.** $4\,\lfloor 484$ **24.** $3\,\overline{)396}$

Exercise 34

You may set these out in any of the ways, shown above:

1. $2\,\overline{)18}$	**11.** $2\,\overline{)614}$	**21.** $4\,\overline{)536}$	**31.** $7\,\overline{)5124}$
2. $2\,\overline{)38}$	**12.** $3\,\overline{)948}$	**22.** $8\,\overline{)344}$	**32.** $9\,\overline{)8037}$
3. $3\,\overline{)45}$	**13.** $6\,\overline{)642}$	**23.** $9\,\overline{)513}$	**33.** $4\,\overline{)3008}$
4. $3\,\overline{)84}$	**14.** $2\,\overline{)146}$	**24.** $9\,\overline{)702}$	**34.** $6\,\overline{)7104}$
5. $4\,\overline{)92}$	**15.** $2\,\overline{)728}$	**25.** $6\,\overline{)858}$	**35.** $8\,\overline{)3440}$
6. $5\,\overline{)75}$	**16.** $3\,\overline{)279}$	**26.** $8\,\overline{)672}$	**36.** $7\,\overline{)6307}$
7. $6\,\overline{)84}$	**17.** $7\,\overline{)847}$	**27.** $7\,\overline{)441}$	**37.** $5\,\overline{)7035}$
8. $8\,\overline{)96}$	**18.** $3\,\overline{)759}$	**28.** $2\,\overline{)5628}$	**38.** $9\,\overline{)8775}$
9. $7\,\overline{)91}$	**19.** $6\,\overline{)846}$	**29.** $3\,\overline{)6726}$	**39.** $8\,\overline{)3400}$
10. $2\,\overline{)438}$	**20.** $3\,\overline{)261}$	**30.** $5\,\overline{)2845}$	**40.** $6\,\overline{)7056}$

Exercise 35

1. (a) I have a piece of string that is 18 m long.
How many lengths of 3 m can I cut from this?
(b) $18 - 3 - 3 - 3 - 3 - 3 - 3 = \boxed{?}$
(c) $18 \div 3 = \boxed{?}$

2. (a) How many fives can be subtracted from 50?
(b) $50 - 5 - 5 - 5 - 5 - 5 - 5 - 5 - 5 - 5 - 5 = \boxed{?}$
(c) $50 \div 5 = \boxed{?}$

3. (a) How many times can 8 be subtracted from 56?
(b) $56 - 8 - 8 - 8 - 8 - 8 - 8 - 8 = \boxed{?}$
(c) $56 \div 8 = \boxed{?}$

4. (a) A piece of ribbon is 54 m long. How many lengths of 9 m can be cut from this?
(b) $54 - 9 - 9 - 9 - 9 - 9 - 9 = \boxed{?}$
(c) $54 \div 9 = \boxed{?}$

Exercise 36

1. How many weeks are there in 98 days?

2. I have 76 tablets. How many days will they last if I take 4 each day?

3. A shopkeeper bought 840 pencils. They were sold in boxes of 10. How many boxes did he buy?

4. 6 people share 102 cards. How many does each get?

5. Buttons are sold in packs of eight. How many packs have I got if I have 272 buttons?

6. Out of a box of 203 sweets, how many girls can be given 7 each?

7. A piece of rope 365 m in length is cut into 5 m lengths. How many pieces are obtained?

8. 684 biscuits are put into 9 boxes. How many biscuits are put into each box?

9. Two people share 76 badges. How many do they each get?

10. 195 kg of potatoes are put into 3 kg bags. How many bags are needed?

11. How many egg boxes are needed to hold 468 eggs if each box holds 6 eggs?

12. How many boxes are needed to hold 18 dozen eggs if each box holds 6 eggs?

13. Stamps are put into packets of nine. How many packets are needed for 1764 stamps?

14. Four people share 1296 counters. How many does each get?

15. 2980 tins are put into boxes. Each box holds 10 tins. How many boxes are needed?

16. 3495 washers are sold in packs of five. How many packs are there?

17. A 162 m length of cable is cut into 3 m lengths. How many lengths are obtained?

18. Eight buns will fit into a box. How many boxes are needed for 1472 buns?

Exercise 37

1. When 11 oranges are shared equally between 2 people, how many are left over?

2. Three people share 14 bars of chocolate equally. How many are left over?

3. Five girls shared 23 balloons. If they each received the same number, how many were left over?

4. Egg boxes hold half a dozen eggs each. How many boxes can be filled from 371 eggs?
How many eggs will be left over?

5. How many cars are needed to carry 98 people if each car will seat four people?
If the last car is the only car that is not full, how many people will be in it?

6. 462 cm of string was cut into 9 cm lengths. How many 9 cm lengths were obtained?
What length was left over?

7. Coloured pencils were packed into boxes of ten. How many full boxes were made up out of 586 pencils?
How many pencils were left over?

8. Certain boxes would only hold nine tins of beans. How many boxes were used for 347 tins if the last box was not filled?
How many tins were there in the last box?

9. How many packets of curtain hooks must I buy if I need 250 hooks and they are sold in packets containing eight?
How many hooks will I have left over?

10. If I divide 185 cm into 7 cm lengths, what length will I have left over?

Exercise 38

A Work these out on your calculator:

1. $168 \div 4$	**4.** $2345 \div 35$	**7.** $15\,750 \div 250$	**10.** $36\,936 \div 18$
2. $1876 \div 7$	**5.** $5719 \div 19$	**8.** $5252 \div 101$	**11.** $36\,936 \div 27$
3. $2637 \div 9$	**6.** $1869 \div 21$	**9.** $11\,877 \div 37$	**12.** $36\,936 \div 108$

B Are these statements true or false? (Check them on your calculator.)

1. $1577 \div 19 = 19 \div 1577$ **2.** $1764 \div 36 = 36 \div 1764$

C Try these:

1. $14 \times 8 \div 8 = \boxed{?}$ **6.** $2856 \div 34 \times 34 = \boxed{?}$

2. $238 \div 7 \times 7 = \boxed{?}$ **7.** $4182 \div 41 \times 41 = \boxed{?}$

3. $649 \div 11 \times 11 = \boxed{?}$ **8.** $2401 \times 49 \div 49 = \boxed{?}$

4. $1140 \times 15 \div 15 = \boxed{?}$ **9.** $7081 \times 73 \div 73 = \boxed{?}$

5. $851 \times 23 \div 23 = \boxed{?}$ **10.** $42\,276 \div 156 \times 156 = \boxed{?}$

D Use your calculator to find the remainder when 3567 is divided by 17.

4 More Work on Numbers and Money

Exercise 1

Find the number that is exactly halfway between the two given numbers:

1. 5 and 13	**11.** 6 and 78	**21.** 136 and 24
2. 4 and 18	**12.** 17 and 83	**22.** 507 and 43
3. 8 and 26	**13.** 37 and 73	**23.** 58 and 624
4. 19 and 27	**14.** 24 and 62	**24.** 139 and 413
5. 13 and 29	**15.** 86 and 32	**25.** 845 and 387
6. 0 and 26	**16.** 97 and 29	**26.** 653 and 135
7. 6 and 34	**17.** 12 and 42	**27.** 615 and 461
8. 12 and 52	**18.** 15 and 45	**28.** 322 and 570
9. 17 and 45	**19.** 6 and 78	**29.** 537 and 269
10. 3 and 39	**20.** 48 and 10	**30.** 834 and 464

Exercise 2

Find all the even numbers in this list. Put them in order of size. Start with the smallest first.

432	199	64	205	73	800	376	277
56	2071	528	1054	390	5215	2403	6318
711	29	456	42	497	3104	7	1062

Exercise 3

For each question, write a sentence using all the given words.
e.g. nine, two, seven, from — 'Two from nine equals seven.'
(Note that other words may also be used.)

1. eight, five, thirteen, sum
2. four, three, twelve, product
3. four, three, twelve, divided by
4. eight, two, divisor

5. eight, two, divisible by
6. seven, twelve, nineteen, plus, equals
7. nine, fifteen, twenty-four, more than
8. six, thirty-one, thirty-seven, difference between

Exercise 4

Copy this number line:

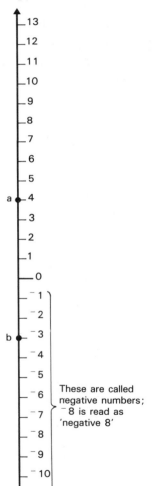

Answer these using a calculator and mark your answers on your number line. (The first two have been answered for you — answers *a* and *b* on the number line.)

e.g. 1   (*a*) 7 − 3 = 4
e.g. 2   (*b*) 5 − 8 = ⁻3

(*c*)   10 − 5

(*d*)   14 − 5

(*e*)   28 − 15

(*f*)   7 − 11

(*g*)   3 − 12

(*h*)   2 − 9

(*i*)   9 − 2

(*j*)   19 − 19

(*k*)   18 − 24

(*l*)   24 − 22

(*m*) 22 − 24

(*n*)   32 − 43

Exercise 5

Copy these, but replace each box with = or ≠ to make each statement correct. (You may use a calculator to help you.)

A
1. 486 + 397 ? 397 + 486
2. 795 + 48 ? 48 + 795
3. 142 − 317 ? 317 − 142
4. 238 − 109 ? 109 − 238
5. 54 × 73 ? 73 × 54
6. 365 × 48 ? 48 × 365
7. 72 ÷ 6 ? 6 ÷ 72
8. 834 ÷ 37 ? 37 ÷ 834

9. 2961 + 4527 ? 4527 + 2961
10. 8946 ÷ 134 ? 134 ÷ 8946
11. 4028 − 1765 ? 1765 − 4028
12. 965 × 488 ? 488 × 965
13. 7650 × 59 ? 59 × 7650
14. 62 351 − 9812 ? 9812 − 62 351
15. 4531 + 996 ? 996 + 4531
16. 70 516 ÷ 8972 ? 8972 ÷ 70 516

B Without calculating, say whether these are true or false:

1. 635 + 812 = 812 + 635
2. 7281 − 1416 = 1416 − 7281
3. 857 ÷ 291 = 291 ÷ 857
4. 703 × 84 = 84 × 703

5. 6142 ÷ 983 = 983 ÷ 6142
6. 4907 + 7163 = 7163 + 4907
7. 6514 − 937 = 937 − 6514
8. 484 ÷ 95 = 95 ÷ 484

Exercise 6

Here is a test. Check the answers. If an answer is wrong, copy its question and show the correct answer.

1.
```
   457
 + 226
   683
```

2.
```
   386
 + 465
   841
```

3.
```
   376
    29
 + 154
   559
```

4.
```
   724
 − 267
   453
```

5.
```
   9003
 − 4655
   4348
```

6.
```
   716
 ×   9
  6435
```

7.
```
   942
 ×   7
  6594
```

8.
```
    242
 4 )968
```

9.
```
 6 )8034
   1324
```

71

10.	5063	12.	7492	14.	384

10.
```
  5063
   958
+   27
  6048
```

11.
```
  9005
- 3768
  5337
```

12.
```
  7492
×    8
 58936
```

13.
```
   257
×   45
 10280
+ 1285
 11565
```

14.
```
   384
×   72
   768
+2688
  3456
```

15.
```
   473
× 205
  2365
+94600
 96965
```

Exercise 7

Replace each box with a digit to make the calculations correct:

1.
```
  7 ? 4
+ 1 6 ?
  ? 8 8
```

2.
```
  5 ? 7
+ ? 3 ?
  8 9 2
```

3.
```
  6 5 ?
- ? 3 5
  5 ? 4
```

4.
```
  9 ? 5
- 4 5 8
  ? 2 ?
```

5.
```
  8 ? 4
- ? 3 ?
  6 3 6
```

6.
```
  4 2 ?
- 1 ? 6
  ? 7 6
```

7.
```
  4 ? 7
×     2
  8 9 ?
```

8.
```
  6 ? ?
×     7
4 3 7 5
```

9.
```
    3 ? 8
×       4
  1 5 9 ?
```

10.
```
    2 ? ?
×       9
  ? ? 0 4
```

11.
```
2 ) 4 ? 6
    ? 4 3
```

12.
```
    ? 6 7
5 ) 8 ? 5
```

72

13. $\boxed{?}\,8\,4$

$4\,)\,\overline{7\,\boxed{?}\,6}$

14. $9\,)\,\overline{6\,1\,\boxed{?}\,\boxed{?}}$

$\qquad \boxed{?}\,8\,4$

15.
$$\begin{array}{r} 6\,4\,5 \\ +\ \boxed{?}\,\boxed{?}\,\boxed{?} \\ \hline 7\,8\,3 \end{array}$$

16.
$$\begin{array}{r} 8\,3\,2\,7 \\ -\ \boxed{?}\,\boxed{?}\,\boxed{?}\,\boxed{?} \\ \hline 2\,6\,3\,3 \end{array}$$

17.
$$\begin{array}{r} \boxed{?}\,\boxed{?}\,\boxed{?}\,\boxed{?} \\ -\ 3\,5\,1\,8 \\ \hline 4\,8\,3\,7 \end{array}$$

18.
$$\begin{array}{r} \boxed{?}\,\boxed{?}\,\boxed{?}\,\boxed{?} \\ \times\ \qquad 7 \\ \hline 9\,5\,6\,9 \end{array}$$

19. $1\,4\,8\,4$

$6\,)\,\overline{\boxed{?}\,\boxed{?}\,\boxed{?}\,\boxed{?}}$

20.
$$\begin{array}{r} \boxed{?}\,\boxed{?}\,5\,3 \\ \times\ \qquad\quad \boxed{?} \\ \hline 5\,4\,0\,\boxed{?}\,4 \end{array}$$

21. $7\,)\,\overline{\boxed{?}\,4\,5}$

$\qquad 1\,\boxed{?}\,\boxed{?}$

Exercise 8

Copy these, but replace each question mark with the signs $+$, $-$, $\times$ or $\div$, to make the calculations correct:

1. $18\ \boxed{?}\ 6 = 3$

2. $10\ \boxed{?}\ 8 = 2$

3. $16\ \boxed{?}\ 2\ \boxed{?}\ 6 = 20$

4. $32\ \boxed{?}\ 4\ \boxed{?}\ 5 = 13$

5. $3\ \boxed{?}\ 2\ \boxed{?}\ 7 = 13$

6. $8\ \boxed{?}\ 3 = 17\ \boxed{?}\ 7$

7. $15\ \boxed{?}\ 3\ \boxed{?}\ 12 = 33$

8. $64\ \boxed{?}\ 8 = 41\ \boxed{?}\ 33$

9. $84\ \boxed{?}\ 4 = 3\ \boxed{?}\ 7$

10. $18\ \boxed{?}\ 3\ \boxed{?}\ 2 = 27$

11. $60\ \boxed{?}\ 5\ \boxed{?}\ 11 = 66$

12. $42\ \boxed{?}\ 3\ \boxed{?}\ 5 = 19$

13. $16\ \boxed{?}\ 2\ \boxed{?}\ 4 = 8$

14. $50\ \boxed{?}\ 2\ \boxed{?}\ 5 = 100\ \boxed{?}\ 25$

15. $16\ \boxed{?}\ 2\ \boxed{?}\ 6 = 40\ \boxed{?}\ 8\ \boxed{?}\ 8$

16. $30\ \boxed{?}\ 3\ \boxed{?}\ 10 = 70\ \boxed{?}\ 10$

17. $48\ \boxed{?}\ 12\ \boxed{?}\ 8 = 2\ \boxed{?}\ 13\ \boxed{?}\ 2$

18. $18\ \boxed{?}\ 6\ \boxed{?}\ 4 = 8\ \boxed{?}\ 2$

Exercise 9

1. John and Ian together have 157 marbles. If Ian has 29 more marbles than John, how many have they each got?

2. Ann and Susan have 875 stamps altogether and Ann has 83 stamps more than Susan. If Ann gives Susan 39 of her stamps, how many stamps does Susan now have?

3. Richard and Paul have the same number of conkers. If Richard gives Paul 8 of his conkers, how many more than Richard has Paul now got?

4. If I read from the top of page 128 of my book to the bottom of page 173, how many pages have I read?

5. The product of three numbers is 12 122. If two of the numbers are 19 and 29, is the third number odd or even?

6. How many people are there in a queue if the middle person is ninth?

7. I have a book of tickets numbered 286, 287, 288, and so on, as far as 350. How many tickets are there in the book?

8. The graph opposite shows the daily attendance at a certain school.
   (a) On which day did the fewest number of pupils attend school?
   (b) Find the difference between the number who attended on Monday and the number who attended on Wednesday.

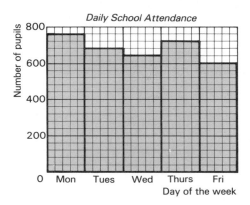

Daily School Attendance

Exercise 10

1. How many more than 18 is the sum of 13, 26, and 35?

2. How many less than 100 is the product of 4 and 17?

3. Divide the product of 15 and 8, by 6.

4. Calculate the answer obtained when the difference between 47 and 83 is multiplied by 7.

5. Take seven times twenty from a quarter of a million.

6. How many times can 7 be subtracted from 80 492?

7. The circumference of my bicycle wheel is 2 m. How far will I travel if my wheel makes 395 turns?

8. What number is three times as large as the sum of 43 and 87?

9. A piece of wood, 900 mm in length, is cut into two pieces so that one piece is 150 mm longer than the other. How long will the longer piece be?

10. In an election, 49 372 people voted for the two candidates. If Mr Brown won by 5846 votes, how many votes did Mr White, the losing candidate, get?

11. Calculate the distance from the surface of the Earth to the surface of the Moon if the diameter of the Earth is 12 757 km and the Moon's diameter is 3476 km, and if the distance from the centre of the Earth to the centre of the Moon is 384 400 km.

12. If Jack is 9 cm taller than Margaret but is 5 cm smaller than Brian, how much taller than Margaret is Brian?

13. What number, when divided by 6 and then multiplied by 3, gives 12?

14. A man, aged 32 years, is four times as old as his daughter. How many times as old as his daughter will he be in 16 years time?

15. If you earn £198 per week, how much per month is that? (You do not just multiply by 4.)

Exercise 11

1. If I add 13 to a number, the answer is 41. What would the answer have been if I had subtracted 13?

2. The first cheque in my cheque book is numbered 581931. The last cheque is number 581960. How many cheques are there?

3. Twelve people went to a concert and sat in the same row in consecutive, odd-numbered seats. If the first person sat in seat 29, what numbered seat could the last person be sitting in?

4. After shopping, I brought home twice as much money as I had spent. If I set off with £54, how much money did I spend?

5. I have £105 made up of an equal number of £10 and £5 notes. How many of each have I got?

6. What is the difference between 8 times £43 and 10 times £43?

7. Joan and Mark, together, have the same number of stamps as Pam and Ian. How many stamps has Pam got if Joan has 762, Mark has 951, and Ian has 839?

8. My car used 27 litres of petrol in travelling 432 km. How many kilometres does it travel per litre?

9. In a test, Les and Val's marks totalled 115. Les and Sue's marks totalled 142. If all three marks totalled 190, how many did each person get?

Exercise 12

1. Two numbers add up to 63. If one of the numbers is 15 more than the other, find both numbers.

2. A certain number is 4 times as big as another. The sum of both numbers is 85. What are they?

3. The product of two numbers is 48 and one of the numbers is 3 times as big as the other. What are the two numbers?

4. The sum of two numbers is 14 and their product is 48, find the two numbers.

5. A certain number is 26 more than another number. If the sum of the two numbers is 64, what are they?

6. The sum of 3 consecutive numbers is 978. Find them.

7. The numbers of two, adjacent, odd-numbered houses add up to 292. Find the house numbers.

8. The product of the numbers of two, adjacent, odd-numbered houses is 195. Find the house numbers.

9. If I write down all the natural numbers from 37 to 84 inclusive, how many digits will I have written altogether?

10. If I write down all the natural numbers from 76 to 213 inclusive, how many digits will I have written altogether?

Exercise 13

Carry out the following calculations using quick methods:

1. $3 + 19 + 7$ **6.** $797 - 388$ **11.** $286 - 198$
2. $37 + 88 + 63$ **7.** $78 + 36 + 22$ **12.** $691 - 348$
3. $99 + 68$ **8.** $523 + 138 - 3$ **13.** $752 - 488$
4. $202 + 179$ **9.** $2 \times 17 \times 5$ **14.** $812 - 449$
5. $399 - 148$ **10.** $5 \times 36 \times 2$ **15.** $6 \times 82 \times 5$

Exercise 14

Carry out these calculations:

1.
$$\begin{array}{r} 87654 \\ + 12345 \\ \hline \end{array}$$
2.
$$\begin{array}{r} 88888 \\ - 12345 \\ \hline \end{array}$$
3.
$$\begin{array}{r} 4444 \\ + 2345 \\ \hline \end{array}$$
4.
$$\begin{array}{r} 60606 \\ + 71717 \\ \hline \end{array}$$

5. Work out:
(*a*) $95 - 59$ (*b*) $84 - 48$ (*c*) $73 - 37$ (*d*) $62 - 26$ (*e*) $51 - 15$

6. Work out:
(*a*) $41 - 14$ (*b*) $52 - 25$ (*c*) $63 - 36$ (*d*) $74 - 47$ (*e*) $85 - 58$
(*f*) $96 - 69$

7. In questions 5 and 6, a 2-digit number is written down (the tens digit is greater than the units).
The digits are reversed to form a second number.
The second number is subtracted from the first.

(*a*) Write down three subtractions which give the answer 54 by carrying out the steps above.

(*b*) Write down seven subtractions which give the answer 18 by carrying out the steps above.

8. Work these out. Try to find a pattern.

$$0 \times 9 + 1 = \boxed{?}$$
$$1 \times 9 + 2 = \boxed{?}$$
$$12 \times 9 + 3 = \boxed{?}$$
$$123 \times 9 + 4 = \boxed{?}$$
$$1234 \times 9 + 5 = \boxed{?}$$

etc.

Exercise 15   A Number Puzzle

Ask a friend to write down two numbers, one under the other,   8
without you seeing them. (I suggest that the numbers be less   13
than 15, e.g. 8 and 13.)   21
These two numbers should be added and the total should be   34
written underneath the first two numbers (e.g. 8 + 13 = 21).   55
The second and third numbers should be added to give the   89
fourth number (13 + 21 = 34).   144
The third and fourth numbers should be added to give the   233
fifth number. Your friend should continue this until there are   377
10 numbers.   <u>610</u>
You can now look at the list of 10 numbers and quickly tell
your friend the total!
(The total can be found by multiplying the seventh number
in the list by 11. $144 \times 11 = 1584$.)

Exercise 16

A Look at each amount of money. If it is correctly written, copy it. If it
is wrongly written, write it in the way you think it should be written:

1. £7	**9.** 8 p	**17.** .84 p
2. 9 £	**10.** £0.08 p	**18.** 476 p
3. £5.62 p	**11.** £0.03	**19.** £6 59 p
4. £8.00	**12.** £0.60	**20.** £725
5. £42 p	**13.** £0.7	**21.** £48.00
6. £.65	**14.** £5.2	**22.** £17.00 p
7. £0.29	**15.** p 47	**23.** £0.49
8. 54 p	**16.** £ 6.0	**24.** p. 87

B Write in figures:

1. Forty-six pounds	6. Sixty-one pounds fifteen
2. Three pounds seventy-two	7. Two pounds forty-one
3. Five pounds six	8. Nine pounds thirty-eight
4. Eight pounds ninety	9. Seventy-four pounds
5. Thirty-seven pounds ten	10. Sixteen pounds twenty-three

C £7.93 is usually written as £7–93 on a cheque.

Write each of these in the normal way:

1. £4–63
2. £18–21
3. £46–82

4. £4–24
5. £61–97
6. £0–38

7. £1–05
8. £87–43
9. £239–76

Write these as on a cheque:

10. £5.12
11. £54.49

12. £9.70
13. £7.06

14. £8.54
15. £26.69

Exercise 17

1. Which single coin is worth:
   (a) 1 ten pence, 1 five pence, 2 two pence and 1 one pence?
   (b) 1 five pence, 1 two pence and 3 one pence?
   (c) 5 two pence, 1 five pence and 5 one pence?
   (d) 3 ten pence, 8 two pence and 4 one pence?

2. How many two pence pieces are worth ten pence?

3. How many two pence pieces are worth fifty pence?

4. How many five pence pieces are worth £1?

5. Five coins have a total value of 20 p. Which coins could they be? (You are allowed more than one of any British coins.)

6. Four coins have a total value of 10 p. Which coins could they be?

7. Five coins have a total value of £1. Give three different lists of coins where this can happen.

8. Can three coins have a total value of 20 p?

9. Can three coins have a total value of 10 p?

10. Can three coins have a total value of 5 p?

11. List five coins that have a total value of £2.75.

12. List four coins that have a total value of £2.05.

79

Exercise 18

1. What was the total cost of a book at £4.35 and a pen at £8.52?

2. I had £462.75 in the bank. I withdrew £47.50. How much was left in my bank account?

3. I spent £7.68 in one shop and £6.89 in another. How much did I spend altogether?

4. Mrs Bailey paid £39.89 for a dress in a sale. If the dress had been reduced by £8.50, what was its price before the sale?

5. A meal cost me £8.45. How much change did I get out of £10?

6. A television set costing £481.25 was reduced by £58.70 in a sale. What was the sale price?

7. I saved £7.25, £9.83, £8.46 and £9.52 in four weeks. How much was that altogether?

8. I spent £8.16 and £5.79 while shopping. How much did I have left out of £20?

9. I gave a shopkeeper £5. He said that, to save change, if I gave him a further 23 p then he would give me 50 p. How much did my goods cost?

10. Joyce spent £37.82 altogether at four shops. If she spent £8.29 at the first shop, £3.87 at the second, and £18.74 at the third, how much did she spend at the fourth shop?

Exercise 19

1. Find the cost of four bars of chocolate at 87 p each.

2. Two identical pens cost £16.74. What was the cost of each?

3. A man saved £5.83 per week for 5 weeks. How much did he save altogether?

4. The single fare on a bus journey was £1.29. What would the total fare for two adults be if they made a return journey at a singles rate?

5. It costs Mrs James £9.30 in fares to travel to work on five days. What is her daily fare?

6. I bought 6 cups at £1.49 each. How much change did I get out of £10?

7. (a) Which is the greater amount of money, £8.64 per month for 6 months or £50.92?
   (b) By how much is it greater?

8. A holiday for four totals £505.48. What is the cost for one person?

9. Material costs £7.99 a yard. What would three yards cost?

10. If eight metres of material costs £53.92, find the cost of one metre.

11. A stereo unit costs £345 cash. It can be bought for that price in a year on HP (hire-purchase) for £29.45 a month. How much extra is paid on HP?

12. A shopkeeper could buy 5 packs of cards for £4.45 to sell at £1.23 per pack. How much profit would he make from 40 packs?

13. A snooker table costs £592.20. It can be bought for that price on HP if twelve, monthly payments are made. Find each monthly payment.

Exercise 20

1. A shopkeeper sold five TV sets in a sale for £1493.25. If each set had been reduced by £38.95, how much more money would the shopkeeper have taken if the five sets were sold at their original price?

2. If 4 metres of material costs £25.28, find the cost of 7 metres.

3. If 4 metres of material costs £30.36, find the cost of 8 metres.

4. 4 yards of material costs £23.48. What is the cost of 6 yards?

5. Which is the cheaper buy, 400 g at £3.52 or 300 g at £2.67?

6. Mrs Black saves the same amount of money each week for several weeks. The weekly amount is a whole number of pence. If she has saved £9.59 so far, for how many weeks has she been saving?

Exercise 21

A Find the change out of £5 when you spend:

1. £2.86	**3.** £3.25	**5.** £2.66	**7.** £3.98	**9.** £4.29
2. £1.53	**4.** £2.17	**6.** £4.21	**8.** £1.94	**10.** £3.02

B Find the change out of £10 when you spend:

1. £7.34	**3.** £8.23	**5.** £3.91	**7.** £7.45	**9.** £2.67
2. £6.82	**4.** £5.48	**6.** £4.09	**8.** £9.36	**10.** £3.14

C Find the change out of £20 when you spend:

1. £17.42	**3.** £15.81	**5.** £16.04	**7.** £4.39	**9.** £10.28
2. £12.83	**4.** £11.47	**6.** £8.13	**8.** £9.65	**10.** £3.76

Exercise 22

Use a calculator for these:

1. Key in another subtraction question that gives the same answer on the display as $243 - 167$.

2. Use only the number keys, the $\boxed{=}$ key and the operation keys $\boxed{+}$ and $\boxed{-}$, which may be used as many times as you wish. ($\boxed{\times}$, $\boxed{\div}$ and other operation keys may not be used.)

Try to find the answers to:

(a) 6×3	(c) 386×5	(e) $108 \div 9$
(b) 4×37	(d) $20 \div 4$	(f) $574 \div 82$

3. Using any keys except $\boxed{8}$ or $\boxed{9}$, find the answer to:

(a) $368 + 452$	(g) $835 - 146$	(m) 7×82
(b) $678 - 246$	(h) $892 - 456$	(n) 16×94
(c) $369 + 144$	(i) $907 + 358$	(o) $84 \div 6$
(d) $579 + 251$	(j) 8×364	(p) $744 \div 8$
(e) $879 + 239$	(k) 9×473	(q) $495 \div 5$
(f) $719 - 253$	(l) 4×78	(r) $368 \div 4$

4. Ask a friend to:

(a) Key in his or her age on a calculator, e.g.	14
(b) Multiply it by 25	350
(c) Add 36	386
(d) Multiply by 4	1544

82

(e) Add the number of the month of his or her birth (e.g. May = 5)   1549
(f) Now take the calculator from your friend and subtract 144. The first two digits give the age and the last two digits give the month of birth.   1405
    The example shows the age to be 14 and the month to be May

5. Ask a friend to:
   (a) Key in his or her age on a calculator, e.g.   13
   (b) Multiply it by 5   65
   (c) Add 12   77
   (d) Multiply by 4   308
   (e) Subtract 4   304
   (f) Multiply by 5   1520
   (g) Add the number of the month of his or her birth (e.g. May = 5)   1525
   (h) Multiply by 25   38 125
   (i) Add 18   38 143
   (j) Multiply by 4   152 572
   (k) Add the date of his or her birthday (e.g. 27 May, so add 27)   152 599
   (l) Subtract 50   152 549
   (m) Now take the calculator from your friend. Subtract 22 022.   130 527

   Look at the display. The last two digits give the day of the birthday. The next two digits give the month. The first digit or digits give the age.

DON'T FORGET to press $\boxed{=}$ at each stage.

Exercise 23

Write down the units digit of the answer to each of these calculations:

1. $384 + 515$	**9.** 73×8	**17.** $872 - 689$
2. $846 - 342$	**10.** $67 + 244$	**18.** 507×39
3. 712×8	**11.** $409 - 385$	**19.** 86×71
4. $68 \div 2$	**12.** $513 - 208$	**20.** $1920 + 862$
5. $419 + 207$	**13.** $513 + 208$	**21.** 748×92
6. $724 - 316$	**14.** 82×43	**22.** $458 \div 2$
7. 317×7	**15.** 584×25	**23.** 490×36
8. $145 \div 5$	**16.** $721 + 569$	**24.** $1940 - 1374$

5 Drawing and Measuring

Exercise 1

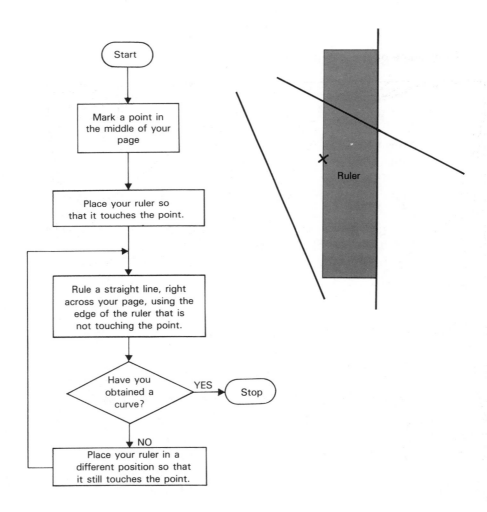

Exercise 2

Copy this pattern:

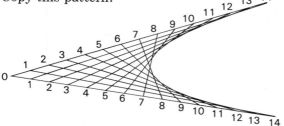

Join the numbers using straight lines so that the total is always 15.

Copy some of these patterns:

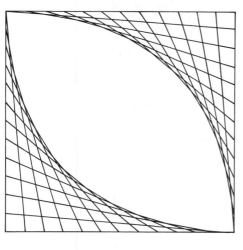

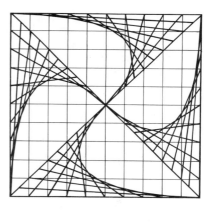

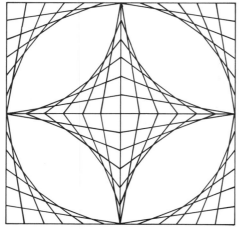

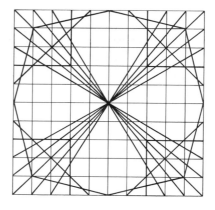

Exercise 3

You can colour in parts of your shapes to make patchwork patterns.

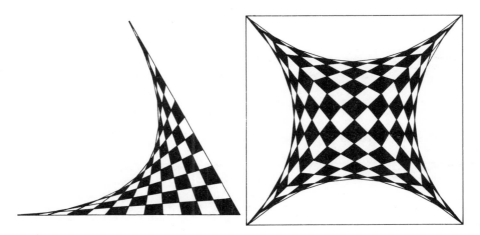

Exercise 4   A Drawing Puzzle

Each time a new line is drawn it is drawn to intersect all the lines that are already there.

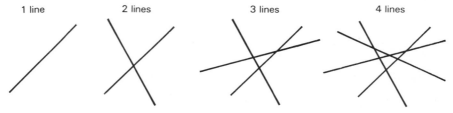

Copy and complete the following table. Look for patterns.

Number of lines	Number of points of intersection	Number of regions
1	0	2
2	1	4
3	3	7
⋮ 12		

Exercise 5

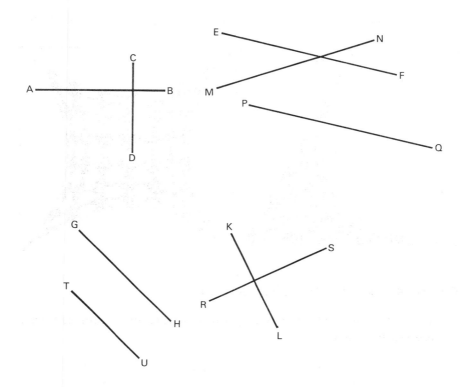

1. Which line segment is perpendicular to KL?

2. Which line segment is parallel to EF?

3. Which line segment is perpendicular to CD?

4. Which line segments intersect but are not perpendicular to each other?

5. Which line segments do not intersect any other lines?

6. Which line segments are parallel?

7. List the pairs of line segments that intersect.

8. Which line segment is parallel to one line and intersects another?

Exercise 6

To construct parallel lines:

1. Mark a straight line on a piece of paper.

2. Mark a point through which you want to draw a line parallel to the first line.

3. Place one edge of your set square along the line, as shown.

4. Place your ruler so that it touches a different side of your set square.

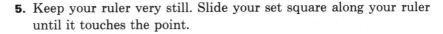

5. Keep your ruler very still. Slide your set square along your ruler until it touches the point.

6. Draw a line along your set square to pass through the point. The line you have drawn should be parallel to your first line.

Exercise 7

To construct a straight line perpendicular to a given straight line:

1. Draw a straight line. Place your set square along the line as shown. Place your ruler along the other short edge of the set square.

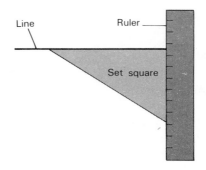

2. Keep your ruler very still.
Slide your set square along the
ruler as shown.

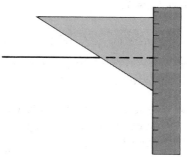

3. Remove the ruler. (Your set
square now crosses the line.)
Draw your answer line along the
edge of the set square which was
touching the ruler.

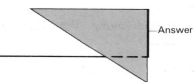

Exercise 8   An Illusion

The four thick black
lines are really parallel.
(Check by measuring.)

They do not look paral-
lel.

It is an *illusion*.

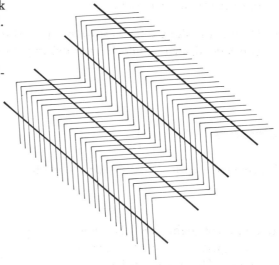

Exercise 9

The word 'line' refers to an infinite line (i.e. a line that is continuous
in both directions).

Lines are said to *intersect* if they meet in a common point.

If a heavy mass is fastened to one end of a piece of thread and allowed to hang, the thread is said to be *vertical*.

A plane surface such as a wall is called a 'vertical plane'.

A line that follows the same direction as the horizon is *horizontal*.

A surface such as a table top or a floor is called a 'horizontal plane'.

Now answer the following questions (note that many of them require very careful thought, so take care):

1. Name some horizontal lines in the classroom.

2. Name some vertical lines in the classroom.

3. Name some horizontal planes in the classroom.

4. Name some vertical planes in the classroom.

5. Is it possible to draw a horizontal line on a vertical plane?

6. Is it possible to draw a vertical line on a horizontal plane?

7. Is it possible to draw a horizontal line on a plane that is neither horizontal nor vertical?

8. A certain plane is neither horizontal nor vertical. Is it possible to draw a vertical line on it?

9. If a plane surface contains a horizontal line, must that surface be a horizontal plane?

10. If a vertical line lies on a plane surface, must that surface be a vertical plane?

11. A horizontal plane contains a straight line. Must that line be horizontal?

12. A straight line lies on a vertical plane. Must that straight line be vertical?

13. Can a horizontal plane have straight lines on it that are not horizontal?

14. Can a vertical plane have straight lines on it that are not vertical?

15. Must two vertical lines point in the same direction?

Exercise 10

fathom, cubit, foot, span, hand, palm, digit, inch

These units of length have something to do with different parts of the body.

Find out what each word means (you may need to use a dictionary), write down the meaning, then draw a sketch of that part of the body.

Measure all the lengths on yourself. (Use centimetres or millimetres.)

e.g.

Digit 21 mm

Exercise 11

Give your answers correct to the nearest whole number.

1. How many of your digits make your palm?

2. How many of your palms make your cubit?

3. How many of your digits make your cubit?

4. How many of your cubits make your fathom?

5. How many of your spans make your fathom?

6. How many of your inches make your foot?

7. Is your span and hand together greater than your foot?

8. Is your hand and foot together greater than your cubit?

9. Are 3 of your spans greater than your cubit?

10. Are 7 of your digits greater than your hand?

Exercise 12

kilometre (km), metre (m), centimetre (cm), millimetre (mm)

Which metric units would you use to measure the following? (Choose from the units given above.)

Write down the name of the metric unit and its abbreviation (e.g. millimetres, mm).

1. The length of your foot.

2. The height of your classroom.

3. The thickness of your exercise book.

4. The distance from London to Manchester.

5. The height of your house.

6. The length of one of your fingers.

7. The height of your chair seat.

8. The width of your pencil.

Exercise 13

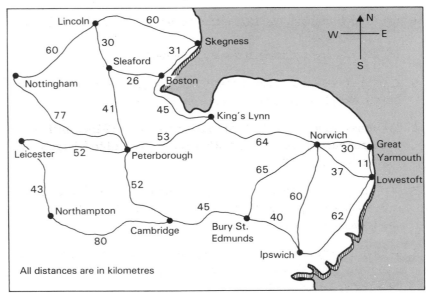

1. How far is it from Lincoln to Skegness?

2. How far is it from King's Lynn to Sleaford travelling through Peterborough?

3. Find the total distance travelled during the following journey: Ipswich to Lowestoft to Norwich to King's Lynn?

4. Mr Short travels from Bury St. Edmunds to Leicester travelling via Northampton. Mr Long travels from Skegness to Leicester travelling through Boston, Sleaford and Peterborough. Who travels the further and by how many kilometres?

5. How far is the shortest journey from Lincoln to Ipswich?

Exercise 14

Use the chart on page 94 to answer the following:

1. How far is it from Dover to York?

2. How far is it from Hull to Preston?

3. How far is it from Oxford to Carlisle?

4. (a) Which journey is further: Cardiff to Norwich or York to Cambridge?
   (b) By how many kilometres is it further?

5. A man travels from Gloucester to Nottingham and then to Edinburgh. What is the total distance he travels?

6. Mr Jones travels from Oxford to Aberdeen while Mrs Smith makes a return journey (i.e. travels both ways) from Hull to Glasgow. Who travels the further?

7. Mrs Long travels from Inverness to Newcastle. She then continues to Manchester, then to Southampton, then to Dover. How far does she travel altogether?

8. Which is further, a return journey from Penzance to Liverpool or a journey from Inverness to Perth to Glasgow to Manchester to Cambridge to London to Bristol?

	Bristol	Cambridge	Cardiff	Carlisle	Dover	Edinburgh	Glasgow	Gloucester	Hull	Inverness	Liverpool	Manchester	Newcastle	Norwich	Nottingham	Oxford	Penzance	Perth	Preston	Southampton	York	London
Aberdeen	806	749	838	368	990	203	229	782	581	170	566	554	378	797	638	782	1110	133	504	898	522	856
Bristol		246	70	440	322	598	594	56	374	851	291	269	483	346	234	118	318	670	299	120	362	192
Cambridge			299	410	205	547	562	189	256	803	314	248	370	99	134	128	563	614	315	211	251	96
Cardiff				474	373	632	630	93	406	853	323	304	512	398	262	170	378	704	330	190	392	245
Carlisle					629	157	152	384	240	414	202	190	93	454	299	418	744	234	138	536	181	491
Dover						789	781	306	456	1035	475	453	587	272	339	222	586	854	483	232	469	125
Edinburgh							72	542	378	256	360	349	174	592	437	579	904	70	296	693	318	648
Glasgow								538	392	275	354	342	240	606	450	571	899	96	293	686	333	643
Gloucester									317	797	230	213	418	288	178	77	362	618	253	152	304	166
Hull										640	202	155	200	302	141	307	675	454	190	413	61	330
Inverness											610	597	432	846	691	829	1155	187	550	942	579	902
Liverpool												58	277	374	166	267	592	430	48	387	162	338
Manchester													230	294	115	245	573	418	53	370	115	318
Newcastle														414	259	416	781	246	210	518	141	448
Norwich															197	227	658	661	362	306	296	184
Nottingham																166	539	507	192	274	139	205
Oxford																	434	650	278	107	296	90
Penzance																		978	605	363	667	464
Perth																			371	763	394	723
Preston																				371	128	350
Southampton																					403	125
York																						334

All the distances in this table are in kilometres.

94

The metric steps

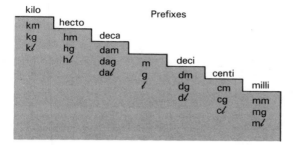

Exercise 15

Measure and state the length of each of the following lines, using centimetres:

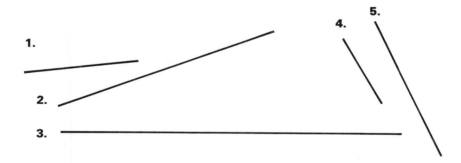

Exercise 16

Draw lines having the following lengths:

1. 8 cm   **3.** 7 cm   **5.** 12 cm   **7.** 7.5 cm   **9.** 11.5 cm

2. 5 cm   **4.** 1 cm   **6.** $4\frac{1}{2}$ cm   **8.** 2.5 cm   **10.** 9.5 cm

Exercise 17

Measure and state the length of each of the following lines, using millimetres:

1.

2.

3.

4.

5.

6.

7.

8.

Exercise 18

Draw lines having the following lengths:

1. 30 mm   **3.** 45 mm   **5.** 27 mm   **7.** 121 mm   **9.** 19 mm

2. 85 mm   **4.** 72 mm   **6.** 56 mm   **8.** 63 mm   **10.** 98 mm

Exercise 19

How long is each line? DO NOT use a ruler. Use these drawings of rulers:

1.

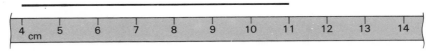

2.

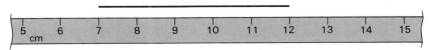

3.

4.

5.

6.

7. I measured a piece of wood with a broken ruler. I had to measure from the 2 cm mark. The ruler showed 17 cm. What was the correct length of the piece of wood?

8. My tape measure gives the length of a shelf as 89 cm. If I measured from the 15 cm mark, what was the true length of the shelf?

Exercise 20

How many millimetres are there in:

1. 7.5 cm?	**3.** 5.7 cm?	**5.** 6.2 cm?	**7.** 0.4 cm?
2. 9.5 cm?	**4.** 3 cm?	**6.** 1.7 cm?	**8.** 15.3 cm?

Exercise 21

How many centimetres are there in:

1. 40 mm?	**3.** 39 mm?	**5.** 58 mm?	**7.** 114 mm?
2. 85 mm?	**4.** 61 mm?	**6.** 16 mm?	**8.** 6 mm?

97

Exercise 22

Draw lines having the following lengths:

1. 39 mm   **3.** 9.1 cm   **5.** 51 mm   **7.** 12.7 cm
2. 6.2 cm   **4.** 7.8 cm   **6.** 108 mm   **8.** 0.8 cm

Exercise 23

Estimate, to the nearest centimetre, the length of each of the following lines. (DO NOT measure.)

1. ―――――――――――――
2. ―――――――――――――――――――
3. ――――――――――――――――
4. ―――――
5. ――――――――――
6. ―――――――――――――――――――――――
7. ――
8. ――――――――――――――――――――――――――
9. ――――――――――――――
10. ――――――――――――――――――――

Exercise 24

Estimate the length of the two grey lines, then measure them:

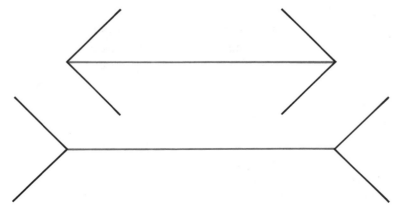

98

Exercise 25

Copy and complete:

1. 7 cm = $\boxed{?}$ mm
2. 5 cm = $\boxed{?}$ mm
3. 2.8 cm = $\boxed{?}$ mm
4. 7.6 cm = $\boxed{?}$ mm
5. 18 cm = $\boxed{?}$ mm
6. 90 mm = $\boxed{?}$ cm
7. 30 mm = $\boxed{?}$ cm
8. 65 mm = $\boxed{?}$ cm
9. 42 mm = $\boxed{?}$ cm
10. 570 mm = $\boxed{?}$ cm

11. 5 m = $\boxed{?}$ cm
12. 4.3 m = $\boxed{?}$ cm
13. 800 cm = $\boxed{?}$ m
14. 780 cm = $\boxed{?}$ m
15. 6000 m = $\boxed{?}$ km
16. 2 km = $\boxed{?}$ m
17. 7.3 km = $\boxed{?}$ m
18. 5400 m = $\boxed{?}$ km
19. 9 m = $\boxed{?}$ mm
20. 3.7 m = $\boxed{?}$ mm

Exercise 26

A Write in millimetres

1. 8 cm
2. 4.5 cm
3. 3.8 cm
4. 4 m
5. 2.9 m
6. 5.27 m
7. 0.8 cm
8. 0.3 m
9. 0.63 m

B Write in centimetres:

1. 7 m
2. 6.2 m
3. 0.6 m
4. 60 mm
5. 82 mm
6. 485 mm
7. 5.18 m
8. 0.54 m
9. 7 mm

C Write in metres:

1. 300 cm
2. 560 cm
3. 236 cm
4. 7000 mm
5. 4200 mm
6. 3540 mm
7. 8917 mm
8. 7 km
9. 9.2 km
10. 6.89 km
11. 0.3 km
12. 0.78 km
13. 50 cm
14. 61 cm
15. 0.029 km

Exercise 27

1. Draw a pair of parallel lines so that one of the lines is 95 mm long, the other line is 75 mm long and the lines are 45 mm apart.

2. Draw a straight line, PQ, 82 mm long.
   Mark a point, R, on this line so that PR = 25 mm. Draw a straight line through R that is perpendicular to PQ. Mark a point, S, on this line so that RS = 36 mm.
   How long is QS?

Exercise 28

1. Copy this rectangle:

   Divide your rectangle into 12 equal columns.
   How wide is each column?
   Divide your large rectangle into 10 rows.
   Into how many small rectangles has your large rectangle been divided?

2. Draw another rectangle, 120 mm by 50 mm, as in question 1.
   Divide this new rectangle into 8 equal columns.
   Divide the rectangle into rows that are each 10 mm wide.
   How wide is each column?
   How many small rectangles have you drawn?

3. Draw a rectangle 100 mm long by 45 mm.
Divide this rectangle into 8 equal columns and 6 equal rows.
How many small rectangles have you drawn?

4. Draw a rectangle 135 mm long by 60 mm.
Divide this rectangle into 7 columns where the first three are each
15 mm wide and the remaining four are all of equal width.
Make 5 rows, the first being 10 mm wide and the other four being
the same width.
Into how many parts has your big rectangle been divided?

Exercise 29

1. How long is a bath towel?
   A. 1.2 m   B. 0.3 km   C. 500 cm   D. 3 m

2. How high is a doorway?
   A. 1 m   B. 2 m   C. 100 mm   D. 15 m

3. How long is a pen?
   A. 12 mm   B. 12 cm   C. 200 mm   D. 2 m

4. The *diameter* of the head of a drawing pin is:
   A. 3 mm   B. 0.4 cm   C. 8 mm   D. 1.2 cm

5. The *circumference* of a football is:
   A. 0.2 m   B. 25 cm   C. 50 cm   D. 75 cm

6. What would have a length of 100 m?
   A. an ordinary house   C. an association football pitch
   B. a tennis court   D. a cricket square

7. What would have a length of about 25 cm?
   A. a shoe   C. a paperclip
   B. a pair of scissors   D. a light bulb

8. What is most likely to be 2 mm thick?
   A. an encyclopaedia   C. a cake
   B. a pen   D. a match

9. What would have a diameter of 80 mm?
   A. a cricket ball   C. a saucer
   B. a football   D. a bucket

10. What would be 7.5 m high?
   A. a small boy   C. a house
   B. a classroom door   D. a church tower

Exercise 30

What length must be added to each of these to make 1 m?

1. 80 cm	**11.** 69 cm	**21.** 380 mm
2. 91 cm	**12.** 42 cm	**22.** 430 mm
3. 76 cm	**13.** 24 cm	**23.** 265 mm
4. 64 cm	**14.** 19 cm	**24.** 176 mm
5. 57 cm	**15.** 11 cm	**25.** 743 mm
6. 32 cm	**16.** 1 cm	**26.** 53 cm
7. 28 cm	**17.** 5 cm	**27.** 27 cm
8. 13 cm	**18.** 990 mm	**28.** 208 mm
9. 96 cm	**19.** 820 mm	**29.** 72 mm
10. 35 cm	**20.** 600 mm	**30.** 72 cm

Exercise 31

How many centilitres must be added to these to make 1 l?

1. 95 cl	**11.** 83 cl
2. 81 cl	**12.** 89 cl
3. 62 cl	**13.** 97 cl
4. 54 cl	**14.** 23 cl
5. 49 cl	**15.** 20 cl
6. 78 cl	**16.** 6 cl
7. 36 cl	**17.** 44 cl
8. 40 cl	**18.** 22 cl
9. 65 cl	**19.** 18 cl
10. 56 cl	**20.** 9 cl

Exercise 32

Find, by measuring and adding, the perimeters of these shapes. Give each answer correct to the nearest centimetre.

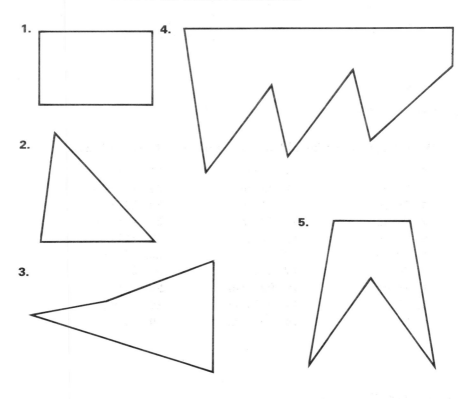

1.

2.

3.

4.

5.

Exercise 33

Find the perimeters as accurately as you can:

1.

2.

3.

4.

5.

Exercise 34

Calculate the perimeter of each of these shapes:

1.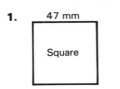

47 mm

Square

4.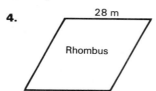

28 m

Rhombus

2.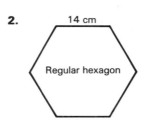

14 cm

Regular hexagon

5.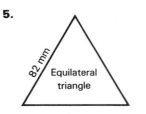

82 mm

Equilateral triangle

3.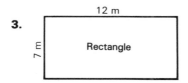

12 m

7 m

Rectangle

6.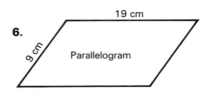

19 cm

9 cm

Parallelogram

104

7.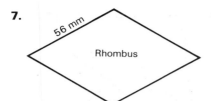

56 mm

Rhombus

12.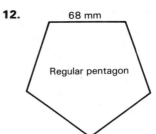

68 mm

Regular pentagon

8.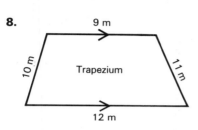

9 m

10 m

Trapezium

11 m

12 m

13.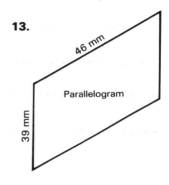

46 mm

Parallelogram

39 mm

9.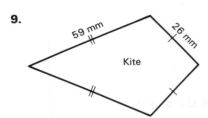

59 mm

26 mm

Kite

10.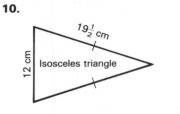

$19\frac{1}{2}$ cm

12 cm

Isosceles triangle

14.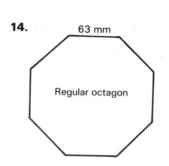

63 mm

Regular octagon

11.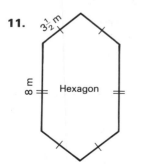

$3\frac{1}{2}$ m

8 m

Hexagon

15.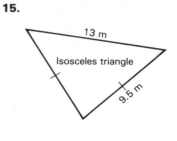

13 m

Isosceles triangle

9.5 m

Exercise 35

Calculate the missing length in each of these shapes:

1.

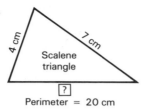

Scalene triangle, 4 cm, 7 cm, ?
Perimeter = 20 cm

2.

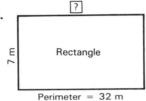

Rectangle, ?, 7 m
Perimeter = 32 m

3.

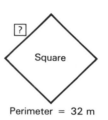

Square, ?
Perimeter = 32 m

4.

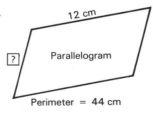

Parallelogram, 12 cm, ?
Perimeter = 44 cm

5.

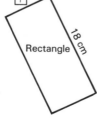

Rectangle, ?, 18 cm
Perimeter = 38 cm

6.

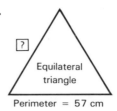

Equilateral triangle, ?
Perimeter = 57 cm

7.

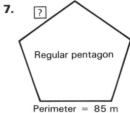

Regular pentagon, ?
Perimeter = 85 m

8.

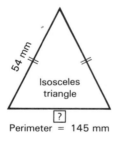

Isosceles triangle, 54 mm, ?
Perimeter = 145 mm

9.

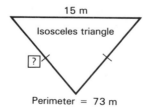

Isosceles triangle, 15 m, ?
Perimeter = 73 m

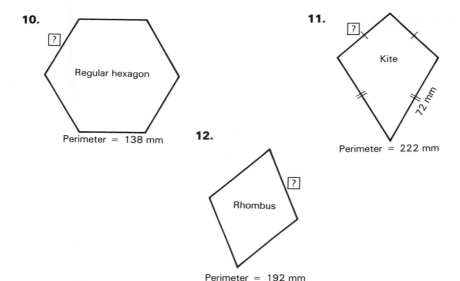

10. Regular hexagon

Perimeter = 138 mm

11. Kite

72 mm

Perimeter = 222 mm

12. Rhombus

Perimeter = 192 mm

Exercise 36

1. Each side of a square is 7 cm. Find its perimeter.

2. A rectangle has a length of 12 m and its breadth is 9 m. Calculate its perimeter.

3. A rectangular field is 87 m long and 52 m wide. Find the length of fencing needed to fence round this field.

4. The perimeter of a square is 36 cm. Find the length of each side.

5. A rectangle with length 11 cm has a perimeter of 34 cm, calculate its breadth.

6. A rectangle's length is 4 times as long as its breadth. Find its perimeter if its length is 28 m.

7. A certain rectangle has a perimeter of 96 mm. If its length is 3 times as long as its breadth, find its length.

8. A piece of wire is 2 m in length. It forms a 5-sided polygon where one side is 32 cm long and where the other 4 sides are all equal. Find the length of the 4 equal sides.

Exercise 37

1. What is the length of the perimeter of an equilateral triangle where each side is:

    (*a*) 1 cm?   (*c*) 3 cm?   (*e*) 5 cm?

    (*b*) 2 cm?   (*d*) 4 cm?   (*f*) 6 cm?

2. Copy and complete the following diagram (you may use the answers above):

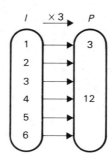

3. Make a table from question 2. Note that you can draw up the table in different ways. Choose and use the method you prefer.

Length of side (cm)	1	2	3	4	5	6
Perimeter (cm)	3			12		

Length of side (cm)	Perimeter (cm)
1	3
2	
3	
4	12
5	
6	

4. Now plot a graph of the perimeter against the length of side. [Suggested scale: 2 cm to 1 unit on the length axis (the horizontal axis) and 1 cm to 1 unit on the perimeter axis (the vertical axis).] Join all the points carefully.

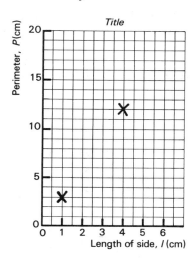

Exercise 38

Give each of these measurements correct to the nearest centimetre:

1. 3.2 cm	**7.** 7.5 cm	**13.** 6.4 cm
2. 5.7 cm	**8.** 8.5 cm	**14.** 5.5 cm
3. 8.6 cm	**9.** 17.6 cm	**15.** 29.7 cm
4. 12.9 cm	**10.** 2.3 cm	**16.** 3.28 cm
5. 1.4 cm	**11.** 9.4 cm	**17.** 6.71 cm
6. 3.8 cm	**12.** 18.5 cm	**18.** 4.49 cm

Exercise 39

Give each of these measurements correct to the nearest kilometre:

1. 4.6 km	**6.** 3.4 km	**11.** 34.72 km
2. 8.1 km	**7.** 6.5 km	**12.** 18.41 km
3. 2.2 km	**8.** 5.4 km	**13.** 8.49 km
4. 5.9 km	**9.** 4.5 km	**14.** 9.99 km
5. 9.3 km	**10.** 26.5 km	**15.** 7.46 km

Exercise 40

Give the following lengths correct to the nearest 10 cm:

1. 264 cm	**10.** 2354 cm	**19.** 2008 cm
2. 326 cm	**11.** 1846 cm	**20.** 14 291 cm
3. 421 cm	**12.** 7908 cm	**21.** 17 186 cm
4. 877 cm	**13.** 4152 cm	**22.** 8139 cm
5. 543 cm	**14.** 8337 cm	**23.** 295 cm
6. 668 cm	**15.** 675 cm	**24.** 5495 cm
7. 867 cm	**16.** 5445 cm	**25.** 6997 cm
8. 148 cm	**17.** 2085 cm	
9. 719 cm	**18.** 3116 cm	

Exercise 41

Give the following lengths correct to the nearest 10 km:

1. 547 km	**10.** 2834 km	**19.** 3209 km
2. 281 km	**11.** 1768 km	**20.** 8066 km
3. 468 km	**12.** 7123 km	**21.** 9871 km
4. 372 km	**13.** 5087 km	**22.** 7148 km
5. 844 km	**14.** 2306 km	**23.** 695 km
6. 759 km	**15.** 765 km	**24.** 7298 km
7. 623 km	**16.** 385 km	**25.** 3996 km
8. 186 km	**17.** 2745 km	
9. 367 km	**18.** 3105 km	

Exercise 42

Give these lengths correct to the nearest 100 km:

1. 3827 km	**10.** 2349 km	**19.** 32 565 km
2. 2183 km	**11.** 4567 km	**20.** 14 118 km
3. 7641 km	**12.** 24 168 km	**21.** 20 671 km
4. 1783 km	**13.** 36 517 km	**22.** 19 355 km
5. 2494 km	**14.** 58 462 km	**23.** 3249 km
6. 4218 km	**15.** 27 371 km	**24.** 8954 km
7. 6329 km	**16.** 9492 km	**25.** 37 986 km
8. 5460 km	**17.** 74 844 km	
9. 3072 km	**18.** 8859 km	

Exercise 43

1. Copy the names of the following mountains, then give their heights correct to the nearest 10 m:

Mountain	Height in metres
(a) Nanga Parbat	8126 m
(b) K2	8611 m
(c) Annapurna 1	8075 m
(d) McKinley	6194 m
(e) Aconcagua	6957 m
(f) Mont Blanc	4807 m
(g) Etna	3263 m
(h) Popocatépetl	5452 m
(i) Manaslu	8125 m
(j) Vesuvius	1277 m

2. Copy the names of the following planets, then give their diameters to the nearest 100 km:

Planet	Diameter
(a) Mercury	4828 km
(b) Venus	12 231 km
(c) Earth	12 757 km
(d) Mars	6759 km
(e) Jupiter	142 745 km
(f) Saturn	120 858 km
(g) Uranus	49 727 km
(h) Neptune	53 107 km

Exercise 44

Find the meaning of each of the following units of measurement (use a dictionary or reference books). Write down the meaning and also the Greek, Latin (or other) words from which it is derived.

1. Metre	6. Pint	11. Micrometre
2. Gram	7. Acre	12. Furlong
3. Litre	8. Centimetre	13. Hectare
4. Kilogram	9. Ton	14. Nanometre
5. Millilitre	10. Tonne	15. Stone

kilometre (km)	litre (ℓ)	kilogram (kg)
metre (m)	centilitre (cℓ)	gram (g)
centimetre (cm)	millilitre (mℓ)	
millimetre (mm)		

Choose, from the metric units above, the unit you would use to measure the following.

1. The height of a tall man.

2. The amount of medicine in a small bottle.

3. How heavy an adult is.

4. The amount of beer in a barrel.

5. How heavy a packet of nuts is.

6. The distance from Liverpool to London.

7. How heavy a 10 p coin is.

8. The amount of petrol put in a car.

9. The length of a garden.

10. How heavy your luggage is.

11. The amount of water in a bucket.

12. How heavy a packet of tea is.

13. The amount of shampoo in a bottle.

14. The length of curtain material.

15. The length (or breadth) of a book.

16. A dose of medicine.

Exercise 46

A Copy and complete:

1. $5 \text{ km} = \boxed{?} \text{ m}$
2. $5 \text{ kg} = \boxed{?} \text{ g}$
3. $3 \text{ m} = \boxed{?} \text{ mm}$
4. $3 \ell = \boxed{?} \text{ m}\ell$
5. $4000 \text{ g} = \boxed{?} \text{ kg}$
6. $9000 \text{ m}\ell = \boxed{?} \ell$
7. $8 \text{ m} = \boxed{?} \text{ cm}$
8. $8 \ell = \boxed{?} \text{ c}\ell$
9. $700 \text{ c}\ell = \boxed{?} \ell$
10. $2 \text{ cm} = \boxed{?} \text{ mm}$
11. $2 \text{ c}\ell = \boxed{?} \text{ m}\ell$
12. $90 \text{ mm} = \boxed{?} \text{ cm}$

13. $90 \text{ m}\ell = \boxed{?} \text{ c}\ell$
14. $3000 \text{ mg} = \boxed{?} \text{ g}$
15. $3.5 \text{ cm} = \boxed{?} \text{ mm}$
16. $1.9 \text{ c}\ell = \boxed{?} \text{ m}\ell$
17. $47 \text{ m}\ell = \boxed{?} \text{ c}\ell$
18. $5.6 \text{ m} = \boxed{?} \text{ cm}$
19. $8.4 \ell = \boxed{?} \text{ c}\ell$
20. $720 \text{ c}\ell = \boxed{?} \ell$
21. $6.8 \text{ km} = \boxed{?} \text{ m}$
22. $3.9 \text{ kg} = \boxed{?} \text{ g}$
23. $2400 \text{ g} = \boxed{?} \text{ kg}$
24. $8270 \text{ g} = \boxed{?} \text{ kg}$

B Copy and complete:

1. $9200 \text{ m}\ell = \boxed{?} \ell$
2. $6.7 \text{ kg} = \boxed{?} \text{ g}$
3. $7.3 \ell = \boxed{?} \text{ m}\ell$
4. $5800 \text{ g} = \boxed{?} \text{ kg}$
5. $4.6 \text{ c}\ell = \boxed{?} \text{ m}\ell$
6. $12 \text{ c}\ell = \boxed{?} \text{ m}\ell$
7. $17.3 \text{ c}\ell = \boxed{?} \text{ m}\ell$
8. $2900 \text{ g} = \boxed{?} \text{ kg}$
9. $9.2 \ell = \boxed{?} \text{ c}\ell$
10. $350 \text{ c}\ell = \boxed{?} \ell$
11. $59 \text{ m}\ell = \boxed{?} \text{ c}\ell$
12. $1.6 \text{ kg} = \boxed{?} \text{ g}$
13. $7.31 \text{ kg} = \boxed{?} \text{ g}$
14. $4.8 \ell = \boxed{?} \text{ c}\ell$
15. $6400 \text{ mg} = \boxed{?} \text{ g}$

16. $5.2 \ell = \boxed{?} \text{ m}\ell$
17. $8200 \text{ m}\ell = \boxed{?} \ell$
18. $4.9 \text{ g} = \boxed{?} \text{ mg}$
19. $5.84 \text{ kg} = \boxed{?} \text{ g}$
20. $6.48 \ell = \boxed{?} \text{ m}\ell$
21. $2760 \text{ g} = \boxed{?} \text{ kg}$
22. $5067 \text{ g} = \boxed{?} \text{ kg}$
23. $930 \text{ c}\ell = \boxed{?} \ell$
24. $2.304 \text{ kg} = \boxed{?} \text{ g}$
25. $8.261 \ell = \boxed{?} \text{ m}\ell$
26. $0.79 \ell = \boxed{?} \text{ m}\ell$
27. $0.67 \text{ kg} = \boxed{?} \text{ g}$
28. $5467 \text{ m}\ell = \boxed{?} \ell$
29. $0.6 \text{ c}\ell = \boxed{?} \text{ m}\ell$
30. $0.08 \text{ kg} = \boxed{?} \text{ g}$

1. How many centimetres are there in 1 m?

2. How many grams are there in 1 kg?

3. How many millilitres are there in 3 ℓ?

4. How many centimetres are there in 3 km?

5. How many 400 mℓ bottles can be filled from 6 ℓ?

6. If you drink 600 mℓ of milk each day, how many litres would you have drunk in a 30-day month?

7. After walking 2470 m, how much further must I walk to finish my journey of 4 km?

8. How many 125 g packets of sweets can be made up out of 6 kg of sweets?

9. How many 160 mm lengths of wood can be cut from a 4 m length?

10. 6 ℓ of water is poured into 12 containers of the same size. How many centilitres will each container hold?

11. If I have 8 packets of sweets, each packet holding 250 g, how many kilograms of sweets do I have?

12. I have 2 ℓ of lemonade. I fill four 300 mℓ glasses with this lemonade then pour the rest into 200 mℓ glasses. How many 200 mℓ glasses will I need if each one is to be filled?

13. If I make up 120 g bags of sweets out of 2 kg of sweets, how many grams will be left over after I have filled a whole number of bags?

14. The distance around a running track is 400 m. How many laps should I run if I want to run 2 km?

15. 4 identical, large boxes each hold 20 small boxes of sweets. Each small box of sweets has a mass of 150 g. If the 4 large boxes have a total mass of 13 kg when all of them are full, find the mass of each large box.

6 Circles

Exercise 1

Copy and learn the names of the parts of a circle:

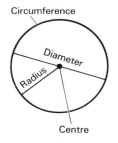

centre (Greek 'kentron' = a sharp point)

circumference (Latin 'circumferre' = to carry round)

diameter (Greek 'dia' = through, + 'metron' = measure)

radius (plural—'radii') (Latin = spoke of a wheel)

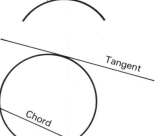

arc (Latin 'arcus' = bow or arch)

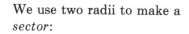

tangent (Latin 'tangere' = to touch)
chord (Greek 'khorde' = string)

We use two radii to make a *sector*:

We use a chord to make a *segment*:

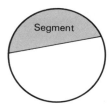

115

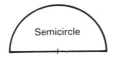

A *semicircle* is half of a circle. We use a diameter to make a semicircle.

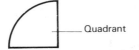

A *quadrant* is a quarter of a circle. We use two radii to make a quadrant.

Exercise 2

1. Draw a circle, radius 3 cm.
Draw a radius in your circle.
Write the length of 3 cm along the radius you have drawn.

2. Draw a circle, diameter 70 mm.
Draw a diameter.
Label this diameter with its length of 70 mm.

3. Draw a circle, radius 25 mm.
Show and name a sector on your circle.

4. On a circle, show and name a segment.

5. On a circle, name the circumference.

6. On a circle, draw and name a chord.

7. Draw and name an arc of a circle.

116

1. Carefully copy the circle pattern shown:

2. Here is another circle pattern idea.

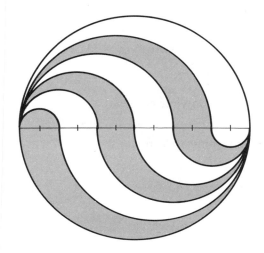

Now make some of your own.

Exercise 4

1. Why are most tins cylindrical?

2. Why are many castle towers cylindrical?

Exercise 5

Copy these, or try some of your own:

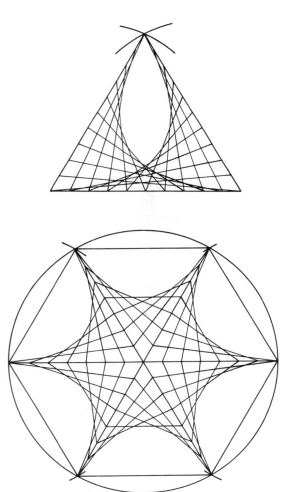

Exercise 6

1. Mark a point on your page. (You need at least 5 cm space to each side and above and below this point.)

2. With centre the marked point, draw a circle of radius 25 mm. This circle will be called the base circle.

3. With centre on the base circle, draw another circle of radius 25 mm.

4. With centre at a different position on the base circle, draw another circle of radius 25 mm.

5. Repeat step 4 over and over again until an interesting pattern is obtained. (The more circles you draw, the better the final shape obtained will be.)

Exercise 7

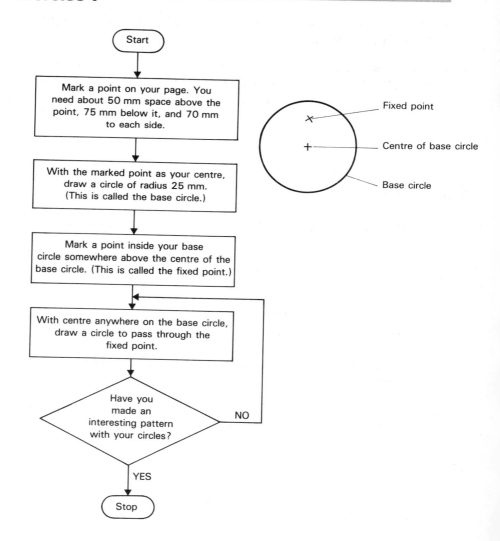

Exercise 8

1. Mark a point on your page. You need about 15 mm space above the point, 80 mm below it and 70 mm to each side.

2. With this point as your centre, draw a circle of radius 25 mm. (This is called the base circle.)

3. Mark a point on the base circle at the top. (This is called the fixed point.)

4. With centre anywhere on the base circle, draw a circle to pass through the fixed point.

5. Repeat step 4 over and over again until an interesting pattern is obtained. (The more circles you draw, the better your final pattern will be.)

Exercise 9

A 1. Mark a point on your page. You need about 60 mm space above the point, 110 mm below it and 80 mm to each side.

2. With this point as your centre, draw a circle of radius 25 mm. (This is called the base circle.)

3. Mark a point above this base circle and no more than 25 mm from it. (This is called the fixed point.)

4. With centre anywhere on the base circle, draw a circle to pass through the fixed point.

5. Repeat step 4 over and over again. (The more circles you draw, the better your final pattern will be.)

B Draw a base circle of radius 25 mm. (You need about 60 mm space above its centre, 110 mm below it, and 80 mm to each side.) Mark a point 25 mm above this base circle (call it the fixed point). Now continue as before.

C Draw a base circle of radius 15 mm. (You need about 50 mm space above its centre, 80 mm below it, and 65 mm to each side.) Mark a fixed point above this base circle between 15 mm and 30 mm from it. (If d mm = distance of the fixed point from the base circle, then radius < distance < diameter of the base circle.) Now continue as before.

D Draw a base circle of radius 15 mm. (You need about 65 mm space above its centre, 95 mm below it and 80 mm to each side.) Mark a fixed point above this base circle between 30 mm and 45 mm from the circle. Now continue as before.

E Look up the words 'Cardioid' and 'Limaçon' in a dictionary. Write down their meanings.

Arches

The roofs of the earliest buildings were supported by slabs of timber or stone laid upon and between two columns. However, stone slabs are easily cracked by heavy weights built on top of them and wooden beams are really only suitable for small buildings. Arches came into use because they enabled larger weights to be built above them. This allowed buildings to be built with higher roofs and also allowed wider gaps to be spanned.

The Romans used arches in many structures. Their arches were round. Arch shapes have changed through the ages. It is possible to guess the approximate age of a structure by the shape of its arch.

Saxon (449–1066) arches were semi-circular.

Norman (1066–1189) arches were also semi-circular, but recessed sub-arches were used; the arches were highly decorated. *Transitional Norman* showed a gradual change to the pointed arches of Gothic architecture (12th–16th century).

Early English (13th century) arches were pointed, with deep-cut mouldings and circular piers. *Decorated* (14th century) arches were also pointed, with more but shallower mouldings. *Perpendicular* (15th century) arches were pointed but more obtuse, often using a four-centred arch.

Renaissance (14th–16th century) showed a gradual change back to the round classical-style arches.

Arches are made using wedge-shaped blocks placed one on top of the other in such a way that the two sides eventually meet at the top.

The various parts of an arch have special names, as shown. The most important stone in an arch is the *keystone*. Without it, the arch would collapse. It is the last piece of the arch to be inserted.

Arches have been built since about 4000 BC.

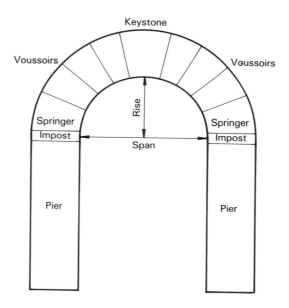

Exercise 10

Carefully copy these arches and those on the next page.

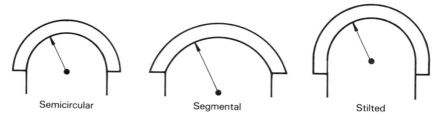

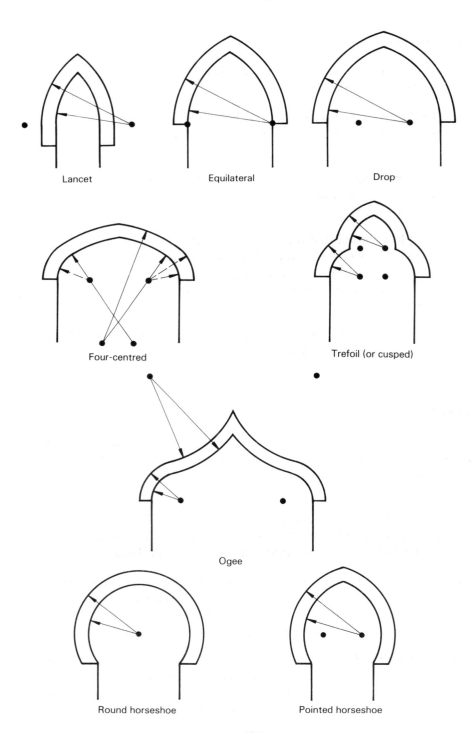

Lancet

Equilateral

Drop

Four-centred

Trefoil (or cusped)

Ogee

Round horseshoe

Pointed horseshoe

Exercise 11

1. On a piece of paper, draw a straight line that you want to bisect.

2. Open a pair of compasses so that the radius is bigger than half the length of your straight line.

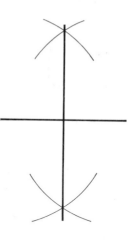

3. Place the point of your pair of compasses at one end of your line. Draw arcs above and below your line.

4. Now place the point of your pair of compasses at the other end of your line. Draw two more arcs, one above and one below the line. These arcs should cross your first arcs to give two points.

5. Join these two points with a straight line. This line should bisect your first line. It is called the *perpendicular bisector* of the line.

Exercise 12

1. Draw a circle having a radius of 30 mm. Draw a chord of length 36 mm inside this circle. How far is this chord from the centre of the circle?

2. Draw a straight line 50 mm in length. Using one end of this line as centre, draw a circle having a radius of 35 mm. Using the other end of the line as centre, draw a circle with a radius of 28 mm. Draw a common chord to these circles. How long is this chord?

3. Draw a circle having a diameter of 80 mm. Draw a second circle of radius 20 mm having its centre on the circumference of the first circle. Draw a straight line through the centres of both circles. Produce the line to meet both circles. How long is this line?

4. Draw 2 *concentric circles* (circles having the same centre). Let one circle have a radius of 45 mm and the other a radius of 25 mm. Now draw one straight line that happens to be a tangent to the smaller circle and a chord of the larger circle. How long is this line?

Exercise 13

1. Draw a circle having a radius of 28 mm.

Mark a point on the circle.

Without altering your pair of compasses, place the point on the marked point and then draw a small arc to cross the circle.

With centre on this new position, mark another small arc to cross the circle again.

Repeat this over and over again.

Into how many parts do these arcs divide the circle?

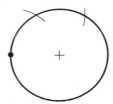

2. Start again and draw another circle with a radius of 28 mm. This time, re-set your pair of compasses to a radius of 14 mm (half-size). Mark a point on the circle. If you continue marking arcs as in question 1, will you obtain 12 equal parts this time?

Check your answer by marking the arcs.

Exercise 14

Construct some of these triangles using a ruler and a pair of compasses. These drawings only give the measurements you must use. They are not drawn to the proper sizes.

1.

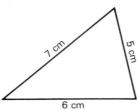

2.

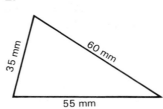

3.

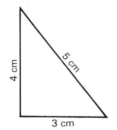

6.

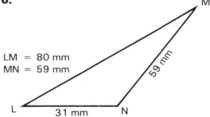

LM = 80 mm
MN = 59 mm

4.

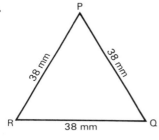

7.

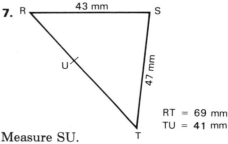

RT = 69 mm
TU = 41 mm

Measure SU.

5.

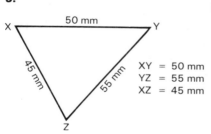

XY = 50 mm
YZ = 55 mm
XZ = 45 mm

8.

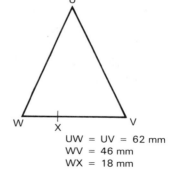

UW = UV = 62 mm
WV = 46 mm
WX = 18 mm

Measure UX.

Exercise 15

1. Construct △PQR such that PQ = 55 mm, QR = 40 mm and PR = 45 mm. Mark a point, S, on PQ, such that PS = 30 mm. How long is RS?

2. Construct △ABC such that BC = 70 mm, AC = 30 mm, and AB = 65 mm. Mark a point, P, where P is the mid-point of BC. How long is AP?

3. Construct △XYZ where all three sides are 50 mm long. Find out the name of this type of triangle.

4. Construct △LMN where LM = MN = 45 mm and where LN = 30 mm.
   (a) What sort of triangle is this?
   (b) If LN is the base of this triangle, measure its perpendicular height.

5. Try to construct △DEF such that EF = 75 mm, FD = 35 mm and DE = 30 mm. What do you notice?

6. Construct △STU where TU = 58 mm, US = 50 mm, and ST = 45 mm. Mark points P and Q where P is the mid-point of TU and Q is the mid-point of US. Join PQ. How long is PQ?

7. Construct △UVW such that UV = 60 mm, VW = 45 mm and WU = 75 mm. P, Q and R are the mid-points of UV, VW and WU *respectively* (i.e. P is the mid-point of UV since both are mentioned first).
   (a) How long is PQ?
   (b) How long is QR?
   (c) How long is PR?

8. Copy the given quadrilateral (the drawing is not accurate). How long is QS?

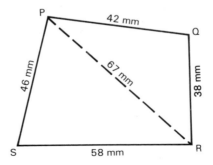

7 Factors, Multiples and Primes

Exercise 1

Copy and complete the following tables:

A Divisibility by 2

Number	Divisible by 2?	Last digit
26	YES	6
37	NO	7
68		8
42	YES	
73		
90		
45		
21		1
92	YES	
89		
54		
108		8
327		
536	YES	
284		
770		
645		

What do you notice about the last digits of all the numbers that are exactly divisible by 2?

B Divisibility by 10

Number	Divisible by 10?	Last digit
40	YES	0
38	NO	8
75		
80		
20		
64		
60		
170		
410		0
200		
206	NO	
771		
450		
283		3
620		
490		
585		

What do you notice about the last digit of each number that is exactly divisible by 10?

C Divisibility by 5

Number	Divisible by 5?	Last digit
42		
60	YES	0
25		
78		
50		
105		
51	NO	1
15		
260		
325		
485		
563		
246	NO	
630		
975		
800		
735		

What do you notice about the last digit of each number that is exactly divisible by 5?

D Divisibility by 3

Number	Divisible by 3?	Sum of the digits	Single-digit sum of digits
18	YES	$1 + 8 = 9$	9
29		$2 + 9 = 11$	$1 + 1 = 2$
51			
78	YES	$7 + 8 = 15$	$1 + 5 = 6$
49			
185			
291			
756			
948			
548			
370	NO		
426			
879			
646			
427			
519			
630			

What do you notice about the single-digit sum of the digits (last column) for each number that is exactly divisible by 3? Divide each third-column entry (sum of digits) by 3. What do you notice about all such divisions when the number is exactly divisible by 3?

E Divisibility by 4

Number	Divisible by 4?	Last 2 digits
32	YES	32
66	NO	66
184	YES	84
321		
576		
652		
742		
294		
530		
860		60
910		
986		
768		
4608		
3992		
7188		

For each number, divide the last 2 digits (in the third column) by 4. What do you notice about the results of these divisions when the number is exactly divisible by 4?

F Divisibility by 9

Number	Divisible by 9?	Sum of the digits	Single-digit sum of digits
54	YES	$5 + 4 = 9$	9
87	NO	$8 + 7 = 15$	$1 + 5 = 6$
99		$9 + 9 = 18$	$1 + 8 = 9$
358		$3 + 5 + 8 = 16$	$1 + 6 = 7$
168			
268			
745			
7652			
5310			
2362			
4689			
1971			
8396			
12587			
52587			
769878			
630927			

Look at the single-digit number found and written in the last column. What do you notice about this value when the given number is exactly divisible by 9? Divide each answer in the third column (sum of digits) by 9. What do you notice about these divisions when the given number is exactly divisible by 9?

Exercise 2

1. Is 38 268 exactly divisible by   (*a*) 9?   (*b*) 3?   (*c*) 5?   (*d*) 4?

2. Is 49 326 exactly divisible by   (*a*) 2?   (*b*) 4?   (*c*) 9?

3. Is 246 810 exactly divisible by   (*a*) 4?   (*b*) 9?   (*c*) 5?   (*d*) 3?

4. Is 3 576 288 exactly divisible by   (*a*) 3?   (*b*) 9?   (*c*) 5?

5. Is 217 348 exactly divisible by   (*a*) 4?   (*b*) 3?   (*c*) 9?

6. Is 52 413 exactly divisible by   (*a*) 3?   (*b*) 9?   (*c*) 4?   (*d*) 5?

Exercise 3

Without dividing each number completely, find the remainder, if any, from the given division:

1. 31 697 ÷ 2

2. 53 478 ÷ 10

3. 726 349 ÷ 5

4. 41 682 ÷ 5

5. 847 634 ÷ 4

6. 2 365 183 ÷ 9

7. 8 512 657 ÷ 5

8. 643 874 ÷ 3

9. 8 981 641 ÷ 10

10. 71 654 ÷ 9

11. 2 698 340 ÷ 9

12. 813 564 ÷ 9

13. 618 253 ÷ 3

14. 276 395 ÷ 4

15. 870 478 ÷ 4

16. 718 656 ÷ 3

17. 2 937 172 ÷ 4

18. 4 165 326 ÷ 10

19. 812 974 ÷ 5

20. 783 493 ÷ 9

21. 1 062 714 ÷ 9

For each divisor used in the above questions, write a brief explanation of the method you used to find the remainder.

Exercise 4

Copy and complete the given multiplication square.

From the multiplication square it can be seen that:

$1 \times 6 = 6$

$2 \times 3 = 6$

$3 \times 2 = 6$

$6 \times 1 = 6$

×	1	2	3	4	5	6	7	8	9	10
1	1	2			5	6				10
2	2	4	6				14		18	
3	3	6		12						
4				16					36	40
5				20					45	
6	6					36			54	
7		14						56		70
8			32							
9	9	18	27					72		90
10	10	20								100

The *factors* of 6 are 1, 2, 3 and 6.

1. Use your multiplication square to find the missing numbers:

$1 \times \boxed{?} = \boxed{10}$ $2 \times \boxed{?} = \boxed{10}$

What are the factors of 10?

2. Find the factors of:

(a) 20	(f) 30	(k) 52	(p) 56
(b) 18	(g) 45	(l) 75	(q) 36
(c) 4	(h) 54	(m) 29	(r) 99
(d) 27	(i) 32	(n) 70	(s) 90
(e) 3	(j) 42	(o) 39	(t) 60

Exercise 5

Find the factors of:

1. 10	**6.** 23	**11.** 121	**16.** 80
2. 12	**7.** 44	**12.** 81	**17.** 126
3. 14	**8.** 64	**13.** 66	**18.** 182
4. 50	**9.** 85	**14.** 105	**19.** 108
5. 25	**10.** 100	**15.** 175	**20.** 231

Copy and complete:

1.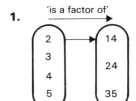

2.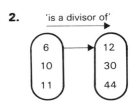

3.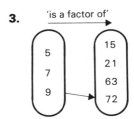

4.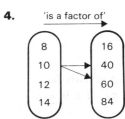

5.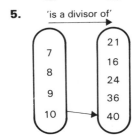

6.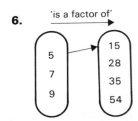

7.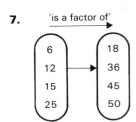

8.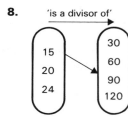

9.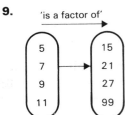

10.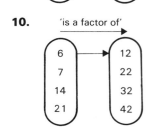

Exercise 7

Find the missing digits that will make each statement true. Note that if a single letter is used more than once in a particular statement, it refers each time to the same digit. Note also that there may be more than one correct answer.

1. 5 is a factor of $437*$.
2. 4 is a factor of $7351*$.
3. 9 is a factor of $615*$.
4. 2 is a factor of $543*$.
5. 10 is a factor of $8192*$.
6. 3 is a factor of $6521*$.
7. 9 is a factor of $46*37$.

8. 9 is a factor of $25x57x$.
9. 4 is a factor of $2753tt$.
10. 3 is a factor of $47c9c5$.
11. 25 is a factor of $685yy$.
12. 25 is a factor of $9342*$.
13. 25 is a factor of $719*5$.

Exercise 8

$63 = 7 \times 9$
We say that 7 and 9 are *factors* of 63.
63 has been written as the product of 2 factors.

Write each of the following numbers as the product of 2 factors (DO NOT use the factor 1):

1. 8	6. 49	11. 133	16. 843
2. 15	7. 51	12. 355	17. 413
3. 22	8. 65	13. 327	18. 45
4. 34	9. 87	14. 187	19. 78
5. 35	10. 91	15. 253	20. 138

Note Some numbers can be written as a product of two factors in more than one way; e.g. 63 can be written as $7 \times 9 = 63$ or $3 \times 21 = 63$ or $1 \times 63 = 63$. To find *all* the factors of 63, *all* possible products are needed.

Exercise 9

1. Write all the factors of 24.

2. Is 6 a factor of 48?

3. Is 7 a factor of 54?

4. Write three factors of 72.

5. Write three numbers that have 6 as a factor.

6. Write three numbers that have 5 as a factor.

7. Write the first three numbers that have both 2 and 5 as factors.

8. Write the first three numbers that have both 3 and 5 as factors.

9. Write the first three numbers that have both 5 and 10 as factors.

10. Write the first three numbers that have both 4 and 8 as factors.

11. Write the first three numbers that have both 4 and 6 as factors.

12. What is the largest factor of 42 other than 42?

13. What is the largest factor of 51 other than 51?

14. What is the largest factor of 405 other than 405?

15. Write all the even numbers that are factors of 40.

16. Write all the odd numbers that are factors of 63.

17. Write all the odd numbers that are factors of 105.

18. Write all the odd numbers that are factors of 50.

19. Which of the following numbers have at least one even factor: {12, 15, 21, 28, 35, 48, 65, 97, 121}?

20. One factor of 91 is 7. Find another factor of 91 other than 1 or 91.

21. One factor of 185 is 5. Find another factor of 185 other than 1 or 185.

22. List all the numbers between 250 and 280 that have 9 as a factor.

23. Find the largest 3-digit number that has 4 as one of its factors.

24. When 3 is added to a certain number, it becomes a factor of 414, but when 4 is subtracted from the same number, it becomes a factor of 429. Find the number.

1. On a 100-number square, shade all the squares that contain a multiple of 2. What do you notice about the pattern?

2. On another 100-number square, shade all the squares that contain multiples of 3. Describe the pattern.

1	2	3	4	5	6	7	8	9	10
11	12	13	14	15	16	17	18	19	20
21	22	23	24	25	26	27	28	29	30
31	32	33	34	35	36	37	38	39	40
41	42	43	44	45	46	47	48	49	50
51	52	53	54	55	56	57	58	59	60
61	62	63	64	65	66	67	68	69	70
71	72	73	74	75	76	77	78	79	80
81	82	83	84	85	86	87	88	89	90
91	92	93	94	95	96	97	98	99	100

Repeat this process, using a different number square each time, for multiples of:

3. 10
4. 4

5. 5
6. 6

7. 7
8. 8

9. 9
10. 11

1. Write six multiples of 4.

2. Write six multiples of 7.

3. Is 68 a multiple of 8?

4. Is 72 a multiple of 9?

5. Is 56 a multiple of 6?

6. Is 370 a multiple of 5?

7. Write the set of multiples of 5 that are less than 52.

8. List the set of multiples of 8 that are less than 90.

9. List the set of odd numbers that lie between 50 and 70.

10. Write the set of multiples of 3 that are greater than 25 but are less than 40.

11. List the set of multiples of 11 that lie between 60 and 100.

12. List the set of multiples of 9 that are greater than 200 but are less than 300.

13. (*a*) List the set of multiples of 2 that are less than 49.
(*b*) List the set of multiples of 3 that are less than 49.
(*c*) Write all the numbers that are less than 49 and are also multiples of *both* 2 *and* 3.
(*d*) List the set of multiples of 6 that are less than 49.

14. What is the smallest number that should be added to 289 to make it a multiple of 6?

15. 5 ⬚?⬚ 73 is a multiple of 9. Find the missing digit.

16. By what number should 45 be multiplied to make it into a multiple of 60? (Give the smallest possible number.)

17. List the numbers that lie between 100 and 140 that are 4 more than a multiple of 7.

18. List the numbers that lie between 100 and 140 that are 3 more than a multiple of 5.

19. Find a number between 100 and 140 that is 4 more than a multiple of 7, and 3 more than a multiple of 5.

20. Find the smallest number that, when multiplied by 8, becomes a multiple of 42.

Exercise 12

Copy the diagram.

On your diagram, write the numbers 1, 2, 3, 4, 5, 6 and 7.

One number should be in each area.

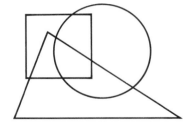

Follow these rules:

1. The sum of the numbers in the circle is a multiple of 6.

2. The sum of the numbers in the square is a multiple of 7.

3. The total of the numbers in the triangle is an even number.

Exercise 13 M

Eratosthenes, an astronomer who lived in Greece about 275–195 BC, devised a method for finding prime numbers. It is known as 'the sieve of Eratosthenes'.

Note   A prime number cannot be divided exactly by any number other than by 1 or itself.

e.g.   To find all the prime numbers up to 100:

1. Write all the numbers from 1 to 100 in the way shown.

2. Cross out the number 1 since it is not a prime number.

3. 2 is the first prime, so do not cross it out, but cross out all the multiples of 2 (4, 6, 8, etc.).

4. The next number, after 2, that has not been crossed out, is 3. Leave it, but, cross out all multiples of 3 (the first few of these have been done for you).

1̶	2	3	4̶	5	6̶	7	8̶	9̶	1̶0̶
11	1̶2̶	13	1̶4̶	1̶5̶	1̶6̶	17	1̶8̶	19	2̶0̶
2̶1̶	2̶2̶	23	2̶4̶	25	2̶6̶	2̶7̶	2̶8̶	29	3̶0̶
31	3̶2̶	3̶3̶	3̶4̶	35	3̶6̶	37	3̶8̶	39	4̶0̶
41	4̶2̶	43	4̶4̶	45	4̶6̶	47	4̶8̶	49	5̶0̶
51	5̶2̶	53	5̶4̶	55	5̶6̶	57	5̶8̶	59	6̶0̶
61	6̶2̶	63	6̶4̶	65	6̶6̶	67	6̶8̶	69	7̶0̶
71	7̶2̶	73	7̶4̶	75	7̶6̶	77	7̶8̶	79	8̶0̶
81	8̶2̶	83	8̶4̶	85	8̶6̶	87	8̶8̶	89	9̶0̶
91	9̶2̶	93	9̶4̶	95	9̶6̶	97	9̶8̶	99	1̶0̶0̶

5. The next number, after 3, that has not been crossed out, is 5. Leave it, but cross out all other multiples of 5.

6. Repeat this process until there are no further multiples left to be crossed out.

139

7. List the remaining numbers. They are all the prime numbers that are less than 100.

8. How many prime numbers are there that are less than 100?

9. How many prime numbers do you think there are between 100 and 200? Check your answer.

10. How many prime numbers are there between 200 and 300?

Exercise 14 === **M**

Instead of using a 10 by 10 number square for the sieve of Eratosthenes, arrange the numbers as shown.

As before:

1. Cross out 1 (not prime).

2. Leave 2. Cross out all the multiples of 2.

3. Leave 3, but cross out all the multiples of 3.

4. Leave the next number that has not been crossed out (i.e. 5) but cross out all its multiples.

5. Repeat step 4 as far as necessary.

1̶	2	3	4̶	5	6̶
7	8̶	9	1̶0̶	11	1̶2̶
13	1̶4̶	15	1̶6̶	17	1̶8̶
19	2̶0̶	21	2̶2̶	23	2̶4̶
25	2̶6̶	27	2̶8̶	29	3̶0̶
31	3̶2̶	33	34	35	36
37	3̶8̶	39	40	41	42
43	4̶4̶	45	46	47	48
49	5̶0̶	51	52	53	54
55	5̶6̶	57	58	59	60
61	6̶2̶	63	64	65	66
67	6̶8̶	69	70	71	72
73	7̶4̶	75	76	77	78
79	8̶0̶	81	82	83	84
85	8̶6̶	87	88	89	90
91	9̶2̶	93	94	95	96
97	9̶8̶	99	100	101	102

The numbers that have not been crossed out are the *prime numbers*. Note how easy it is to see them (they are only in certain columns). Try this for other arrangements (say 8 across, or 12, or 9).

Exercise 15

1. List all the prime numbers that are factors of 84.

2. Give three prime numbers that have a units digit of 9.

3. The sum of the digits of a 2-digit prime number is 11. Find all such prime numbers.

4. Is it possible to find any prime numbers where the sum of the digits is 5?

5. Is it possible to find any prime numbers where the sum of the digits is 9?

6. List all the prime numbers between 60 and 90 that remain prime when their digits are reversed.

7. The sum of two prime numbers is 40. Find all possible pairs of such primes.

8. Find, where possible, all the pairs of prime numbers where the sum of the two primes is:
   (a) 16   (c) 28   (e) 32   (g) 37
   (b) 22   (d) 31   (f) 35   (h) 42

9. The sum of two prime numbers is 34. Find both if one of them is a factor of 187.

10. Find, where possible, several pairs of prime numbers such that the difference between the two primes is:
    (a) 4   (c) 6   (e) 15   (g) 19
    (b) 5   (d) 7   (f) 16   (h) 22

Exercise 16

1. (a) List the set of factors of 140.
   (b) Which of the factors of 140 are prime?

2. What are the prime factors of 100?

3. List the prime factors of 34.

4. Write all the prime factors of 105.

5. How many 2-digit numbers are there that are multiples of 21?

6. Write all the multiples of 9 that lie between 843 and 912.

7. Find the largest, even, 3-digit number that has 6 as one of its factors.

8. Find all possible numbers between 50 and 90 that are 3 less than a multiple of 7.

9. Find all possible numbers between 320 and 360 that are 5 less than a multiple of 8.

10. Find the product of the smallest multiple of 6 that lies between 40 and 50 and the largest factor of 24 other than 24 itself.

11. Find the product of the smallest 2-digit factor of 78 and the largest prime number that is less than 50.

12. What is the smallest 3-digit number that has 14 as a factor?

13. Which multiple of 24 is closest to 400?

14. Find the smallest possible number that has each of the prime numbers 3, 5 and 7 as its factors.

15. Find a 2-digit prime factor of 3672.

Exercise 17

The factors of 36 are $\{1, 2, 3, 4, 6, 9, 12, 18, 36\}$.

These can be shown as:

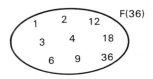

The factors of 54 are {1, 2, 3, 6, 9, 18, 27, 54}.

These can be shown as:

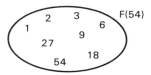

The two sets of factors overlap:

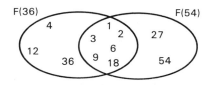

Since {1, 2, 3, 6, 9, 18} are factors of both 36 and 54, they are called *common factors*.

The *highest* of these factors is 18, so 18 is called the HCF of 36 and 54 (HCF stands for 'highest common factor').

It is sometimes called the 'greatest common divisor'.

In the same way as above (using diagrams), find the HCF of:

1. 6 and 8	**5.** 16 and 24	**9.** 24 and 72
2. 10 and 12	**6.** 25 and 35	**10.** 18 and 38
3. 8 and 12	**7.** 40 and 48	**11.** 75 and 125
4. 16 and 20	**8.** 42 and 63	**12.** 13 and 19

Exercise 18

A List the common factors of:

1. 4 and 6	**8.** 26 and 39	**15.** 12 and 25
2. 15 and 40	**9.** 44 and 132	**16.** 6, 9 and 12
3. 6 and 9	**10.** 45 and 48	**17.** 15, 35 and 75
4. 12 and 18	**11.** 60 and 45	**18.** 75, 45 and 15
5. 20 and 30	**12.** 21 and 35	**19.** 9, 15 and 12
6. 6 and 12	**13.** 42 and 140	**20.** 16, 24 and 56
7. 7 and 21	**14.** 54 and 63	

B Find the highest common factor (the HCF) of the numbers given in each of the questions above.

1. (a) Using a 100-number square, cross out all multiples of 2 using vertical lines (|).
   (b) Cross out all multiples of 3 using diagonal lines (/).
   (c) Which numbers are crossed out with 2 marks (✗)? (i.e. which 'times table' are they?)

1	2	3	4	5	6	7	8	9	10
11	12	13	14	15	16	17	18	19	20
21	22	23	24	25	26	27	28	29	30
31	32	33	34	35	36	37	38	39	40
41	42	43	44	45	46	47	48	49	50
51	52	53	54	55	56	57	58	59	60
61	62	63	64	65	66	67	68	69	70
71	72	73	74	75	76	77	78	79	80
81	82	83	84	85	86	87	88	89	90
91	92	93	94	95	96	97	98	99	100

Note that the numbers that are crossed out with 2 marks are multiples of 2 and 3.

They are called the *common multiples* of 2 and 3.

The smallest of these common multiples is called the lowest (or least) common multiple (LCM for short). What is the LCM of 2 and 3?

2. (a) On another 100-number square, cross out all multiples of 4 using diagonal lines (\), and all multiples of 9 using diagonal lines (/).
   (b) List the common multiples of 4 and 9.
   (c) What is the LCM of 4 and 9?

3. (a) On another 100-number square, cross out all multiples of 8 using horizontal lines (—), and all multiples of 10 using vertical lines (|).
   (b) List the common multiples of 10 and 8.
   (c) What is the LCM of 10 and 8?

4. (a) On another 100-number square, cross out all multiples of 5 using vertical lines (|), and all multiples of 10 using horizontal lines (—).
   (b) List the common multiples of 5 and 10.
   (c) What is the LCM of 5 and 10?

Exercise 20

1	2	3	4	5	6	7	8	9	10
11	12	13	14	15	16	17	18	19	20
21	22	23	24	25	26	27	28	29	30
31	32	33	34	35	36	37	38	39	40
41	42	43	44	45	46	47	48	49	50
51	52	53	54	55	56	57	58	59	60
61	62	63	64	65	66	67	68	69	70
71	72	73	74	75	76	77	78	79	80
81	82	83	84	85	86	87	88	89	90
91	92	93	94	95	96	97	98	99	100

Use a 100-number square as shown.

Cross out all multiples of 2 using vertical (|) lines.

Cross out all multiples of 3 using diagonal (/) lines.

Cross out all multiples of 4 using horizontal (—) lines.

Cross out all multiples of 5 using diagonal (\) lines.

(Some of these crossings out have already been done.)

Look carefully at the crossed-out numbers, then cover the number square before answering these questions:

1. Which numbers are crossed out with a ┼?

2. Which numbers are crossed out with a ✕?

3. Which numbers are crossed out with a ⟋?

4. What is the first number that is crossed out by 3 marks?

5. What is the first number that is crossed out by 4 marks?

6. Where possible, list the numbers that are crossed out by *only* the given mark:
   (a) \   (b) /   (c) —   (d) |

7. What sort of mark will cross out the following numbers (draw the mark):
   (a) 10?   (c) 76?   (e) 30?   (g) 42?
   (b) 15?   (d) 24?   (f) 96?   (h) 80?

8. If the number square continued beyond 100, by what sort of mark would the following be crossed out:
   (a) 108?   (b) 120?   (c) 225?   (d) 320?   (e) 296?

145

Exercise 21

Find the LCM (lowest or least common multiple) of the following:

1. 3 and 4

2. 2 and 7

3. 4 and 5

4. 3 and 9

5. 6 and 12

6. 6 and 24

7. 4 and 6

8. 8 and 12

9. 8 and 18

10. 9 and 12

11. 12 and 18

12. 20 and 8

13. 24 and 18

14. 10 and 21

15. 26 and 39

16. 18 and 27

17. 21 and 28

18. 2, 3 and 4

19. 2, 3 and 5

20. 3, 9 and 18

21. 6, 8 and 12

22. 6, 9 and 15

23. 10, 4 and 6

24. 15, 25 and 35

25. 12, 9 and 21

Exercise 22

1. A man and a woman set off walking together. They are in step for their first pace. If the man's stride is 80 cm while the woman's stride is 60 cm, how far will they walk before they are in step again?

2. A light is flashed every 20 s while a second light is flashed every 50 s. If they flash at the same time, after how many seconds will they once again flash together?

3. Two bells begin to toll at the same time. If the first bell tolls every 3 s while the second bell tolls every 5 s, after how many seconds will they again toll together?

4. Two pendulums start their swing at the same time. One pendulum makes 5 swings every 3 s while the second pendulum swings 7 times every 4 s. After how many seconds will they start to swing together for the second time?

5. I belong to two societies. Both meet on a Wednesday. If one meeting is held every 4 weeks while the other meeting is held every 6 weeks, after how many weeks will there be a clash?

6. Three bells start to toll at the same time. One tolls every 4 s, one every 8 s, and one every 12 s. After how many seconds will they again toll together?

7. A certain number of pupils can be grouped in groups of 8, or 9, or 12 without anyone being left over. How many pupils must there be if there are less than 100 altogether?

Exercise 23

Copy the following sequences and fill in the missing numbers:

1. 6, 8, 10, 12, ? , 16, 18, ?

2. 12, 16, 20, ? , 28, 32, ? , 40

3. 5, 10, ? , 20, ? , 30, 35, 40

4. 3, 6, 9, ? , 15, ? , 21

5. 11, 22, 33, ? , ? , 66, 77

6. 1, 4, 7, 10, ? , 16, ?

7. 2, 9, 16, 23, ? , ? , 44

8. 48, 44, 40, ? , 32, 28, ?

9. 65, 58, 51, 44, ? , 30, ? , 16, 9

10. 128, 119, 110, 101, 92, ? , 74, ? , 56

11. 1, 3, 9, ? , 81, 243, ?

12. 3, 6, 12, ? , 48, 96, ?

13. 128, ? , 32, 16, 8, ? , 2, 1

14. 320, 160, ? , 40, 20, 10, ?

15. 1, 2, 4, 7, 11, 16, ? , ?

16. 2, 3, 7, 14, ? , 37, 53, ?

17. 40, 39, 37, 34, ? , 25, ? , 12, 4

18. 1, 3, 7, 13, ? , 31, 43, ?

19. 85, 64, 46, 31, ? , 10, ? , 1

20. 3, 5, 9, ? , 33, 65, ?

21. 3, 4, 6, 10, ? , 34, ? , 130

22. 5, 6, 8, 6, 11, 6, 14, ? , 17, 6, ?

23. 2, 3, 6, 7, 10, 11, 14, ? , 18, 19, ?

24. 1, 3, 4, 6, 9, 11, ? , 18, 25, ? , 36, 38

25. 123, 234, 345, ? , 567, ?

Rectangular Numbers

Any number that can be shown as a rectangular pattern of dots is called a *rectangular number*.

12 is a rectangular number:

12 can also be shown as:

Note that ●●●● is the same as ●●●

7 is not a rectangular number. ● ● ● ● ● ● ●

A straight line of dots is not called a rectangle.

Exercise 24

Draw dot patterns to show which of these numbers are rectangular numbers:

1. 8	**3.** 5	**5.** 11	**7.** 20	**9.** 28
2. 10	**4.** 18	**6.** 15	**8.** 21	**10.** 9

Exercise 25

Show the number 24 as a rectangular dot pattern in as many different ways as possible.

Exercise 26

1. List the first 15 numbers that are not rectangular numbers (miss 1; start with 2, 3, 5, 7, and so on).

2. What are these non-rectangular numbers called?

Square Numbers

Square numbers are numbers that can be shown as a square of dots.

16 is a square number:

We also call the number 1 a square number.

Exercise 27

Show which of these are square numbers by drawing a square pattern of dots (you may like to use pegboard):

1. 4   **2.** 7   **3.** 9   **4.** 18   **5.** 25

Exercise 28

1. Write down the first eight square numbers.
2. What is the tenth square number?
3. What is the twelfth square number?
4. Find the fifteenth square number.
5. Find the twentieth square number.

Exercise 29

Copy and complete these, then give the next 3 steps:

1. (a) 1   = 1   (c) 1   = 1
        1 + 2 + 1   = 4   1 + 3   = 4
        1 + 2 + 3 + 2 + 1   = 9   1 + 3 + 5   = 9
        1 + 2 + 3 + 4 + 3 + 2 + 1 =   1 + 3 + 5 + 7 =

   (b) 1 × 1 = 1
        2 × 2 = 4
        3 × 3 = 9
        4 × 4 =
        5 × 5 =

2. What is the sum of the first 10 odd numbers?

3. What is the sum of the first 15 odd numbers?

4. What is the sum of the first 20 odd numbers?

Exercise 30

A

1	= 1	
1 + 3	= 4	
1 + 3 + 5	= 9	
1 + 3 + 5 + 7	= 16	
etc.		

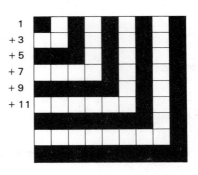

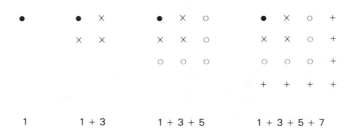

The figures above both show how the odd numbers can be added to give the square numbers.

Copy both figures.
Show the next step in both cases.

B

×	1	2	3	4	5	6	7	8	9	10
1	①					6				
2			6							
3					15					
4									36	
5				20						
6		12								
7								56		
8										80
9						54				
10				40						

Copy and complete this multiplication square.

Draw a circle around each of the numbers on the main diagonal.

What sort of numbers are they?

Exercise 31

Plot a graph to show the square numbers.

Draw a pair of axes as shown. (Suggested scale: 2 cm to 1 unit on the horizontal axis. 2 cm to 5 units on the vertical axis.)

A point has been plotted to show that the fifth square number is 25 (i.e. $5 \times 5 = 25$ which is written as $5^2 = 25$).

Do not forget to give your graph a title.

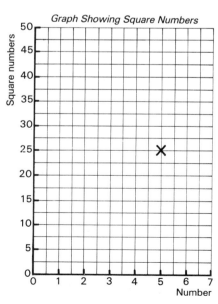

Graph Showing Square Numbers

Square numbers

Number

151

Exercise 32   Triangular Numbers

Here are the first five triangular numbers:

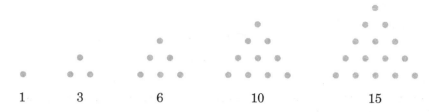

1   3   6   10   15

1. Draw a dot pattern to show the sixth triangular number. What is this sixth triangular number?

2. What is the eighth triangular number?
Draw its dot pattern.

3. Which of these numbers are triangular numbers:
24? 28? 45? 55? 65? 81? 91? 100? 120?

4. List the first seventeen triangular numbers.
Underneath each one, print O if it is odd and E if it is even. The first five of these are:

1   3   6   10   15
O   O   E   E   O

What do you notice about your answers?

5. Copy this number pattern.
Give the next three rows of the pattern

$1 = 1$
$1 + 2 = 3$
$1 + 2 + 3 = 6$
$1 + 2 + 3 + 4 = 10$
$1 + 2 + 3 + 4 + 5 = 15$
etc.

What sort of numbers are obtained in the answers?

Exercise 33

e.g.

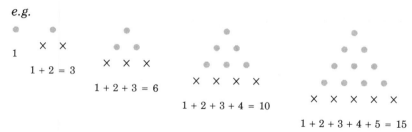

1

$1 + 2 = 3$

$1 + 2 + 3 = 6$

$1 + 2 + 3 + 4 = 10$

$1 + 2 + 3 + 4 + 5 = 15$

The above patterns show that the sum of consecutive numbers gives the triangular numbers.

A Copy these and give the next three steps:

$2 = 2$
$2 + 4 = 6$
$2 + 4 + 6 = 12$
$2 + 4 + 6 + 8 = 20$
$2 + 4 + 6 + 8 + 10 = 30$
etc.

Now divide each of your answers by 2.
What do you notice about the numbers you obtained?

		e.g. 1	*e.g. 2*
B	**1.** Select any triangular number.	6	15
	2. Double it	12	30
	3. Note your answer.		
	4. Note which triangular number you selected.	third	fifth
	5. If the third triangular number was selected, find 3×4. If the ninth triangular number was selected, find 9×10, and so on.	12	30
	6. Compare your answer with that obtained in step 2.		
	7. Try this again using a different triangular number.		
	8. What do you notice about the answers obtained in steps 2 and 5?		

Exercise 34

A Find the difference between successive triangular numbers. Copy these. Give the next five steps.

1	3	6	10	15	21	–	–	–	–	–
	2	3	4	5	6	–	–	–	–	–

B 1   3   6   10   15   21
     5×6

         3×10

	e.g.
1. Write any triangular number.	3
2. Miss the next triangular number.	
3. Write the one following that.	10
4. Multiply the two numbers together and note the answer.	$3 \times 10 = 30$
5. Now write the triangular number that you missed out.	6
6. Subtract 1.	5
7. Multiply these two numbers.	$5 \times 6 = 30$

8. Repeat these steps using different triangular numbers.

9. In each case, what do you notice about the two answers you obtained?

C Plot a graph to show the first 6 triangular numbers.

The fifth triangular number (i.e. 15) has been shown on the graph on the opposite page.

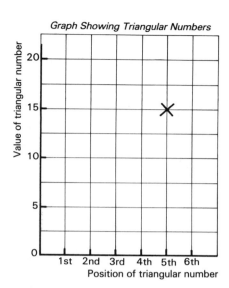

Graph Showing Triangular Numbers

Value of triangular number (y-axis)

Position of triangular number (x-axis): 1st 2nd 3rd 4th 5th 6th

Exercise 35

Copy these and give the next three steps:

1.
$1 \times 9 = 9$
$21 \times 9 = 189$
$321 \times 9 = 2889$
$4321 \times 9 = 38\,889$
etc.

2. $11 \times 9 = 99$
$21 \times 9 = 189$
$31 \times 9 = 279$
$41 \times 9 = 369$
etc.

3.
$1 \times 8 + 1 = 9$
$12 \times 8 + 2 = 98$
$123 \times 8 + 3 = 987$
$1234 \times 8 + 4 = 9876$
etc.

4.
$3 \times 9 = 27$
$33 \times 9 = 297$
$333 \times 9 = 2997$
$3333 \times 9 = 29\,997$
etc.

5. $1 \times 1 \times 1 = 1$
$2 \times 2 \times 2 = 3 + 5$
$3 \times 3 \times 3 = 7 + 9 + 11$
$4 \times 4 \times 4 = 13 + 15 + 17 + 19$
etc.

6.
$1 \times 1 = 1$
$11 \times 11 = 121$
$111 \times 111 = 12\,321$
$1111 \times 1111 = 1\,234\,321$
etc.

155

7. $1 \times 8 = 10 - 2$
$2 \times 8 = 20 - 4$
$3 \times 8 = 30 - 6$
$4 \times 8 = 40 - 8$
etc.

9.
$$6 \times 6 = 36$$
$$66 \times 66 = 4356$$
$$666 \times 666 = 443\,556$$
$$6666 \times 6666 = 44\,435\,556$$
etc.

8. $3 \times 37 = 111$
$6 \times 37 = \boxed{?}$
$9 \times 37 = \boxed{?}$
$12 \times 37 = \boxed{?}$
etc.

10. $\dfrac{22 \times 22}{1 + 2 + 1} = \boxed{?}$

$$\dfrac{333 \times 333}{1 + 2 + 3 + 2 + 1} = \boxed{?}$$

$$\dfrac{4444 \times 4444}{1 + 2 + 3 + 4 + 3 + 2 + 1} = \boxed{?}$$
etc.

Exercise 36

The following anagrams are of mathematical words. Find the words and, for each one, either state its meaning or draw a sketch to illustrate it.

1. CAR
2. FOR CATS
3. NICER TEST
4. TILER
5. GNAT NET
6. DAD NOT II
7. DREAM TIE
8. TREK O MILE
9. REAL PALL
10. MEGS TEN
11. CUT BRATS
12. RIPER MEET
13. M RIPE
14. CC MICE RUN FREE
15. L ZORINO HAT
16. RIPELAND PURE C
17. TERM E
18. LIVE CART
19. IV DIED
20. SEC ROT
21. PIT MULE L
22. U SAID R
23. MY PULL IT
24. CL RICE
25. ROD HC

8 Fractions and Decimals

Latin 'frangere' = to break or fracture

$$\begin{array}{l} 2 \longleftarrow numerator\ (number) \\ \overline{3} \longleftarrow denominator\ (French\ 'le\ nom' = 'the\ name') \end{array}$$

2-thirds   Thirds is the family *name* of the fraction.

Exercise 1   M

Copy these shapes.
Shade each as asked.

1. Shade $\dfrac{1}{2}$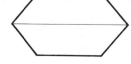

4. Shade $\dfrac{3}{4}$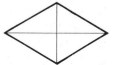

2. Shade $\dfrac{1}{4}$

5. Shade $\dfrac{2}{3}$

3. Shade $\dfrac{1}{3}$

6. Shade $\dfrac{5}{8}$

7. Shade $\frac{3}{10}$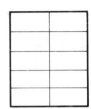

12. Shade $\frac{5}{6}$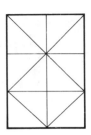

8. Shade $\frac{7}{12}$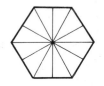

13. Shade $\frac{1}{4}$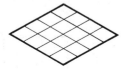

9. Shade $\frac{2}{8}$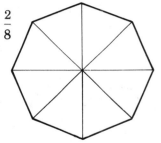

14. Shade $\frac{2}{3}$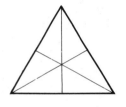

10. Shade $\frac{3}{6}$

15. Shade $\frac{3}{4}$

11. Shade $\frac{1}{2}$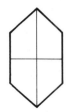

Exercise 2

What fraction of each of these shapes has been shaded?

1.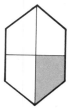

6.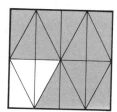

2.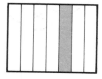

7.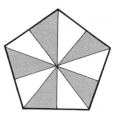

10.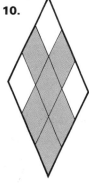

3.

4.

8.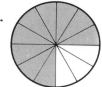

11.

5.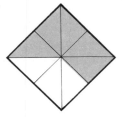

9.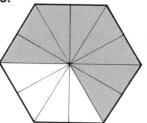

12.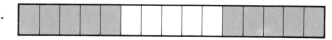

159

Exercise 3

What fraction is:

1.

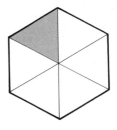

Shaded?
Unshaded?

4.

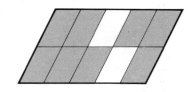

Shaded?
Unshaded?

2.

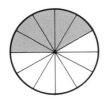

Shaded?
Unshaded?

5.

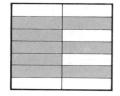

Shaded?
Unshaded?

3.

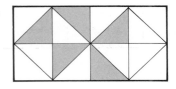

Shaded?
Unshaded?

6.

Shaded?
Unshaded?

Exercise 4 M

Copy these blocks. Divide each block into the correct number of parts so that you can shade the given fractions. Make your parts as nearly equal as you can. On each of your blocks, only shade the first part. Question 8 has been done for you.

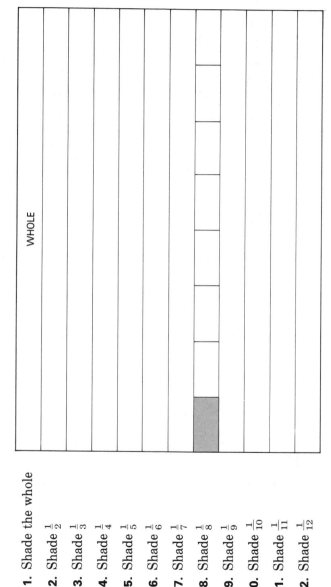

WHOLE

1. Shade the whole
2. Shade $\frac{1}{2}$
3. Shade $\frac{1}{3}$
4. Shade $\frac{1}{4}$
5. Shade $\frac{1}{5}$
6. Shade $\frac{1}{6}$
7. Shade $\frac{1}{7}$
8. Shade $\frac{1}{8}$
9. Shade $\frac{1}{9}$
10. Shade $\frac{1}{10}$
11. Shade $\frac{1}{11}$
12. Shade $\frac{1}{12}$

161

Exercise 5

What fraction of each of the above equal-sized rectangles has been shaded?

Exercise 6

A Write in figures:

1. one-half
2. two-thirds
3. four-fifths
4. three-sixths
5. two-quarters

6. three-sevenths
7. five-tenths
8. seven-eighths
9. six-elevenths
10. thirteen-fifteenths

B Write in words:

1. $\dfrac{1}{3}$ 4. $\dfrac{5}{7}$ 7. $\dfrac{2}{6}$ 10. $\dfrac{7}{11}$

2. $\dfrac{3}{4}$ 5. $\dfrac{4}{8}$ 8. $\dfrac{8}{9}$ 11. $\dfrac{9}{14}$

3. $\dfrac{3}{5}$ 6. $\dfrac{6}{10}$ 9. $\dfrac{10}{12}$ 12. $\dfrac{12}{16}$

C Write the numerator of each of these fractions:

1. $\dfrac{5}{8}$ 2. $\dfrac{9}{10}$ 3. $\dfrac{3}{14}$ 4. $\dfrac{1}{9}$ 5. $\dfrac{12}{19}$

162

D Write the denominator of each of these fractions:

1. $\dfrac{1}{6}$ **2.** $\dfrac{4}{7}$ **3.** $\dfrac{7}{12}$ **4.** $\dfrac{4}{8}$ **5.** $\dfrac{11}{15}$

Exercise 7

A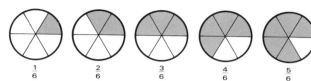

$\frac{1}{6}$ $\frac{2}{6}$ $\frac{3}{6}$ $\frac{4}{6}$ $\frac{5}{6}$ $\frac{6}{6}$

1. Why are the denominators all alike?

2. Why are the numerators all different?

B Draw a line:

  1.   50 mm long. Divide it into halves.

  2.   80 mm long. Divide it into quarters.

  3. 100 mm long. Divide it into tenths.

  4.   91 mm long. Divide it into sevenths.

  5. 108 mm long. Divide it into eighths.

C Each of these lines is divided into equal parts.
What fraction is shown?

1.

2.

3.

4.

5.

D *e.g.* 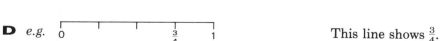   This line shows $\frac{3}{4}$.

1.

    Copy the line above. Show $\frac{5}{6}$.

163

2.

```
┌─                                                      ─┐
└
0                                                         1
```

Copy the line above. Show $\frac{3}{8}$.

3. Draw a line 105 mm in length. Show $\frac{1}{3}$.

4. Draw a line 108 mm in length. Show $\frac{8}{9}$.

5. Draw a line 112 mm in length. Show $\frac{11}{16}$.

Exercise 8

Copy and complete:

1. [?] halves make a whole. $\dfrac{?}{2} = 1$

2. [?] thirds make a whole. $\dfrac{?}{3} = 1$

3. [?] quarters make a whole. $\dfrac{?}{4} = 1$

4. [?] sixths make a whole. $\dfrac{?}{6} = 1$

5. [?] eighths make a whole. $\dfrac{?}{8} = 1$

6. [?] tenths make a whole. $\dfrac{?}{10} = 1$

7. [?] twentieths make a whole. $\dfrac{?}{20} = 1$

8. [?] hundredths make a whole. $\dfrac{?}{100} = 1$

Exercise 9

crotchet | quaver | 2 quavers
(a quarter note, $\frac{1}{4}$) | (an eighth note, $\frac{1}{8}$) | (2 eighth notes)

Copy this music and divide it into bars. 4 quarter notes fill a whole bar. (8 eighth notes fill a bar.)

Exercise 10

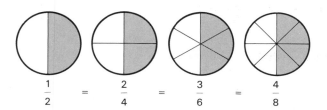

$$\frac{1}{2} = \frac{2}{4} = \frac{3}{6} = \frac{4}{8}$$

A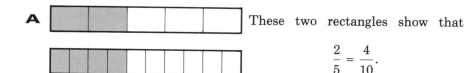

These two rectangles show that $\frac{2}{5} = \frac{4}{10}$.

1. Draw two rectangles 6 cm long by $\frac{1}{2}$ cm wide (i.e. 60 mm by 5 mm). Shade the rectangles to show that $\frac{4}{6} = \frac{2}{3}$.

2. Draw two rectangles 8 cm long by $\frac{1}{2}$ cm wide. Shade the rectangles to show that $\frac{3}{4} = \frac{6}{8}$.

165

B Write the shaded part of each rectangle in two different ways (as in the example):

e.g. 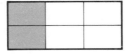 $\frac{2}{6} = \frac{1}{3}$

1.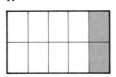

2.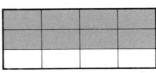

3.

C 1. Draw a rectangle, 5 cm by 2 cm. Shade it to show that $\frac{6}{10} = \frac{3}{5}$.

2. Draw a rectangle, 4 cm by 2 cm. Show that $\frac{1}{4} = \frac{2}{8}$.

3. Draw a square, 3 cm by 3 cm. Show that $\frac{6}{9} = \frac{2}{3}$.

4. Draw a rectangle, 4 cm by 3 cm. Show that $\frac{9}{12} = \frac{3}{4}$.

Exercise 11   **M**

1.

Make rectangular strips of paper, 12 cm by 1 cm, as shown.
Shade and label 6 rectangles to show:

(a) $\dfrac{6}{12}$ (c) $\dfrac{3}{6}$ (e) $\dfrac{4}{8}$

(b) $\dfrac{1}{2}$ (d) $\dfrac{2}{4}$ (f) $\dfrac{5}{10}$

Compare the shaded parts.

We can write $\dfrac{1}{2} = \dfrac{2}{4} = \dfrac{3}{6} = \dfrac{4}{8} = \dfrac{5}{10} = \dfrac{6}{12}$.

166

2. Use 3 rectangular strips.
Shade and label:

(a) $\dfrac{3}{12}$ (b) $\dfrac{1}{4}$ (c) $\dfrac{2}{8}$

Compare the shaded parts.

3. Use 4 rectangular strips.
Shade and label:

(a) $\dfrac{1}{3}$ (b) $\dfrac{2}{6}$ (c) $\dfrac{4}{12}$ (d) $\dfrac{8}{24}$

Compare the shaded parts.

4. Use 3 rectangular strips.
Shade and label:

(a) $\dfrac{2}{12}$ (b) $\dfrac{1}{6}$ (c) $\dfrac{4}{24}$

Compare the shaded parts.

5. Use 4 rectangular strips.
Shade and label:

(a) $\dfrac{8}{12}$ (b) $\dfrac{2}{3}$ (c) $\dfrac{4}{6}$ (d) $\dfrac{16}{24}$

Compare the shaded parts.

6. Use 3 rectangular strips.
Shade and label:

(a) $\dfrac{10}{12}$ (b) $\dfrac{5}{6}$ (c) $\dfrac{20}{24}$

Compare the shaded parts.

7. Use 3 rectangular strips.
Shade and label:

(a) $\dfrac{12}{12}$ (b) $\dfrac{6}{6}$ (c) $\dfrac{24}{24}$

Compare the shaded parts.

Exercise 12

A Copy these shapes carefully:

1. 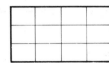 Shade $\frac{1}{2}$.
How many quarters have been shaded?

2. Shade $\frac{1}{2}$.
How many eighths have been shaded?

3. Shade $\frac{1}{3}$.
How many sixths have been shaded?

4. Shade $\frac{2}{3}$.
How many sixths have been shaded?

5.
Shade $\frac{3}{4}$.
How many twelfths have been shaded?

6. Shade $\frac{3}{4}$.
How many eighths have been shaded?

B Copy each pair of fractions. Fill in the missing numbers.

1. $\dfrac{1}{2} = \dfrac{\boxed{?}}{6}$

2.  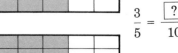 $\dfrac{3}{5} = \dfrac{\boxed{?}}{10}$

3. $\dfrac{3}{9} = \dfrac{\boxed{?}}{3}$

4. 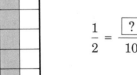 $\dfrac{1}{2} = \dfrac{\boxed{?}}{10}$

168

5. 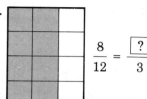 $\dfrac{8}{12} = \dfrac{\boxed{?}}{3}$

6.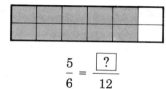

$\dfrac{5}{6} = \dfrac{\boxed{?}}{12}$

Exercise 13

A Copy the questions and fill in the missing numbers:

1. $\dfrac{1}{2}$ $\overset{\times 4}{\underset{\times 4}{=}}$ $\dfrac{\boxed{?}}{8}$

2. $\dfrac{1}{6}$ $\overset{\times 2}{\underset{\times 2}{=}}$ $\dfrac{\boxed{?}}{12}$

3. $\dfrac{1}{4}$ $\overset{\times 3}{\underset{\times 3}{=}}$ $\dfrac{3}{\boxed{?}}$

4. $\dfrac{2}{7}$ $\overset{\times 2}{\underset{\times 2}{=}}$ $\dfrac{\boxed{?}}{14}$

5. $\dfrac{4}{5}$ $\overset{\times 3}{\underset{\times 3}{=}}$ $\dfrac{12}{\boxed{?}}$

6. $\dfrac{3}{8} = \dfrac{9}{\boxed{?}}$

7. $\dfrac{3}{4} = \dfrac{\boxed{?}}{16}$

8. $\dfrac{4}{5} = \dfrac{8}{\boxed{?}}$

9. $\dfrac{5}{6} = \dfrac{15}{\boxed{?}}$

10. $\dfrac{3}{5} = \dfrac{\boxed{?}}{25}$

B Copy these questions and fill in the missing numbers:

1. $\dfrac{4}{12} = \dfrac{1}{\boxed{?}}$ ($\div 4$ / $\div 4$)

2. $\dfrac{7}{14} = \dfrac{\boxed{?}}{2}$ ($\div 7$ / $\div 7$)

3. $\dfrac{20}{25} = \dfrac{4}{\boxed{?}}$ ($\div 5$ / $\div 5$)

4. $\dfrac{30}{40} = \dfrac{3}{\boxed{?}}$ ($\div 10$ / $\div 10$)

5. $\dfrac{25}{30} = \dfrac{\boxed{?}}{6}$ ($\div 5$ / $\div 5$)

6. $\dfrac{24}{28} = \dfrac{\boxed{?}}{7}$

7. $\dfrac{28}{40} = \dfrac{\boxed{?}}{10}$

8. $\dfrac{24}{36} = \dfrac{2}{\boxed{?}}$

9. $\dfrac{24}{64} = \dfrac{3}{\boxed{?}}$

10. $\dfrac{22}{33} = \dfrac{2}{\boxed{?}}$

Exercise 14

A Copy and answer (fill in the missing numbers):

1. $\dfrac{1}{2} = \dfrac{1}{2} \times \dfrac{4}{4} = \dfrac{\boxed{?}}{8}$

2. $\dfrac{1}{6} = \dfrac{1 \times 2}{6 \times 2} = \dfrac{\boxed{?}}{12}$

3. $\dfrac{1}{4} = \dfrac{1 \times 3}{4 \times 3} = \dfrac{3}{\boxed{?}}$

4. $\dfrac{2}{7} = \dfrac{2}{7} \times \dfrac{2}{2} = \dfrac{\boxed{?}}{14}$

5. $\dfrac{4}{5} = \dfrac{4}{5} \times \dfrac{3}{3} = \dfrac{12}{\boxed{?}}$

6. $\dfrac{3}{8} = \dfrac{3}{8} \times \dfrac{3}{3} = \dfrac{9}{\boxed{?}}$

170

7. $\dfrac{3}{4} = \dfrac{3 \times 4}{4 \times 4} = \dfrac{\boxed{?}}{16}$

9. $\dfrac{5}{6} = \dfrac{5}{6} \times \dfrac{3}{3} = \dfrac{\boxed{?}}{\boxed{?}}$

8. $\dfrac{4}{5} = \dfrac{4 \times 2}{5 \times 2} = \dfrac{\boxed{?}}{\boxed{?}}$

10. $\dfrac{3}{5} = \dfrac{3}{5} \times \dfrac{5}{5} = \dfrac{\boxed{?}}{\boxed{?}}$

Compare your answers with those in the previous exercise.

B Copy and answer (fill in the missing numbers):

1. $\dfrac{4}{12} = \dfrac{4 \div 4}{12 \div 4} = \dfrac{1}{\boxed{?}}$

6. $\dfrac{24}{28} = \dfrac{24}{28} \div \dfrac{4}{4} = \dfrac{\boxed{?}}{7}$

2. $\dfrac{7}{14} = \dfrac{7 \div 7}{14 \div 7} = \dfrac{\boxed{?}}{2}$

7. $\dfrac{28}{40} = \dfrac{28 \div 4}{40 \div 4} = \dfrac{\boxed{?}}{10}$

3. $\dfrac{20}{25} = \dfrac{20}{25} \div \dfrac{5}{5} = \dfrac{4}{\boxed{?}}$

8. $\dfrac{24}{36} = \dfrac{24}{36} \div \dfrac{12}{12} = \dfrac{2}{\boxed{?}}$

4. $\dfrac{30}{40} = \dfrac{30}{40} \div \dfrac{10}{10} = \dfrac{3}{\boxed{?}}$

9. $\dfrac{24}{64} = \dfrac{24 \div 8}{64 \div 8} = \dfrac{3}{\boxed{?}}$

5. $\dfrac{25}{30} = \dfrac{25}{30} \div \dfrac{5}{5} = \dfrac{\boxed{?}}{6}$

10. $\dfrac{22}{33} = \dfrac{22}{33} \div \dfrac{11}{11} = \dfrac{2}{\boxed{?}}$

Compare your answers with those in the previous exercise.

Exercise 15

For each of these questions, draw a straight line 120 mm in length.

e.g. Divide your line into halves (label above the line).
Divide your line into quarters (label below the line).

$\dfrac{1}{2} = \dfrac{\boxed{?}}{6}$ 1 half = 2 quarters

1. Divide your line into halves (label above the line).
   Divide your line into sixths (label below).

$$\frac{1}{2} = \frac{\boxed{?}}{6}$$ 1 half = $\boxed{?}$ sixths

2. Divide your line into 2 equal parts (label above).
   Divide your line into eighths (label below).

$$\frac{1}{2} = \frac{\boxed{?}}{8}$$ 1 half = $\boxed{?}$ eighths

3. Divide your line into halves (label above).
   Divide your line into 10 equal parts (label below).

$$\frac{1}{2} = \frac{\boxed{?}}{10}$$ 1 half = $\boxed{?}$ tenths

4. Divide your line into 6 equal parts (label above).
   Divide your line into twelfths (label below).

(a) $\dfrac{1}{6} = \dfrac{\boxed{?}}{12}$ 1 sixth = $\boxed{?}$ twelfths

(b) $\dfrac{2}{6} = \dfrac{\boxed{?}}{12}$ 2 sixths = $\boxed{?}$ twelfths

(c) $\dfrac{\boxed{?}}{6} = \dfrac{6}{12}$ $\boxed{?}$ sixths = 6 twelfths

(d) $\dfrac{4}{6} = \dfrac{\boxed{?}}{12}$ 4 sixths = $\boxed{?}$ twelfths

(e) $\dfrac{5}{6} = \dfrac{\boxed{?}}{12}$ 5 sixths = $\boxed{?}$ twelfths

Exercise 16

For each of these questions, draw a straight line 120 mm in length.

e.g. Divide your line into fifths (label above the line).
Divide each fifth into 2 equal parts (mark below).

Into how many equal parts is your line divided?

(i) The line is now divided into 10 equal parts.
(ii) Each part is called a tenth.

Answer these questions.
Copy and complete the sentences (*a*) and (*b*).

1. Divide your line into thirds (label above).
Divide each third into 2 equal parts (mark below).
(*a*) The line is now divided into ⬚? equal parts.
(*b*) Each part is called a ⬚? .

2. Divide your line into thirds (label above).
Divide each third into 4 equal parts (mark below).
(*a*) The line is now divided into ⬚? equal parts.
(*b*) Each part is called a ⬚? .

3. Divide your line into quarters (label above).
Divide each quarter into 2 equal parts (mark below).
(*a*) The line is now divided into ⬚? equal parts.
(*b*) Each part is called an ⬚? .

4. Divide your line into quarters (label above).
Divide each quarter into 3 equal parts (mark below).
(*a*) The line is now divided into ⬚? equal parts.
(*b*) Each part is called an ⬚? .

173

Exercise 17

1. (a) There were 16 cups and John washed half of them. How many did he wash?

   (b) There were 16 cups and Ann washed two-quarters of them. How many did she wash?

   (c) There were another 16 cups and Susan washed four-eighths of them. How many did she wash?

   (d) Copy and complete: $\dfrac{1}{2} = \dfrac{\boxed{?}}{4} = \dfrac{\boxed{?}}{8}$

2. (a) Jane ate one-third of 24 sweets. How many was that?

   (b) Dave ate two-sixths of 24 sweets. How many was that?

   (c) Ken ate four-twelfths of 24 sweets. How many was that?

   (d) Copy and complete: $\dfrac{1}{3} = \dfrac{\boxed{?}}{6} = \dfrac{\boxed{?}}{12}$

Exercise 18

Copy and complete to make sets of equivalent fractions:

1. $\dfrac{1}{2} = \dfrac{\boxed{?}}{4} = \dfrac{\boxed{?}}{6} = \dfrac{4}{\boxed{?}} = \dfrac{\boxed{?}}{10} = \dfrac{6}{12} = \dfrac{7}{\boxed{?}} = \dfrac{\boxed{?}}{16}$

2. $\dfrac{1}{3} = \dfrac{\boxed{?}}{6} = \dfrac{3}{\boxed{?}} = \dfrac{\boxed{?}}{12} = \dfrac{\boxed{?}}{15} = \dfrac{\boxed{?}}{18} = \dfrac{7}{21} = \dfrac{8}{\boxed{?}}$

3. $\dfrac{2}{3} = \dfrac{\boxed{?}}{6} = \dfrac{\boxed{?}}{9} = \dfrac{8}{\boxed{?}} = \dfrac{\boxed{?}}{15} = \dfrac{12}{\boxed{?}} = \dfrac{14}{\boxed{?}} = \dfrac{16}{\boxed{?}}$

4. $\dfrac{1}{4} = \dfrac{2}{\boxed{?}} = \dfrac{\boxed{?}}{12} = \dfrac{\boxed{?}}{16} = \dfrac{5}{\boxed{?}} = \dfrac{\boxed{?}}{24} = \dfrac{\boxed{?}}{28} = \dfrac{\boxed{?}}{32}$

5. $\dfrac{3}{4} = \dfrac{6}{\boxed{?}} = \dfrac{\boxed{?}}{12} = \dfrac{12}{\boxed{?}} = \dfrac{15}{\boxed{?}} = \dfrac{\boxed{?}}{24} = \dfrac{\boxed{?}}{28} = \dfrac{\boxed{?}}{32}$

6. $\dfrac{2}{5} = \dfrac{\boxed{?}}{10} = \dfrac{6}{\boxed{?}} = \dfrac{8}{\boxed{?}} = \dfrac{\boxed{?}}{25} = \dfrac{12}{\boxed{?}} = \dfrac{\boxed{?}}{35} = \dfrac{16}{\boxed{?}}$

Exercise 19

A Copy these fractions. Fill in the missing numbers to make the fractions *equivalent*.

1. $\dfrac{1}{4} = \dfrac{\boxed{?}}{12}$ **9.** $\dfrac{2}{6} = \dfrac{\boxed{?}}{3}$ **17.** $\dfrac{18}{27} = \dfrac{2}{\boxed{?}}$ **25.** $\dfrac{56}{96} = \dfrac{7}{\boxed{?}}$

2. $\dfrac{1}{5} = \dfrac{4}{\boxed{?}}$ **10.** $\dfrac{6}{10} = \dfrac{3}{\boxed{?}}$ **18.** $\dfrac{7}{10} = \dfrac{\boxed{?}}{50}$ **26.** $\dfrac{3}{7} = \dfrac{\boxed{?}}{56}$

3. $\dfrac{3}{4} = \dfrac{\boxed{?}}{16}$ **11.** $\dfrac{10}{15} = \dfrac{2}{\boxed{?}}$ **19.** $\dfrac{30}{100} = \dfrac{3}{\boxed{?}}$ **27.** $\dfrac{1}{3} = \dfrac{20}{\boxed{?}}$

4. $\dfrac{4}{5} = \dfrac{\boxed{?}}{20}$ **12.** $\dfrac{20}{30} = \dfrac{2}{\boxed{?}}$ **20.** $\dfrac{4}{7} = \dfrac{\boxed{?}}{63}$ **28.** $\dfrac{300}{800} = \dfrac{\boxed{?}}{8}$

5. $\dfrac{1}{6} = \dfrac{3}{\boxed{?}}$ **13.** $\dfrac{12}{18} = \dfrac{\boxed{?}}{3}$ **21.** $\dfrac{55}{66} = \dfrac{5}{\boxed{?}}$ **29.** $\dfrac{56}{63} = \dfrac{\boxed{?}}{9}$

6. $\dfrac{5}{6} = \dfrac{\boxed{?}}{30}$ **14.** $\dfrac{10}{22} = \dfrac{\boxed{?}}{11}$ **22.** $\dfrac{7}{8} = \dfrac{\boxed{?}}{32}$ **30.** $\dfrac{7}{13} = \dfrac{\boxed{?}}{52}$

7. $\dfrac{3}{8} = \dfrac{6}{\boxed{?}}$ **15.** $\dfrac{5}{7} = \dfrac{35}{\boxed{?}}$ **23.** $\dfrac{4}{5} = \dfrac{400}{\boxed{?}}$ **31.** $\dfrac{44}{55} = \dfrac{4}{\boxed{?}}$

8. $\dfrac{6}{7} = \dfrac{\boxed{?}}{28}$ **16.** $\dfrac{5}{8} = \dfrac{\boxed{?}}{48}$ **24.** $\dfrac{36}{48} = \dfrac{\boxed{?}}{4}$ **32.** $\dfrac{63}{108} = \dfrac{7}{\boxed{?}}$

B Simplify these fractions (i.e. give the simplest equivalent fraction in each case). *Note* Some books say 'cancel', or 'simplify by cancelling'.

1. $\dfrac{9}{12}$ 7. $\dfrac{32}{40}$ 13. $\dfrac{54}{63}$ 19. $\dfrac{63}{144}$ 25. $\dfrac{108}{132}$

2. $\dfrac{9}{18}$ 8. $\dfrac{33}{36}$ 14. $\dfrac{45}{72}$ 20. $\dfrac{96}{144}$ 26. $\dfrac{224}{252}$

3. $\dfrac{12}{32}$ 9. $\dfrac{12}{40}$ 15. $\dfrac{42}{77}$ 21. $\dfrac{400}{600}$ 27. $\dfrac{175}{325}$

4. $\dfrac{30}{35}$ 10. $\dfrac{35}{42}$ 16. $\dfrac{48}{78}$ 22. $\dfrac{60}{108}$ 28. $\dfrac{90}{162}$

5. $\dfrac{6}{36}$ 11. $\dfrac{18}{48}$ 17. $\dfrac{45}{65}$ 23. $\dfrac{150}{250}$ 29. $\dfrac{210}{546}$

6. $\dfrac{20}{36}$ 12. $\dfrac{15}{27}$ 18. $\dfrac{48}{84}$ 24. $\dfrac{105}{135}$ 30. $\dfrac{192}{264}$

Exercise 20

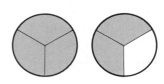

The shaded circles show that

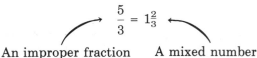

$$\frac{5}{3} = 1\tfrac{2}{3}$$

An improper fraction   A mixed number

This line also shows that $\dfrac{5}{3} = 1\tfrac{2}{3}$

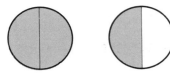

1. How many halves are there in $1\tfrac{1}{2}$?

2. How many thirds are there in $2\tfrac{1}{3}$?

3. How many fifths are there in 2?

4. How many quarters are there in $3\frac{3}{4}$?

5. $2\frac{3}{5} = \dfrac{\boxed{?}}{5}$

6. $\dfrac{\boxed{?}}{3} = 4$

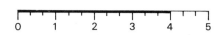

7. $1\frac{5}{8} = \dfrac{\boxed{?}}{8}$

8. $7\frac{1}{2} = \dfrac{\boxed{?}}{2}$

9. $3\frac{2}{3} = \dfrac{\boxed{?}}{3}$

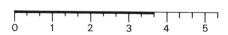

10. $\dfrac{\boxed{?}}{6} = 2\frac{1}{6}$

Exercise 21

Change these mixed numbers into improper fractions:

1. $1\frac{1}{2} = \dfrac{\boxed{?}}{2}$ **2.** $1\frac{2}{3} = \dfrac{\boxed{?}}{3}$ **3.** $1\frac{3}{4} = \dfrac{\boxed{?}}{4}$ **4.** $1\frac{2}{5} = \dfrac{\boxed{?}}{5}$

5. $1\frac{4}{5} = \dfrac{\boxed{?}}{5}$ **14.** $3\frac{2}{9} = \dfrac{\boxed{?}}{9}$ **23.** $10\frac{1}{5} = \dfrac{\boxed{?}}{5}$ **32.** $4\frac{29}{100} = \dfrac{\boxed{?}}{100}$

6. $2\frac{1}{6} = \dfrac{\boxed{?}}{6}$ **15.** $4\frac{1}{8} = \dfrac{\boxed{?}}{8}$ **24.** $6\frac{3}{8} = \dfrac{\boxed{?}}{8}$ **33.** $35\frac{1}{2} = \dfrac{\boxed{?}}{2}$

7. $3\frac{3}{4} = \dfrac{\boxed{?}}{4}$ **16.** $7\frac{1}{2} = \dfrac{\boxed{?}}{2}$ **25.** $9\frac{2}{3} = \dfrac{\boxed{?}}{3}$ **34.** $15\frac{3}{4} = \dfrac{\boxed{?}}{4}$

8. $4\frac{1}{3} = \dfrac{\boxed{?}}{3}$ **17.** $3\frac{5}{8} = \dfrac{\boxed{?}}{8}$ **26.** $8\frac{1}{3} = \dfrac{\boxed{?}}{3}$ **35.** $21\frac{2}{3} = \dfrac{\boxed{?}}{3}$

9. $2\frac{7}{8} = \dfrac{\boxed{?}}{8}$ **18.** $2\frac{3}{11} = \dfrac{\boxed{?}}{11}$ **27.** $6\frac{3}{10} = \dfrac{\boxed{?}}{10}$ **36.** $3\frac{9}{13} = \dfrac{\boxed{?}}{13}$

10. $1\frac{1}{6} = \dfrac{\boxed{?}}{6}$ **19.** $4\frac{5}{12} = \dfrac{\boxed{?}}{12}$ **28.** $9\frac{7}{10} = \dfrac{\boxed{?}}{10}$ **37.** $7\frac{8}{13} = \dfrac{\boxed{?}}{13}$

11. $3\frac{5}{7} = \dfrac{\boxed{?}}{7}$ **20.** $7\frac{1}{9} = \dfrac{\boxed{?}}{9}$ **29.** $4\frac{11}{12} = \dfrac{\boxed{?}}{12}$ **38.** $5\frac{7}{15} = \dfrac{\boxed{?}}{15}$

12. $6\frac{1}{3} = \dfrac{\boxed{?}}{3}$ **21.** $2\frac{5}{6} = \dfrac{\boxed{?}}{6}$ **30.** $12\frac{3}{4} = \dfrac{\boxed{?}}{4}$ **39.** $2\frac{9}{14} = \dfrac{\boxed{?}}{14}$

13. $5\frac{3}{4} = \dfrac{\boxed{?}}{4}$ **22.** $2\frac{1}{5} = \dfrac{\boxed{?}}{5}$ **31.** $11\frac{2}{5} = \dfrac{\boxed{?}}{5}$ **40.** $4\frac{9}{17} = \dfrac{\boxed{?}}{17}$

Exercise 22

Write these improper fractions as mixed numbers in their simplest form:

1. $\dfrac{4}{3}$ **4.** $\dfrac{9}{4}$ **7.** $\dfrac{19}{2}$ **10.** $\dfrac{25}{6}$

2. $\dfrac{7}{2}$ **5.** $\dfrac{23}{6}$ **8.** $\dfrac{30}{7}$ **11.** $\dfrac{39}{8}$

3. $\dfrac{8}{5}$ **6.** $\dfrac{28}{5}$ **9.** $\dfrac{38}{7}$ **12.** $\dfrac{41}{9}$

13. $\dfrac{45}{8}$ **20.** $\dfrac{29}{5}$ **27.** $\dfrac{61}{14}$ **34.** $\dfrac{33}{6}$

14. $\dfrac{37}{4}$ **21.** $\dfrac{45}{7}$ **28.** $\dfrac{73}{16}$ **35.** $\dfrac{48}{9}$

15. $\dfrac{33}{5}$ **22.** $\dfrac{58}{9}$ **29.** $\dfrac{53}{3}$ **36.** $\dfrac{50}{8}$

16. $\dfrac{83}{10}$ **23.** $\dfrac{51}{11}$ **30.** $\dfrac{95}{4}$ **37.** $\dfrac{44}{10}$

17. $\dfrac{37}{11}$ **24.** $\dfrac{361}{100}$ **31.** $\dfrac{93}{5}$ **38.** $\dfrac{68}{12}$

18. $\dfrac{27}{2}$ **25.** $\dfrac{87}{20}$ **32.** $\dfrac{18}{4}$ **39.** $\dfrac{66}{15}$

19. $\dfrac{47}{9}$ **26.** $\dfrac{41}{15}$ **33.** $\dfrac{20}{6}$ **40.** $\dfrac{66}{18}$

Exercise 23

Write as mixed numbers:

1. 9 halves   **6.** 27 eighths
2. 7 thirds   **7.** 47 tenths
3. 11 fifths   **8.** 33 sevenths
4. 13 quarters   **9.** 50 ninths
5. 17 sixths   **10.** 29 quarters

Exercise 24

Write as improper fractions:

1. Two and three-quarters
2. Three and four-fifths
3. Five and one-eighth
4. Seven and two-thirds
5. Six and five-sevenths

Exercise 25

Write as a whole number:

1. 6 halves   **6.** 30 tenths   **11.** $\dfrac{21}{3}$ **16.** $\dfrac{56}{8}$

2. 8 quarters   **7.** 48 sixths   **12.** $\dfrac{80}{10}$ **17.** $\dfrac{42}{7}$

3. 18 thirds   **8.** 72 eighths   **13.** $\dfrac{40}{5}$ **18.** $\dfrac{75}{5}$

4. 25 fifths   **9.** $\dfrac{10}{2}$ **14.** $\dfrac{6}{6}$ **19.** $\dfrac{108}{4}$

5. 32 eighths   **10.** $\dfrac{24}{4}$ **15.** $\dfrac{45}{9}$ **20.** $\dfrac{78}{6}$

Exercise 26   M

Copy the graph on p. 181, which shows fractions. It is called a *Farey lattice*.
Try to work out how it was made.

1. One straight line shows the fractions $\{\frac{1}{2}, \frac{2}{4}, \frac{3}{6}, \frac{4}{8}, \frac{5}{10}, \frac{6}{12}, \text{etc.}\}$.
What do you notice about these fractions?

2. $\frac{4}{6} = \frac{2}{3}$. Find $\frac{4}{6}$ and $\frac{2}{3}$ on your Farey lattice.
What do you notice?

3. $\dfrac{1}{5} = \dfrac{\boxed{?}}{10} = \dfrac{3}{\boxed{?}} = \dfrac{4}{\boxed{?}} = \dfrac{\boxed{?}}{25}$.

Find these fractions on your graph.
What do you notice?

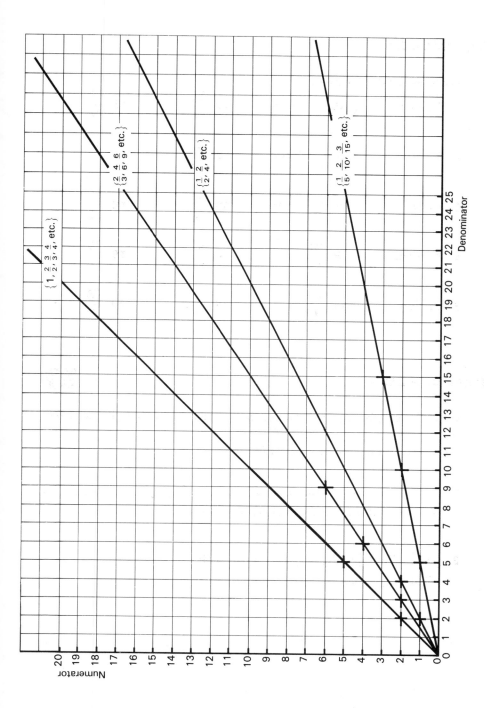

4. $\frac{4}{5} = \frac{8}{10}$. Show $\frac{4}{5}$ and $\frac{8}{10}$ on your graph.

Draw a straight line from the origin to pass through $\frac{8}{10}$. (The origin is the point where the two axes meet. The axes are the two numbered lines.)
Do you need to draw a different straight line to join the origin to the fraction $\frac{4}{5}$?

5. Use your graph to help you to list two more fractions that are equivalent to $\frac{4}{5}$.

6. (a) Which fraction is bigger, $\frac{3}{4}$ or $\frac{1}{2}$?
   (b) Draw a straight line from the origin to pass through $\frac{3}{4}$.
   (c) Which line is steeper, the line that passes through $\frac{3}{4}$, or the line that passes through $\frac{1}{2}$?

7. (a) Which line is steeper, the line that passes through $\frac{2}{3}$, or the line that passes through $\frac{1}{2}$?
   (b) Which fraction is bigger, $\frac{2}{3}$ or $\frac{1}{2}$?

8. Use your graph to find out whether these statements are true or false:

(a) $\dfrac{4}{6} = \dfrac{10}{15}$

(b) $\dfrac{5}{8} > \dfrac{2}{3}$

(c) $\dfrac{7}{10} < \dfrac{6}{9}$

(d) $\dfrac{16}{20} < \dfrac{4}{5}$

(e) $\dfrac{5}{7} > \dfrac{11}{15}$

(f) $\dfrac{12}{18} = \dfrac{10}{14}$

(g) $\dfrac{8}{15} < \dfrac{7}{12}$

(h) $\dfrac{5}{7} < \dfrac{11}{16}$

(i) $\dfrac{5}{9} > \dfrac{7}{13}$

(j) $\dfrac{6}{11} > \dfrac{10}{18}$

(k) $\dfrac{6}{8} = \dfrac{15}{20}$

(l) $\dfrac{3}{4} < \dfrac{11}{14}$

Exercise 27

Now use your fraction graph for these:

1. Does $\dfrac{7}{7} = \dfrac{4}{4}$?

2. Is $\dfrac{7}{4} > \dfrac{5}{4}$?

3. Is $\dfrac{4}{7} > \dfrac{4}{5}$?

4. Is $\dfrac{3}{8} > \dfrac{2}{7}$?

5. Is $\dfrac{8}{3} > \dfrac{7}{2}$?

6. Does $\dfrac{6}{2} = \dfrac{9}{3}$?

7. Does $\dfrac{9}{2} = \dfrac{18}{4}$?

8. Does $\dfrac{10}{3} = \dfrac{18}{6}$?

9. Does $\dfrac{10}{3} = \dfrac{16}{5}$?

10. Is $\dfrac{12}{5} < \dfrac{17}{7}$?

11. Is $\dfrac{14}{9} < \dfrac{11}{7}$?

12. Is $\dfrac{12}{12} > \dfrac{14}{14}$?

13. Is $\dfrac{10}{3} < \dfrac{13}{4}$?

14. Is $\dfrac{17}{6} > \dfrac{14}{5}$?

15. Is $\dfrac{19}{8} < \dfrac{17}{7}$?

Exercise 28 M

A Copy these shapes. Shade the given fraction. State which is the larger fraction.

1. 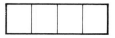 Shade $\frac{2}{3}$

Shade $\frac{3}{4}$

Which is larger, $\frac{2}{3}$ or $\frac{3}{4}$?

2.

Shade $\frac{7}{8}$ Shade $\frac{5}{6}$

Which is larger, $\frac{7}{8}$ or $\frac{5}{6}$?

3. 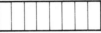 Shade $\frac{5}{8}$

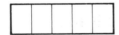 Shade $\frac{3}{5}$

Which is larger, $\frac{5}{8}$ or $\frac{3}{5}$?

4. Shade $\frac{5}{8}$ 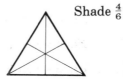 Shade $\frac{4}{6}$

Which is larger, $\frac{5}{8}$ or $\frac{4}{6}$?

B Look at these shaded shapes. State which is the larger fraction.

1. 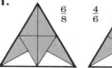 $\frac{6}{8}$ $\frac{4}{6}$

3.  $\frac{7}{8}$

$\frac{9}{10}$

2.

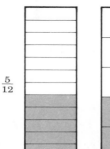

$\frac{5}{12}$ $\frac{2}{5}$

4.

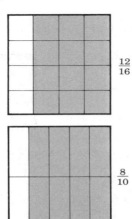

$\frac{12}{16}$

$\frac{8}{10}$

184

Exercise 29

A Which is bigger:

1. $\frac{1}{4}$ or $\frac{1}{2}$?   9. $\frac{2}{10}$ or $\frac{2}{6}$?   **17.** 5 tenths or 5 sixths?

2. $\frac{1}{3}$ or $\frac{1}{5}$?   **10.** $\frac{5}{12}$ or $\frac{5}{6}$?   **18.** 3 quarters or 3 fifths?

3. $\frac{1}{2}$ or $\frac{1}{8}$?   **11.** $\frac{7}{10}$ or $\frac{7}{12}$?   **19.** 8 twelfths or 8 ninths?

4. $\frac{1}{6}$ or $\frac{1}{3}$?   **12.** $\frac{4}{7}$ or $\frac{4}{6}$?   **20.** 7 eighths or 7 ninths?

5. $\frac{1}{5}$ or $\frac{1}{6}$?   **13.** $\frac{9}{16}$ or $\frac{9}{15}$?   **21.** 2 thirds or 2 twelfths?

6. $\frac{1}{10}$ or $\frac{1}{8}$?   **14.** $\frac{7}{8}$ or $\frac{7}{14}$?   **22.** 4 sevenths or 4 fifths?

7. $\frac{1}{12}$ or $\frac{1}{9}$?   **15.** $\frac{10}{12}$ or $\frac{10}{15}$?   **23.** 6 sevenths or 6 eighths?

8. $\frac{3}{5}$ or $\frac{3}{8}$?   **16.** $\frac{13}{20}$ or $\frac{13}{18}$?   **24.** 10 sixteenths or 10 fourteenths?

   25. 9 twentieths or 9 twelfths?

B 1. Ann divided her bar of chocolate into sixths.
Brenda divided the same sort of chocolate bar into eighths.
Who had the smaller pieces? Who had the most pieces?

2. Chris and Dave had the same amount of money.
Chris spent $\frac{7}{10}$ of his money. Dave spent $\frac{7}{9}$ of his.
Who spent the most money?

3. Edwin ate $\frac{5}{9}$ of a cake while Fiona ate $\frac{5}{12}$ of the same size cake.
Who ate the least cake?

C Look at this bar of chocolate:

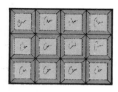

1. Which is the most, $\frac{1}{2}$ or $\frac{7}{12}$?   5. Which is the most, $\frac{3}{4}$ or $\frac{5}{6}$?

2. Which is the least, $\frac{1}{2}$ or $\frac{3}{4}$?   6. Which is the most, $\frac{4}{6}$ or $\frac{7}{12}$?

3. Which is the smaller, $\frac{2}{3}$ or $\frac{5}{6}$?   7. Which is the larger, $\frac{9}{12}$ or $\frac{2}{3}$?

4. Which is the least, $\frac{2}{3}$ or $\frac{3}{4}$?   8. Which is the least, $\frac{3}{6}$ or $\frac{5}{12}$?

Exercise 30

A Copy these fractions. Put a sign, $<$, $>$, or $=$, in place of each box to make the statements true:

1. $\dfrac{1}{2}$? $\dfrac{3}{8}$

2. $\dfrac{2}{6}$? $\dfrac{1}{3}$

3. $\dfrac{1}{4}$? $\dfrac{1}{6}$

4. $\dfrac{3}{7}$? $\dfrac{5}{7}$

5. $\dfrac{3}{5}$? $\dfrac{6}{10}$

6. $\dfrac{5}{8}$? $\dfrac{3}{4}$

7. $\dfrac{5}{6}$? $\dfrac{11}{12}$

8. $\dfrac{9}{12}$? $\dfrac{3}{4}$

9. $\dfrac{6}{8}$? $\dfrac{8}{12}$

10. $\dfrac{3}{5}$? $\dfrac{10}{15}$

11. $\dfrac{3}{5}$? $\dfrac{2}{3}$

12. $\dfrac{2}{3}$? $\dfrac{8}{12}$

13. $\dfrac{4}{7}$? $\dfrac{7}{14}$

14. $\dfrac{4}{7}$? $\dfrac{1}{2}$

15. $\dfrac{9}{12}$? $\dfrac{5}{6}$

16. $\dfrac{3}{4}$? $\dfrac{5}{6}$

17. $\dfrac{6}{8}$? $\dfrac{5}{6}$

18. $\dfrac{6}{8}$? $\dfrac{9}{12}$

19. $\dfrac{4}{6}$? $\dfrac{10}{15}$

20. $\dfrac{9}{12}$? $\dfrac{12}{16}$

21. $\dfrac{5}{8}$? $\dfrac{3}{5}$

22. $\dfrac{2}{5}$? $\dfrac{3}{7}$

23. $\dfrac{7}{9}$? $\dfrac{3}{4}$

24. $\dfrac{7}{10}$? $\dfrac{5}{7}$

B Write in order of size, smallest first:

1. $\dfrac{1}{3}, \dfrac{1}{8}, \dfrac{1}{10}, \dfrac{1}{4}, \dfrac{1}{2}$

2. $\dfrac{3}{8}, \dfrac{3}{5}, \dfrac{3}{7}, \dfrac{3}{12}, \dfrac{3}{4}$

3. $\dfrac{1}{2}, \dfrac{3}{4}, \dfrac{7}{12}, \dfrac{4}{6}$

4. $\dfrac{3}{8}, \dfrac{1}{2}, \dfrac{2}{3}, \dfrac{1}{4}, \dfrac{5}{6}$

5. $\dfrac{4}{9}, \dfrac{2}{3}, \dfrac{3}{4}, \dfrac{5}{8}, \dfrac{7}{10}$

6. $\dfrac{8}{15}, \dfrac{5}{10}, \dfrac{3}{5}, \dfrac{11}{20}, \dfrac{7}{12}$

186

C **1.** (*a*) Which is larger, $\frac{5}{8}$ or $\frac{7}{12}$?

(*b*) What is the LCM of 8 and 12?

(*c*) $\dfrac{5}{8} = \dfrac{\boxed{?}}{24}$ and $\dfrac{7}{12} = \dfrac{\boxed{?}}{24}$. Find the missing numbers.

2. (*a*) $\dfrac{3}{5} = \dfrac{\boxed{?}}{35}$ and $\dfrac{4}{7} = \dfrac{\boxed{?}}{35}$. Find the missing numbers.

(*b*) What is the LCM of 5 and 7?

(*c*) Which is smaller, $\frac{3}{5}$ or $\frac{4}{7}$?

3. Which is larger:

(*a*) $\frac{2}{5}$ or $\frac{3}{8}$?　　(*b*) $\frac{5}{9}$ or $\frac{3}{5}$?　　(*c*) $\frac{7}{11}$ or $\frac{5}{8}$?　　(*d*) $\frac{3}{7}$ or $\frac{5}{12}$?

Exercise 31

1. A firm made a bar of chocolate called 'Fours or Fives' because it could be shared equally between either four or five people (without breaking any square of chocolate).
How many squares could the bar of chocolate have?
What is the smallest number of squares it could have?

2. Since the firm believed that people should share, they made another bar called 'Threes or Fours'.
How many chocolate squares could it have?
What is the smallest number of squares it could have?

3. What is the smallest number of squares a bar called 'Threes or Sixes' could have?

4. What is the smallest number of squares a bar called 'Sixes or Eights' could have?

Exercise 32

1. Write a fraction that is bigger than $\frac{1}{4}$ but less than $\frac{1}{2}$.

2. Write a fraction that is bigger than $\frac{1}{3}$ but less than $\frac{1}{2}$.

3. Write a fraction that lies between $\frac{1}{4}$ and $\frac{1}{3}$.

4. Give a fraction that lies between $\frac{1}{5}$ and $\frac{1}{4}$.

5. Give a fraction that lies between $\frac{3}{5}$ and $\frac{3}{4}$.

6. Give a fraction that lies between $\frac{5}{9}$ and $\frac{5}{8}$.

Exercise 33

Partition the given set of fractions into the three subsets:
$\quad L = \{$fractions less than 1$\}$
$\quad E = \{$fractions equal to 1$\}$
$\quad G = \{$fractions greater than 1$\}$

$\{\frac{3}{5}, \frac{9}{8}, \frac{4}{4}, \frac{6}{3}, \frac{7}{2}, \frac{2}{9}, \frac{7}{10}, \frac{12}{12}, \frac{1}{8}, \frac{6}{4}, \frac{9}{1}, \frac{10}{10}, \frac{37}{12}, \frac{100}{100}, \frac{125}{64}, \frac{13}{125}, \frac{52}{52}\}$

Set out your answers like this:

1. $L = \{$fractions less than 1$\} = \{\frac{3}{5},\qquad\}$

2. $E = \{$fractions equal to 1$\} = \{\frac{4}{4},\qquad\}$

3. $G = \{$fractions greater than 1$\} = \{\frac{9}{8}, \frac{6}{3},\qquad\}$

Exercise 34

1. $9\frac{4}{8} = 8\dfrac{\boxed{?}}{8}$

2. $6\frac{7}{5} = 7\dfrac{\boxed{?}}{5}$

3. $3\frac{1}{2} = 2\dfrac{\boxed{?}}{2}$

4. $7\frac{5}{12} = 6\dfrac{\boxed{?}}{12}$

5. $4\frac{12}{7} = 5\dfrac{\boxed{?}}{7}$

6. $2\frac{9}{8} = 3\dfrac{\boxed{?}}{8}$

7. $5\frac{1}{4} = 4\dfrac{\boxed{?}}{4}$

8. $7\frac{2}{3} = 6\dfrac{\boxed{?}}{3}$

9. $12\frac{5}{6} = 11\dfrac{\boxed{?}}{6}$

10. $6\dfrac{1}{9} = 5\dfrac{\boxed{?}}{9}$

11. $3\dfrac{4}{3} = 4\dfrac{\boxed{?}}{3}$

12. $5\dfrac{13}{11} = 6\dfrac{\boxed{?}}{11}$

13. $11\dfrac{19}{14} = 12\dfrac{\boxed{?}}{14}$

14. $8\dfrac{6}{7} = 7\dfrac{\boxed{?}}{7}$

15. $13\dfrac{1}{3} = 12\dfrac{\boxed{?}}{3}$

16. $9\dfrac{11}{6} = 10\dfrac{\boxed{?}}{6}$

17. $13\dfrac{7}{10} = 12\dfrac{\boxed{?}}{10}$

18. $13\dfrac{13}{7} = 14\dfrac{\boxed{?}}{7}$

19. $9\dfrac{3}{8} = 8\dfrac{\boxed{?}}{8}$

20. $2\dfrac{1}{4} = 1\dfrac{\boxed{?}}{4}$

Exercise 35

A Write in centimetres:

e.g. 27 mm = 2.7 cm

1. 46 mm

2. 71 mm

3. 19 mm

4. 68 mm

5. 32 mm

6. 53 mm

7. 84 mm

8. 95 mm

9. 5 mm

10. 1 mm

1 millimetre is one-tenth of a centimetre

1 mm = 0.1 cm

one-tenth $= \frac{1}{10} = 0.1$

B Write in order of size, smallest first:

1. 0.6 cm, 0.2 cm, 1.5 cm, 4.7 cm, 2.8 cm, 0.7 cm

2. 5 mm, 0.8 cm, 72 mm, 3 mm, 5.4 cm, 0.4 cm, 3.9 cm

3. 0.5, 0.3, 0.1, 0.8, 0.7, 0.4, 0.6

C Write, using the pound sign (£):

e.g. 29 p = £0.29

1. 26 p	**5.** 70 p	**9.** 41 p
2. 87 p	**6.** 62 p	**10.** 55 p
3. 54 p	**7.** 13 p	**11.** 7 p
4. 39 p	**8.** 98 p	**12.** 1 p

1 p is one-hundredth of £1

1 p = £0.01

one-hundredth = 0.01 = $\frac{1}{100}$

D Write in order of size, largest first:

1. £0.76, £0.35, £0.07, £0.89, £0.26, £0.19, £3.30

2. £0.52, 75 p, £0.18, 9 p, £0.83, £0.06, 54 p, 37 p

3. 0.46, 0.21, 0.08, 0.73, 0.97, 0.15, 0.68, 0.56

You can use a calculator to find out if two fractions are equal or if one is bigger than the other. Calculators use decimals (short for *decimal fractions*).

The fractions we have been using are called *vulgar fractions* or *common fractions*.

0.6 is a decimal

↑

This is called a *decimal point*

To find the decimal value of the fraction $\frac{5}{8}$, we key in $\boxed{5}$ $\boxed{\div}$ $\boxed{8}$ $\boxed{=}$. Try it.

What is your decimal answer? It should be 0.625.

Exercise 36

Change these common fractions to decimals using a calculator:

1. $\dfrac{1}{10}$ **2.** $\dfrac{2}{10}$ **3.** $\dfrac{3}{10}$ **4.** $\dfrac{4}{10}$

5. $\dfrac{5}{10}$ 11. $\dfrac{2}{100}$ 17. $\dfrac{8}{100}$ 23. $\dfrac{42}{100}$

6. $\dfrac{6}{10}$ 12. $\dfrac{3}{100}$ 18. $\dfrac{9}{100}$ 24. $\dfrac{51}{100}$

7. $\dfrac{7}{10}$ 13. $\dfrac{4}{100}$ 19. $\dfrac{16}{100}$ 25. $\dfrac{64}{100}$

8. $\dfrac{8}{10}$ 14. $\dfrac{5}{100}$ 20. $\dfrac{23}{100}$ 26. $\dfrac{75}{100}$

9. $\dfrac{9}{10}$ 15. $\dfrac{6}{100}$ 21. $\dfrac{27}{100}$ 27. $\dfrac{89}{100}$

10. $\dfrac{1}{100}$ 16. $\dfrac{7}{100}$ 22. $\dfrac{39}{100}$ 28. $\dfrac{98}{100}$

Look carefully at the questions and the answers.
Could you have found the answers without using a calculator?

Exercise 37

Write in words the value of the underlined digit:

e.g. 1 4̲6 four tens.   *e.g. 2* 3.6̲5 five hundredths.

(*Words:* thousands, hundreds, tens, units, tenths, hundredths)

1. 5̲96	11. 4̲8̲	21. 1̲15.7
2. 7̲2̲4	12. 0.9̲2	22. 323.4̲
3. 0.8̲	13. 0.7̲7̲	23. 781.6̲2̲
4. 3.7̲6	14. 12.3̲5̲	24. 90.2̲4
5. 15.7̲	15. 9̲60	25. 315̲.07
6. 2̲6.3	16. 37̲5	26. 4063̲.2
7. 2.1̲4	17. 0.0̲8̲	27. 8̲407.3
8. 8̲6̲	18. 6̲503	28. 2914.7̲4̲
9. 5.0̲3̲	19. 3.6̲0	29. 800.0̲1̲
10. 6̲0	20. 49̲.32	30. 799.3̲9

History of decimals

When decimals were first used, the decimal point did not exist.

Consider the decimal number 3.142.

Jemshid Al-Kashi, a Persian mathematician who is believed to have died in 1436, would have written 3 142 (he would have left a space).

Pellos, an Italian, would have written 3.142 in 1492. However, he did not fully understand its significance.

In 1530, Christoff Rudolff, a German, would have written 3|142. Rudolff understood how to use decimals. Others, at that time, did not understand his work.

Simon Stevin (or Stevinus), a Belgian, would have written 3 ⓪ 1 ① 4 ② 2 ③ in 1585.

Jost Bürgi, from Switzerland, in 1592 would have written 3,142 or 3.142 or 3$\overset{\circ}{1}$42. (He could not make up his mind!)

William Oughtred, from England, would have written 3 | 142 in 1631.

Adriaen Metius (1571–1635) would have written 3° : 1'4"2''' or 3|1'4"2'''.

John Napier used the notation 3,1'4"2''' in 1617, the year in which he died. In the same year his friend Henry Briggs is believed to have used the decimal point.

Frans Van Schooten, a Dutchman, used the notation 3142... ③ in 1657.

Even today there is no agreement. In the United Kingdom and in the United States a decimal point is used, while in Europe a comma is used.

Exercise 38

A Change these fractions to decimals using a calculator:

1. $\dfrac{2}{5}$ 3. $\dfrac{1}{4}$ 5. $\dfrac{1}{8}$ 7. $\dfrac{1}{20}$ 9. $\dfrac{7}{20}$

2. $\dfrac{1}{2}$ 4. $\dfrac{3}{4}$ 6. $\dfrac{3}{8}$ 8. $\dfrac{3}{20}$ 10. $\dfrac{13}{20}$

11. $\dfrac{17}{20}$ **14.** $\dfrac{11}{25}$ **17.** $\dfrac{1}{16}$ **20.** $\dfrac{15}{16}$ **23.** $\dfrac{37}{80}$

12. $\dfrac{1}{25}$ **15.** $\dfrac{19}{25}$ **18.** $\dfrac{3}{16}$ **21.** $\dfrac{13}{40}$ **24.** $\dfrac{3}{7}$

13. $\dfrac{4}{25}$ **16.** $\dfrac{23}{25}$ **19.** $\dfrac{7}{16}$ **22.** $\dfrac{21}{40}$ **25.** $\dfrac{5}{6}$

B Change these fractions to decimals *without using a calculator*:

1. $\dfrac{1}{2}$ **4.** $\dfrac{4}{5}$ **7.** $\dfrac{7}{8}$ **10.** $\dfrac{13}{20}$ **13.** $\dfrac{2}{3}$

2. $\dfrac{1}{5}$ **5.** $\dfrac{3}{4}$ **8.** $\dfrac{9}{20}$ **11.** $\dfrac{14}{25}$ **14.** $\dfrac{1}{7}$

3. $\dfrac{3}{5}$ **6.** $\dfrac{5}{8}$ **9.** $\dfrac{11}{20}$ **12.** $\dfrac{9}{16}$ **15.** $\dfrac{4}{7}$

C Use a calculator to change these fractions to decimals. Compare the decimals. Hence find out which fraction is bigger.

1. $\dfrac{3}{4}$ or $\dfrac{5}{7}$ **6.** $\dfrac{7}{11}$ or $\dfrac{2}{3}$ **11.** $\dfrac{8}{11}$ or $\dfrac{5}{7}$

2. $\dfrac{2}{5}$ or $\dfrac{5}{11}$ **7.** $\dfrac{2}{9}$ or $\dfrac{3}{14}$ **12.** $\dfrac{16}{25}$ or $\dfrac{2}{3}$

3. $\dfrac{2}{7}$ or $\dfrac{7}{25}$ **8.** $\dfrac{4}{7}$ or $\dfrac{5}{9}$ **13.** $\dfrac{7}{15}$ or $\dfrac{5}{11}$

4. $\dfrac{5}{8}$ or $\dfrac{2}{3}$ **9.** $\dfrac{4}{5}$ or $\dfrac{7}{9}$ **14.** $\dfrac{13}{20}$ or $\dfrac{2}{3}$

5. $\dfrac{5}{8}$ or $\dfrac{7}{11}$ **10.** $\dfrac{3}{10}$ or $\dfrac{2}{7}$ **15.** $\dfrac{19}{25}$ or $\dfrac{3}{4}$

Try quickly to find the answers to the last exercise without using a calculator. It may be quicker without a calculator. (See the next exercise for a quick method.)

Exercise 39

Look carefully at these:

A. $\dfrac{3}{7} > \dfrac{2}{5}$

and $3 \times 5 > 2 \times 7$

C. $\dfrac{7}{10} > \dfrac{11}{16}$

and $7 \times 16 > 11 \times 10$

B. $\dfrac{3}{4} > \dfrac{8}{11}$

and $3 \times 11 > 8 \times 4$

D. $\dfrac{3}{8} > \dfrac{1}{3}$

and $3 \times 3 > 1 \times 8$

Now find out which is the larger of the two fractions in each question:

1. $\dfrac{3}{5}$ or $\dfrac{2}{3}$

2. $\dfrac{3}{4}$ or $\dfrac{4}{5}$

3. $\dfrac{3}{8}$ or $\dfrac{4}{11}$

4. $\dfrac{2}{5}$ or $\dfrac{5}{12}$

5. $\dfrac{3}{4}$ or $\dfrac{10}{13}$

6. $\dfrac{4}{5}$ or $\dfrac{9}{11}$

7. $\dfrac{4}{7}$ or $\dfrac{9}{16}$

8. $\dfrac{5}{8}$ or $\dfrac{16}{25}$

Try to find out why this method works.

Exercise 40

To what value is the arrow pointing?
Give each answer as a decimal.

1.

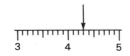

2.

3.

4.

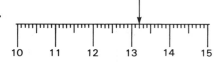

5.

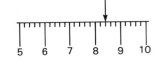

6.

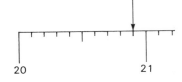

7.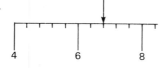

8.

9.

10.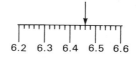

11.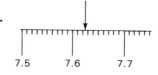

12.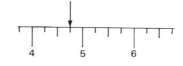

Exercise 41 M

Carefully copy each of these scales.
Only some of the points have been numbered.
Number all the points on your drawings.

1.   **2.**   **3.**   **4.**   **5.**

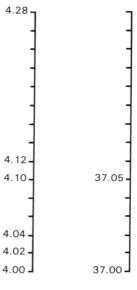

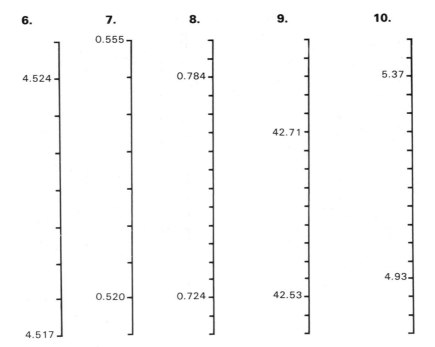

6. 4.524 — 4.517

7. 0.555 — 0.520

8. 0.784 — 0.724

9. 42.71 — 42.53

10. 5.37 — 4.93

Exercise 42

It is possible to use a graph to change fractions into decimals.

Make a copy of the graph on p. 197. Use a scale of 1 cm to 1 unit on the denominator axis and 2 cm to 1 unit on the numerator axis.

The graph shows that $\dfrac{1}{2} = 0.5$, $\dfrac{4}{5} = 0.8$, $\dfrac{1}{8} = 0.125$, and $\dfrac{2}{7} = 0.285$.

Use your graph to change these to decimals:

1. $\dfrac{1}{4}$ **3.** $\dfrac{2}{5}$ **5.** $\dfrac{3}{8}$ **7.** $\dfrac{7}{10}$ **9.** $\dfrac{1}{6}$

2. $\dfrac{3}{4}$ **4.** $\dfrac{3}{5}$ **6.** $\dfrac{5}{8}$ **8.** $\dfrac{1}{3}$ **10.** $\dfrac{1}{12}$

11. $\dfrac{5}{9}$ **12.** $\dfrac{3}{16}$ **13.** Try to show $\dfrac{11}{24}$ on the same graph.

196

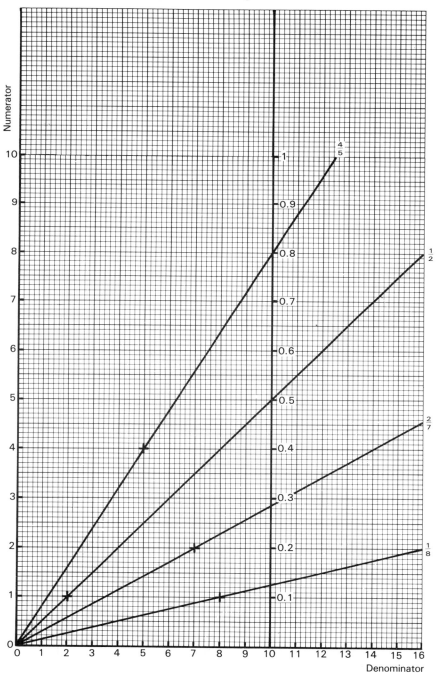

Exercise 43

Write these fractions in decimal form:

e.g. 1 $5\frac{7}{10} = 5.7$ *e.g. 2* $2\frac{9}{100} = 2.09$ *e.g. 3* $3\frac{19}{100} = 3.19$

1. $4\frac{3}{10}$ **6.** $6\frac{45}{100}$ **11.** $12\frac{28}{100}$

2. $9\frac{1}{10}$ **7.** $5\frac{72}{100}$ **12.** $3\frac{12}{100}$

3. $6\frac{8}{100}$ **8.** $4\frac{96}{100}$ **13.** $15\frac{47}{100}$

4. $1\frac{24}{100}$ **9.** $7\frac{53}{100}$ **14.** $22\frac{76}{100}$

5. $2\frac{31}{100}$ **10.** $9\frac{88}{100}$ **15.** $73\frac{55}{100}$

Exercise 44

Change these decimals into common fractions in their simplest form:

1. 0.3   **6.** 0.125   **11.** 0.37

2. 0.8   **7.** 0.825   **12.** 0.03

3. 0.15   **8.** 0.56   **13.** 0.08

4. 0.24   **9.** 0.675   **14.** 0.005

5. 0.78   **10.** 0.48   **15.** 0.225

Exercise 45

$\frac{1}{3}$ of 6 = 2

$$6 \times \frac{1}{3} = 6 \text{ thirds} = 2$$

$$6 \times \frac{1}{3} = \frac{6}{3} = 2$$

198

1. Three people share a bar of chocolate. There were 12 squares altogether.

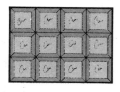

Ann ate $\frac{1}{3}$ of the bar.

Bob ate $\frac{1}{4}$ of the bar.

Chris ate $\frac{1}{6}$ of the bar.

Write down the number of squares each person ate. Set out your work like this:

(a) Ann   ate $\frac{1}{3}$ of 12 squares = ⬚ squares

(b) Bob   ate $\frac{1}{4}$ of 12 squares = ⬚ squares

(c) Chris ate $\frac{1}{6}$ of 12 squares = ⬚ squares

2. How many squares were left?

3. What fraction of the bar of chocolate was left?

Exercise 46

A 1. (a) What is one-fifth of 20 marbles?

   (b) What is two-fifths of 20 marbles?

2. (a) Find $\frac{1}{4}$ of 24 sweets.

   (b) Find $\frac{3}{4}$ of 24 sweets.

3. (a) Find $\frac{1}{6}$ of 30 stamps.

   (b) Find $\frac{5}{6}$ of 30 stamps.

4. (a) Find one-eighth of 24 metres.

   (b) Find three-eighths of 24 metres.

   (c) What is $\frac{7}{8}$ of 24 metres?

5. (a) What is $\frac{1}{3}$ of 18 hours?

   (b) Find $\frac{2}{3}$ of 18 hours.

B 1. Find $\frac{2}{3}$ of 15 km.

2. What is $\frac{3}{4}$ of 24 apples?

3. Find $\frac{3}{5}$ of 35 pounds.

199

4. Find $\frac{5}{8}$ of 56 minutes.

5. What is five-sixths of 54 cm?

6. Find $\frac{2}{7}$ of 42 kg.

7. What is $\frac{3}{10}$ of 80 sheets of paper?

8. Find $\frac{5}{7}$ of 56 sheep.

9. Find $\frac{7}{10}$ of 360°.

10. Find $\frac{11}{20}$ of 120 days.

Exercise 47

A **1.** Write $\frac{1}{2}$ m in cm.

2. Find one-quarter of £1. Give your answer in pence.

3. Give $\frac{1}{6}$ h in minutes.

4. Give $\frac{3}{4}$ km in metres.

5. Find two-thirds of a day in hours.

6. Write $\frac{7}{10}$ kg in grams.

7. Find $\frac{5}{12}$ of a day in hours.

8. Find $\frac{4}{5}$ ℓ in millilitres.

9. How many pence are there in $\frac{13}{20}$ of £1?

10. How many weeks are there in $\frac{3}{4}$ of a year?

B {half, third, quarter, fifth, sixth, seventh, eighth, ninth, tenth}

Copy these sentences and complete them by filling in the missing word. Select the missing word from the set of words above. (The same missing word may be used in more than the sentence.)

1. There are 15 minutes in ⬚ of an hour.

2. There are 3 hours in an ⬚ of a day.

3. 100 mm is a ⬚ of a metre.

4. There are 12 s in a ⬚ of a minute.

5. 200 ml is one ⬚ of a litre.

6. One ⬚ of an hour is 20 minutes.

7. 10 s is one ⬚ of a minute.

8. There are 125 m in one ⬚ of a kilometre.

200

Exercise 48

The *pie chart* shows the sports enjoyed by 48 people:

1. What fraction liked swimming?
2. What fraction liked squash?
3. What fraction liked tennis?
4. What fraction liked badminton?
5. How many liked swimming?
6. How many liked squash?
7. How many liked tennis?
8. How many liked badminton?

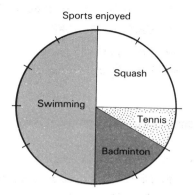

Sports enjoyed

Exercise 49

1. A rectangle measures 14 cm by 8 cm. Draw this rectangle to $\frac{1}{2}$ size.

2. A triangle has sides of length 183 mm, 156 mm and 138 mm. Construct a triangle with sides $\frac{1}{3}$ of these sizes.

3. In $\triangle ABC$, AB = 96 mm, BC = $\frac{2}{3}$ of AB and AC = $\frac{3}{4}$ of BC. Construct this triangle.

4. Draw a circle of radius 42 mm. Divide the circle into 6 equal parts (draw the 6 radii). Label the points where the radii meet the circle, A, B, C, D, E and F (anticlockwise). Let the centre of the circle be point O. Mark points on each radius in turn (A_1 on OA, B_1 on OB, etc.) such that:

   $OA_1 = \frac{1}{6}OA$

   $OB_1 = \frac{1}{3}OB$

   $OC_1 = \frac{1}{2}OC$

   $OD_1 = \frac{2}{3}OD$

   $OE_1 = \frac{5}{6}OE$

   $OF_1 = OF.$

   Join A_1 to B_1 to C_1 to D_1 to E_1 to F_1.

Exercise 50

The graph opposite can be used to find fractions of a kilometre. Try to find out how it works. Make a copy of this graph. Use a scale of 1 cm to 1 unit on the denominator axis and 2 cm to 1 unit on the numerator axis.

1. Now use your graph to find these fractions of a kilometre (in metres):

   (a) $\frac{2}{5}$ (b) $\frac{7}{10}$ (c) $\frac{1}{8}$ (d) $\frac{3}{4}$ (e) $\frac{5}{8}$ (f) $\frac{7}{16}$

2. Try to draw a graph that will help you to find fractions of £1, in pence.

3. Try to draw a graph that will help you to find fractions of an hour in minutes. (This time, the answer line should not be drawn at the number 10 in the denominator. Try to think of the best place for this answer line.)

Exercise 51

1. Find $\frac{1}{2}$ of 3 h in minutes.

2. Find $\frac{1}{5}$ of 2 minutes in seconds.

3. Write $\frac{1}{3}$ of 3 m in centimetres.

4. Find $\frac{3}{4}$ of £2 in pence.

5. Write $\frac{3}{7}$ of 2 weeks in days.

6. What is $\frac{5}{8}$ of 2 h in minutes?

7. Find $\frac{7}{12}$ of 3 km in metres.

8. Find $\frac{4}{9}$ of 3 days in hours.

202

Fractions of a kilometre

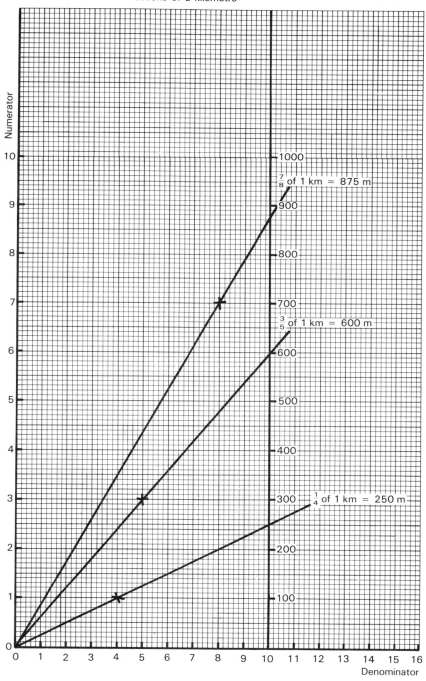

Exercise 52

e.g. 1 To find $\frac{3}{8}$ of 136, key in ⎡3⎤ ⎡÷⎤ ⎡8⎤ ⎡×⎤ ⎡1⎤ ⎡3⎤ ⎡6⎤ ⎡=⎤
Try it.

Sometimes you may not obtain a sensible answer. Try this:

e.g. 2 $\frac{4}{7}$ of 175. ⎡4⎤ ⎡÷⎤ ⎡7⎤ ⎡×⎤ ⎡1⎤ ⎡7⎤ ⎡5⎤ ⎡=⎤

My calculator gives 99.999999. (Some calculators may give slightly different answers.) A sensible answer would be 100.

Work these out on a calculator. Give sensible answers.

1. $\frac{3}{8}$ of 272 days

2. $\frac{6}{7}$ of 329 pupils

3. $\frac{5}{6}$ of 1584 stamps

4. $\frac{7}{9}$ of 486 km

5. $\frac{4}{5}$ of 205 boxes

6. $\frac{7}{12}$ of 4332 eggs

7. $\frac{9}{25}$ of 5 h, in minutes

8. $\frac{7}{15}$ of 1 h, in minutes

Exercise 53

1. Things on the Moon weigh about one-sixth of what they weigh on Earth. How heavy is someone on the Moon who weighs
   (*a*) 720 N on the Earth?
   (*b*) 630 N on the Earth?

2. Three-fifths of a class of 30 pupils were girls.
   (*a*) How many girls were there?
   (*b*) How many boys were there?
   (*c*) What fraction of the class were boys?

3. My car's petrol tank holds 72 *l*. How much petrol does it contain when the tank is $\frac{2}{3}$ full?

4. $\frac{3}{8}$ of a magazine contains adverts. The magazine has 152 pages. How many full pages of adverts would there be?

5. $\frac{9}{10}$ of a group of 40 people can swim. How many is that?

6. A kilometre is five-eighths of a mile. If I travel 32 km, how many miles is that?

7. A pound is $\frac{5}{11}$ of a kilogram. How many kilograms are there in 55 lb?

8. One pint is $\frac{4}{7}$ of a litre. How many litres are there in 56 pints?

9. A girl gave $\frac{2}{9}$ of her stamps away. If she had 1242 stamps, how many had she left?

10. Would you prefer $\frac{2}{5}$ of £935 or $\frac{3}{4}$ of £504?

11. Our planned journey was 468 km. After travelling $\frac{7}{12}$ of this journey, how many kilometres had we travelled?

12. 2400 children live in a certain town; $\frac{1}{3}$ attend secondary school and $\frac{7}{15}$ are at primary school; the rest do not go to school.

(*a*) How many do not attend school?

(*b*) $\frac{9}{16}$ of the secondary-school pupils are boys. How many are girls?

9 Angles

Use any piece of paper. Tear a piece into any shape.

Using only two folds, make a right-angle with your piece of paper.

The two lines on this drawing may help:

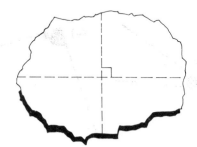

Exercise 2

1. List these angles in order of size. Give the smallest first.

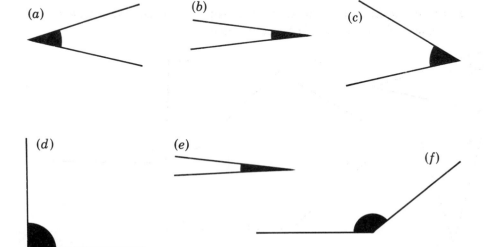

2. State, for each angle, whether it is bigger than, or smaller than, or equal to a right-angle. (Your folded right-angle may help you.)

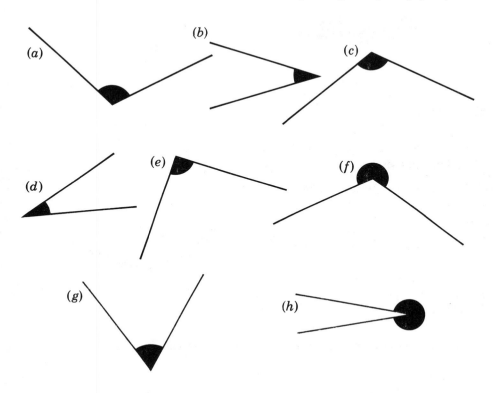

3. State whether each angle is an acute angle, an obtuse angle, a reflex angle, a right-angle, or a straight angle:

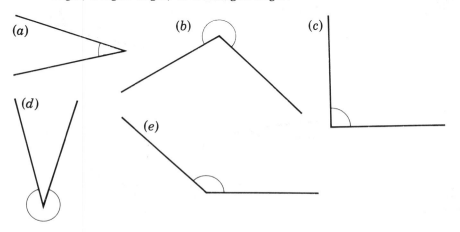

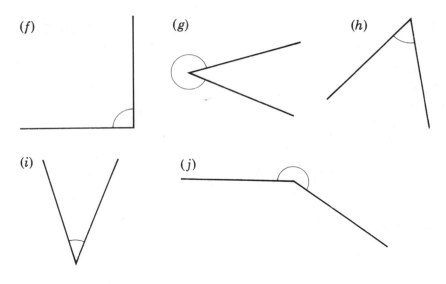

(f)

(g)

(h)

(i)

(j)

(Note that (f) is *not* a left-angle!)

Exercise 3 ▨▨▨▨▨▨▨▨▨▨▨▨▨▨▨▨▨▨▨▨▨▨ **M**

Use the map of Garstangle on p. 209.

Copy the table and write the type of angle through which you turn (acute angle, obtuse angle, reflex angle or right-angle) if:

	You are at the	You face the	You turn	You now face the	Type of angle
1.	garage	station	clockwise	castle ruins	
2.	school	green	clockwise	crescent	
3.	post office	garage	clockwise	cul-de-sac	
4.	church	farm	clockwise	river	
5.	church	farm	anticlockwise	river	
6.	farm	crossroads	clockwise	marsh	
7.	railway bridge	marsh	anticlockwise	station	
8.	crossroads	embankment	clockwise	school	
9.	green	post office	anticlockwise	station	
10.	inn	school	clockwise	garage	

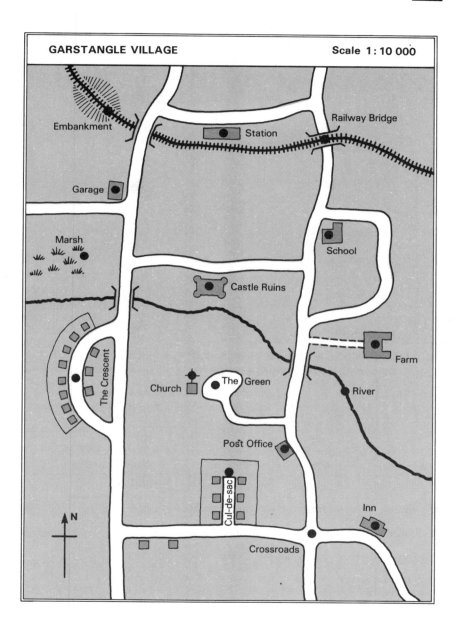

GARSTANGLE VILLAGE

Scale 1:10 000

Embankment

Railway Bridge

Station

Garage

Marsh

School

Castle Ruins

The Crescent

Farm

Church

The Green

River

Post Office

Cul-de-sac

Inn

N

Crossroads

Exercise 4

Write, for each drawing, what fraction of a full turn it shows:

1.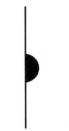

2.

3.

4.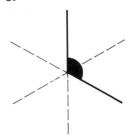

5.

6.

7.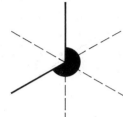

8.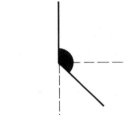

9.

10.

Copy these. For each question, rotate the line QR about R.
Mark a dot S such that angle QRS is a right angle. (S shows the new position of Q.)

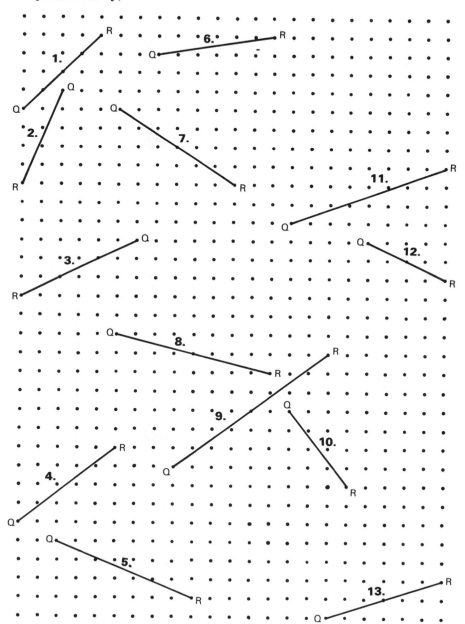

Exercise 6

Use a piece of filter paper, or cut out a circle from a piece of paper.

1. Fold it in half: **2.** Halve it again: **3.** Halve it once more:

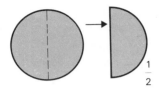 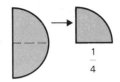 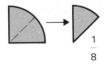

Number 1 shows $\frac{1}{2}$ turn.

Number 2 shows $\frac{1}{4}$ turn.

Number 3 shows $\frac{1}{8}$ turn.

Keep your folded circle. You will need it later.

History!

There are 360° in a full turn.

Why divide a full turn into 360 equal parts?

Why not use some easier number such as 100?

It was possibly divided into 360 parts because thousands of years ago the Greeks and the Sumerians divided their year into 360 days. Each degree would be the daily amount of turning as the Earth followed its path around the Sun.

Exercise 7

A full turn = 360°.

How many degrees are there in:

1. $\frac{1}{2}$ turn? **2.** $\frac{1}{4}$ turns? **3.** $\frac{1}{3}$ turn?

4. $\dfrac{2}{3}$ turn?

5. $\dfrac{1}{6}$ turn?

6. $\dfrac{5}{6}$ turn?

7. $\dfrac{3}{4}$ turn?

8. 2 turns?

9. 3 turns?

10. 4 turns?

11. 5 turns?

12. $\dfrac{1}{10}$ turn?

13. $\dfrac{3}{10}$ turn?

14. $\dfrac{7}{10}$ turn?

15. $\dfrac{1}{5}$ turn?

16. $\dfrac{4}{5}$ turn?

17. $\dfrac{1}{12}$ turn?

18. $\dfrac{5}{12}$ turn?

19. $\dfrac{11}{12}$ turn?

20. 10 turns?

21. $\dfrac{2}{5}$ turn?

22. $\dfrac{9}{10}$ turn?

23. $\dfrac{1}{36}$ turn?

24. $\dfrac{1}{360}$ turn?

Exercise 8

Estimate the number of degrees in each of these angles (your folded circle may help you):

1.

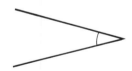

2.

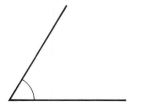

3.

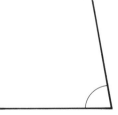

4.

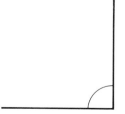

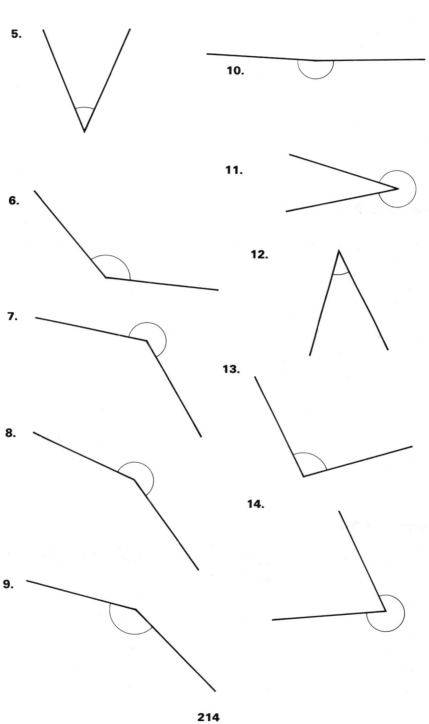

5.

10.

11.

6.

12.

7.

13.

8.

14.

9.

214

15.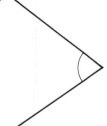

16.

Exercise 9

Without using a protractor, try to draw two straight lines to show these angles. (Label each angle.)

e.g.

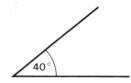

1. 45°	**6.** 160°	**11.** 100°	**16.** 325°
2. 20°	**7.** 120°	**12.** 35°	**17.** 340°
3. 70°	**8.** 270°	**13.** 95°	**18.** 250°
4. 90°	**9.** 300°	**14.** 155°	**19.** 195°
5. 135°	**10.** 225°	**15.** 275°	**20.** 115°

Exercise 10

Give the correct name (acute angle, obtuse angle, reflex angle, right-angle) for each of the following angles:

1. 28°	**7.** 90°	**13.** 5°
2. 74°	**8.** 326°	**14.** 270°
3. 80°	**9.** 170°	**15.** 91°
4. 140°	**10.** 234°	**16.** 89°
5. 200°	**11.** 350°	**17.** 269°
6. 125°	**12.** 21°	**18.** 271°

19. 101°	**23.** 195°	**27.** 232°
20. 310°	**24.** 295°	**28.** 332°
21. 10°	**25.** 32°	**29.** 17°
22. 95°	**26.** 132°	**30.** 248°

Exercise 11

Most protractors have two scales.
One reads clockwise and the other anticlockwise.

The protractor that is drawn here
shows the scale that reads anticlockwise.

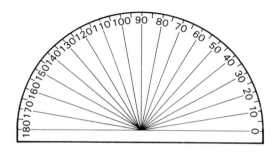

Look at the scales on your protractor.
Find the scale that reads anticlockwise.

Now use the anticlockwise scale (as shown) to measure these angles.
(Estimate each angle before measuring.)

1.

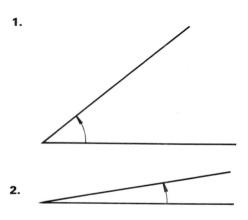

2.

3.

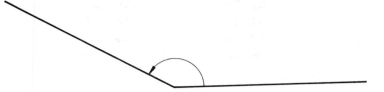

4.

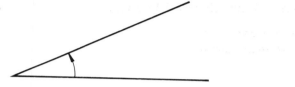

5.

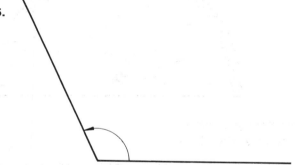

6.

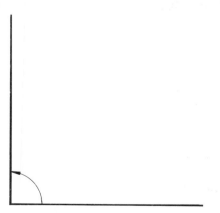

Exercise 12

This time, the protractor shown uses the clockwise scale.

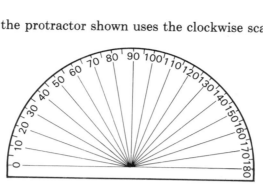

Use the clockwise scale on your protractor to measure these angles.
(Estimate first.)

1.

3.

2.

4.

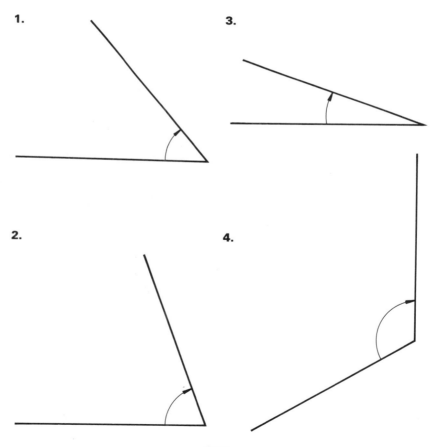

5.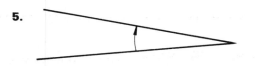

6.

7.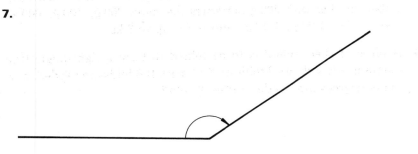

8.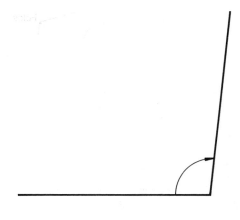

Exercise 13

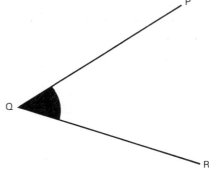

1. Measure this angle by placing the zero line of your protractor along QR.
   Read the anticlockwise scale.

2. Now measure the angle again. This time, place the zero line of your protractor along PQ.
   Read the clockwise scale.

3. What do you notice about your answers to questions 1 and 2?

Exercise 14

Measure these angles.

Estimate each angle first. Your estimate should help you to decide which scale to use on your protractor.

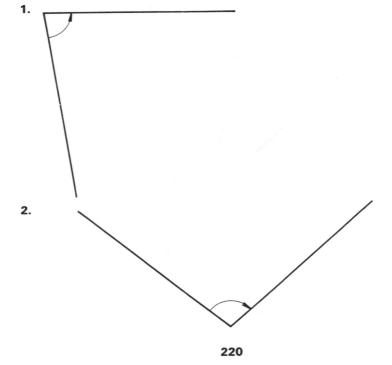

1.

2.

220

3.

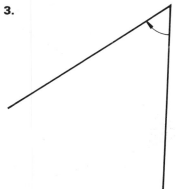

4.

5.

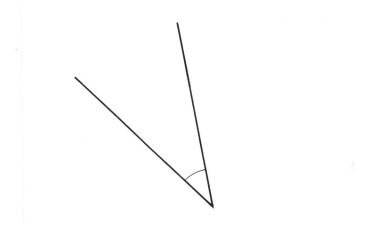

6.

7.

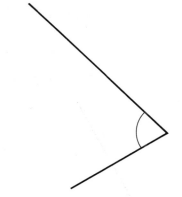

8.

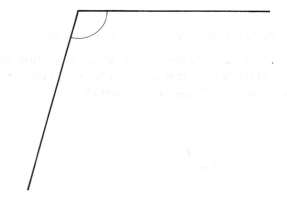

9.

10.

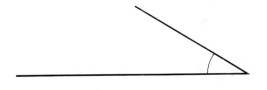

11.

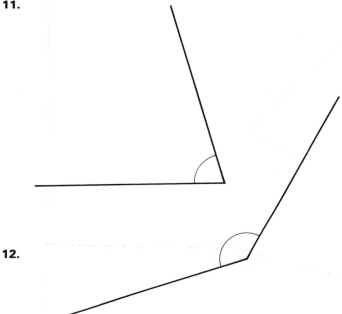

12.

When drawing angles, measure them as accurately as you can.

If a space ship flies on a straight course for the Moon (a journey of about 240 000 miles or 384 000 km), but it is 1° out when it takes off, it will miss the Moon by over 4000 miles (over 6400 km).

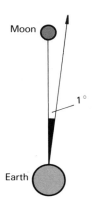

Moon

1°

Earth

Carefully and accurately draw
and label angles of the following
sizes (as in the example):

e.g.

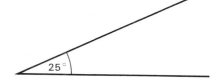

1. 20°	**5.** 60°	**9.** 130°	**13.** 140°	**17.** 15°
2. 75°	**6.** 80°	**10.** 50°	**14.** 10°	**18.** 175°
3. 45°	**7.** 90°	**11.** 165°	**15.** 160°	**19.** 115°
4. 15°	**8.** 120°	**12.** 95°	**16.** 105°	**20.** 55°

Exercise 16

Copy and complete:

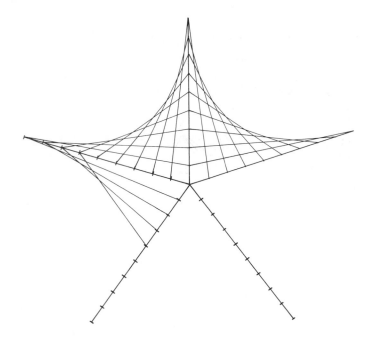

Copy some of these patterns. Complete them if they have not been finished.

1.

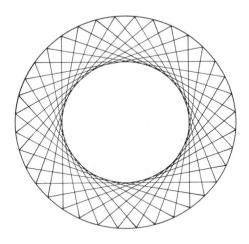

2. Join every point to every other point:

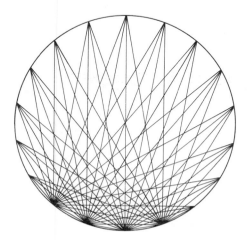

3. Join the numbers using your 2-times table:

$1 \rightarrow 2$
$2 \rightarrow 4$
$3 \rightarrow 6$
$4 \rightarrow 8$
$\vdots$
$18 \rightarrow 36$

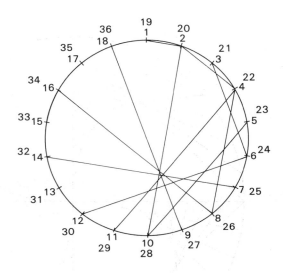

4. Join the numbers using your 3-times table:

$1 \rightarrow 3$
$2 \rightarrow 6$
$3 \rightarrow 9$
$4 \rightarrow 12$
$\vdots$
$18 \rightarrow 54$

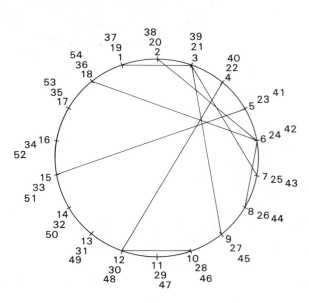

Exercise 18

Copy this. Use a radius of 4.5 cm (45 mm).

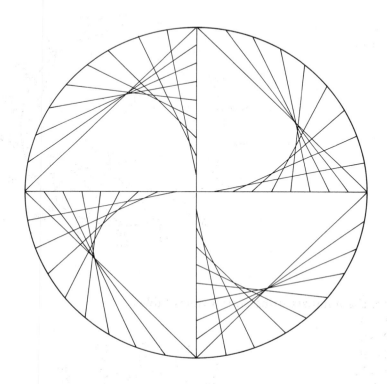

Exercise 19

A Try to do these calculations in your head:

1. $360° - 50°$	**5.** $360° - 165°$	**9.** $360° - 93°$
2. $360° - 70°$	**6.** $360° - 122°$	**10.** $360° - 37°$
3. $360° - 100°$	**7.** $360° - 146°$	**11.** $360° - 81°$
4. $360° - 35°$	**8.** $360° - 64°$	**12.** $360° - 158°$

B Measure these angles. (The calculations you have just done may help.)

1.

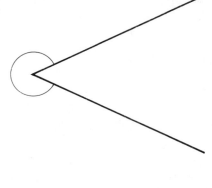

3.

2.

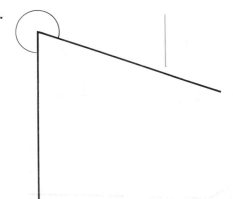

4.

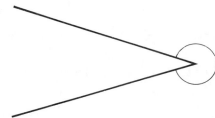

5.

6.

7.

8.

9.

10.

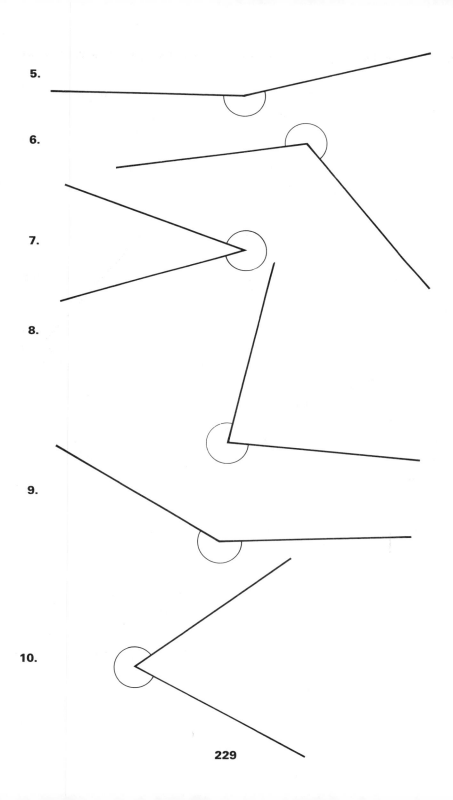

Exercise 20

Carefully and accurately draw and label angles of the following sizes:

1.	35°	**6.**	200°	**11.**	281°
2.	145°	**7.**	185°	**12.**	117°
3.	170°	**8.**	350°	**13.**	217°
4.	190°	**9.**	275°	**14.**	17°
5.	235°	**10.**	42°	**15.**	317°

Exercise 21   **M**

Use the map of Garstangle on p. 209

A Through how many degrees do you turn if you are at the church, you point North, then you turn clockwise to point to each of the named places on the map?

B Copy and complete the table below.

You are at the	You face the	You turn to face the	You turn	Number of degrees
marsh	station	castle ruins	clockwise	
post office	inn	school	anticlockwise	
school	green	farm	clockwise	
green	school	river		56°
crescent	crossroads		anticlockwise	80°
post office		farm	clockwise	110°
castle ruins	garage	school		109°
castle ruins	school		clockwise	251°
crescent	inn		clockwise	250°
	farm	inn	clockwise	63°

Exercise 22

Greek letters are often used to stand for angles.
We shall use the letter θ ('theta').

Calculate the missing angles. DO NOT measure.

e.g.

$$\theta = 145°$$

35°

1.

150° θ

2.

20°
θ

3.

40° θ

4.

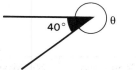

θ 75°

5.

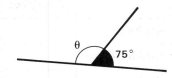

315°
θ

6.

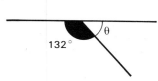

θ
132°

7.

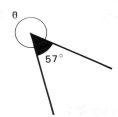

θ

57°

8.

69° θ

9.

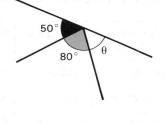

50°
80° θ

10.

40° 35°
θ

11.

90° 105°

θ

231

12.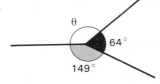

14.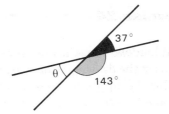

13.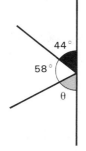

15.

Exercise 23   To Bisect an Angle

Draw any angle ABC.

With centre B, and any radius, draw an arc to cut AB at D and to cut BC at E.

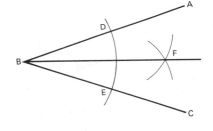

Check that your pair of compasses is set to a radius that is greater than $\frac{1}{2}$DE.

With centre at D, draw an arc between the arms and away from B.

With centre at E, using the *same* radius, draw another arc to cut the previous one at F.

Draw a straight line from B, through F.

This straight line, BF, *bisects* angle ABC.

Exercise 24

When two straight lines intersect (as in the drawing), the two angles that lie opposite each other are called *vertically opposite angles*.

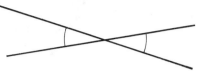

On separate diagrams, draw six pairs of intersecting lines. (All six drawings should be different.)

On each drawing, measure a pair of vertically opposite angles. What do you notice about vertically opposite angles?

Exercise 25

Calculate the missing angles. Look for vertically opposite angles.

1.

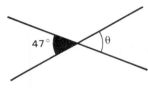

2.

3.

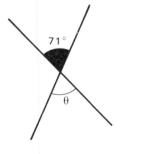

4.

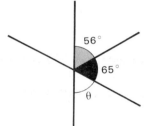

5.

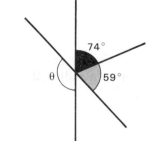

6.

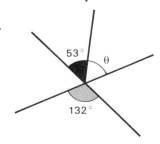

1. A wheel is turned through 273°. Through how many more degrees must it be turned to complete one revolution?

2. My kitchen scales will weigh up to 4 kg. In weighing 4 kg, the pointer turns through 360°.
   (a) Through how many degrees will the pointer turn to weigh 1 kg?
   (b) Through how many degrees will the pointer turn if I weigh 200 g of sweets?
   (c) In weighing some apples, I see the pointer turn through 63°. How heavy are the apples?
   (d) If some potatoes weigh 2.5 kg, through how many degrees will the pointer turn in weighing them?

3. Draw the dial of some kitchen weighing scales that will weigh up to 3 kg with one revolution of the pointer (the pointer turns clockwise). Label the dial with 200 g markings (i.e. show 200 g, 400 g, 600 g, 800 g, 1 kg, 1.2 kg, 1.4 kg, and so on up to 3 kg).

4. A piece of sheet metal is to be folded to form a right-angle (the diagram below shows 3 folds of 30° each). If 6 folds are needed, how many degrees are needed for each fold?

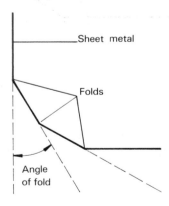

Sheet metal

Folds

Angle of fold

5. The Earth rotates once (through 360°) on its axis in 24 h. Through how many degrees does it turn in
   (a) 4 h?   (b) 1 h?   (c) 4 min?   (d) 48 min?

Exercise 27

1. How much time has passed when the hour hand of a clock turns through:

   (a) 90°?   (b) 60°?   (c) 120°?   (d) 270°?   (e) 300°?

2. How much time has passed when the minute hand of a clock turns through:

   (a) 180°?   (b) 90°?   (c) 60°?   (d) 30°?   (e) 240°?

3. Through how many degrees does the minute hand turn between:

   (a) 12.00 and 12.20?   (b) 10.25 and 11.10?

4. Through how many degrees does the hour hand turn between:

   (a) 10.00 and 11.00?   (c) 14.00 and 16.30?
   (b) 02.00 and 08.00?   (d) 07.10 and 15.40?

5. How many degrees are there between the hour and the minute hands of a clock at (give the smaller angle):

   (a) 10 o'clock?   (b) half past two?   (c) twenty past eight?

6. The slowest cutting speed on a milling machine is 35 r.p.m. (revolutions per minute).

   (a) How many seconds does it take to make 7 revolutions?
   (b) Through how many degrees does the cutter turn in 1 s?

7. If the cutting speed on a milling machine was 330 r.p.m., how many revolutions would it make in 2 s?

8. 40 revolutions of a dividing head handle turn the workpiece once (through 360°).

   (a) How many revolutions are needed to turn it through 72°?
   (b) Through how many degrees do 5 revolutions turn the workpiece?
   (c) Through how many degrees do 12 revolutions turn the workpiece?

9. Ten revolutions of the handle on a vice, close (or open) the vice by 32 mm.

   (a) By how many millimetres do 5 turns of the handle open or close the vice?
   (b) To open the vice by 2 mm, through how many degrees must the handle turn?

Exercise 28

What part of a turn is:

1.	1°	**11.**	2°	**21.**	204°
2.	180°	**12.**	280°	**22.**	360°
3.	240°	**13.**	24°	**23.**	540°
4.	45°	**14.**	225°	**24.**	48°
5.	40°	**15.**	315°	**25.**	1440°
6.	200°	**16.**	80°	**26.**	325°
7.	12°	**17.**	14°	**27.**	1260°
8.	135°	**18.**	100°	**28.**	450°
9.	20°	**19.**	252°	**29.**	960°
10.	50°	**20.**	132°	**30.**	3600°

Exercise 29

The major points of the compass are shown.

Through how many degrees does someone turn in turning:

1. anticlockwise from N to W?

2. clockwise from NE to SE?

3. clockwise from SE to NW?

4. clockwise from SW to W?

5. anticlockwise from E to NW?

6. clockwise from E to NW?

7. anticlockwise from S to SW?

8. anticlockwise from NW to NE?

9. clockwise from NW to NE?

10. anticlockwise from NE to S?

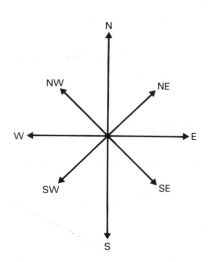

10 Triangles and Constructions

Cut out any triangle from a piece of paper.

Tear off all three corners.

Now place all three corners together as shown below.

What can you say about the sum of the angles of a triangle?

Exercise 2

Measure, then state the size of the following angles:

1.

$\alpha = \boxed{?}$ $\beta = \boxed{?}$ $\gamma = \boxed{?}$

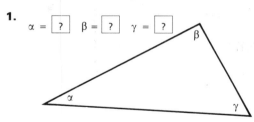

237

2.

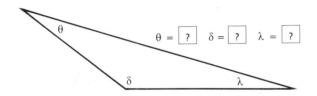

$\theta = $ [?] $\delta = $ [?] $\lambda = $ [?]

3.

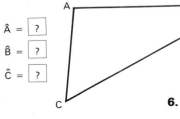

$\hat{A} = $ [?]
$\hat{B} = $ [?]
$\hat{C} = $ [?]

6.

$\hat{P} = $ [?]
$\hat{Q} = $ [?]
$\hat{R} = $ [?]

4.

$\hat{D} = $ [?]
$\hat{E} = $ [?]
$\hat{F} = $ [?]

7.

S$\hat{T}$U $= $ [?]
S$\hat{U}$T $= $ [?]
U$\hat{S}$T $= $ [?]

5.

J$\hat{K}$L $= $ [?]
K$\hat{L}$J $= $ [?]
L$\hat{J}$K $= $ [?]

8.

$\hat{X} = $ [?]
$\hat{Y} = $ [?]
$\hat{Z} = $ [?]

9.

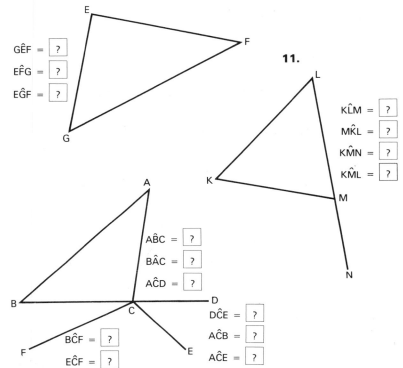

GÊF = ?

EF̂G = ?

EĜF = ?

11.

KL̂M = ?

MK̂L = ?

KM̂N = ?

KM̂L = ?

10.

AB̂C = ?

BÂC = ?

AĈD = ?

DĈE = ?

AĈB = ?

AĈE = ?

BĈF = ?

EĈF = ?

Exercise 3

Calculate the missing angles in the following triangles:

1.

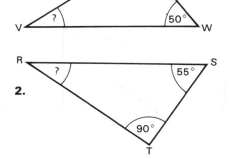

2.

3.

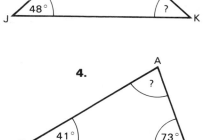

4.

5.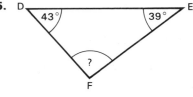

9.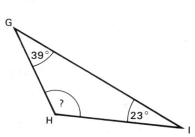

6.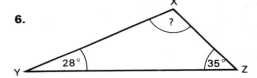

10.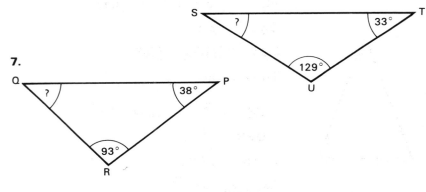

7.

8.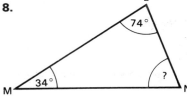

Exercise 4

Copy these triangles. Measure each angle and each side.

Also, copy and complete each sentence with the word 'different' or 'equal'.

1.

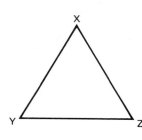

Equilateral triangle

XY = ⬚? mm, YZ = ⬚? mm,

XZ = ⬚? mm

All sides are ⬚? .

∠ XYZ = ⬚? °, ∠ XZY = ⬚? °,

∠ YXZ = ⬚? °

All angles are ⬚? .

2.

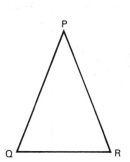

Isosceles triangle

PQ = ⬚? mm, PR = ⬚? mm,

QR = ⬚? mm,

PQ = ⬚? (Which side?)

Two sides are ⬚? .

∠ PQR = ⬚? °, ∠ PRQ = ⬚? °,

∠ QPR = ⬚? °,

∠ PQR = ∠⬚?

Two angles are ⬚? .

Equal angles are opposite ⬚? sides.

3.

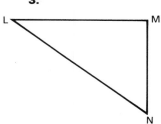

Right-angled triangle

∠ LMN = ⬚? °

Right-angled triangles have one right-angle.

241

4. *Scalene triangle*

AB = $\boxed{?}$ mm, BC = $\boxed{?}$ mm,

AC = $\boxed{?}$ mm.

All sides are $\boxed{?}$.

∠ ABC = $\boxed{?}$ °, ∠ ACB = $\boxed{?}$ °,

∠ BAC = $\boxed{?}$ °.

All angles are $\boxed{?}$.

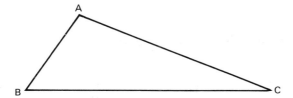

Exercise 5

You need to use 9-pin Geoboard (3 × 3 pinboard) and/or some 3 × 3 dotty paper.

It is easier to do this work using Geoboard.

Show your answers on the dotty paper.

These two triangles are the same:

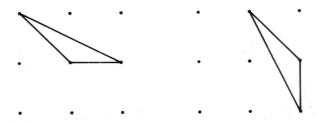

Two triangles are the same if, when cut out, one fits exactly on top of the other.

Check that the two triangles above are the same.

1. Make as many different triangles as you can.

2. How many of your triangles are right-angled triangles?

3. How many of your triangles are isosceles triangles?

4. Are there any equilateral triangles?

5. Are there any scalene triangles?

Exercise 6

Calculate the angles marked with a question mark:

1.

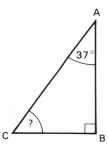

4.

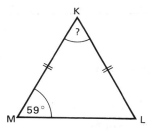

2.

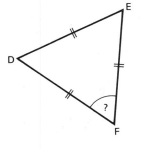

5.

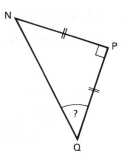

3.

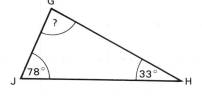

6.

7.

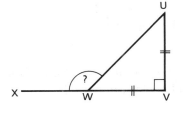

10.

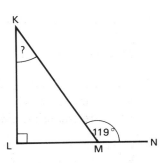

8.

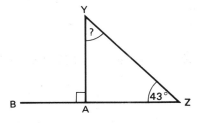

11.

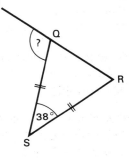

9.

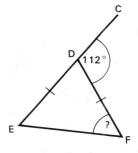

12.

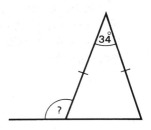

Exercise 7

Use a ruler, a protractor, a setsquare and a pair of compasses to carry out these constructions.
The given drawings are not to the correct size.

1. Construct △PQR with PQ = 56 mm, ∠QPR = 62°, and PR = 49 mm. How long is QR?

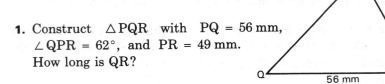

244

2. Construct an isosceles triangle ABC where BC = 37 mm, where AB = AC, and where the equal angles each measure 48°. Measure AB.

3. Construct an isosceles triangle where the equal sides are both 54 mm long and where the equal angles are both 68°. Measure the other side.

4. Construct a right-angled triangle XYZ in which ∠ XZY = 90°, XZ = 31 mm, and XY = 72 mm.
Measure ∠ ZXY and ∠ XYZ.
Find the sum of these two angles.
What do you notice?

5. Construct △JKL such that KL = 57 mm, ∠ JLK = 42° and ∠ KJL = 59°.
Measure JK.

6. Construct △DEF with DE = 44 mm, EF = 62 mm, and FD = 70 mm.

Measure angle DEF. Bisect EF. Let the perpendicular bisector of EF meet DF at G. Measure EG.

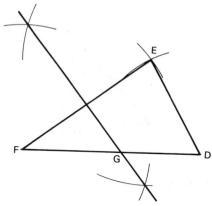

7. Construct an equilateral triangle UVW where each side is 45 mm long. Bisect all three sides.
What do you notice about the three perpendicular bisectors?

8. Construct △STU such that ST = 87 mm, ∠ STU = 34° and TU = 68 mm. Mark a point V on SU where SV = 23 mm. Construct VW parallel to ST so that W lies on TU.
Measure UW.

Exercise 8

1. Two angles of a triangle are 50° and 70°; find the third angle.

2. Two angles of a triangle add up to 140°; find the third angle.

3. Two angles of a triangle are 65° and 45°; find the third angle.

4. Two angles of a triangle are 70° and 40°. If the triangle is an isosceles triangle, find the third angle.

5. One angle of a triangle is 50°. If the other two angles are equal, find them.

6. One angle of an isosceles triangle is 110°, what size can the other angles be?

7. One angle of an isosceles triangle is 80°, what size can the other angles be?

8. If the sum of two angles of a triangle is less than the third angle, must the triangle be an obtuse-angled triangle?

9. A ladder makes an angle of 32° with a wall.
   What angle does it make with the ground?

10. A plank makes an angle of 21° with the horizontal.
    What angle does it make with the vertical?

11 Calculations with Fractions and Decimals

1. Draw a rectangle, 4 cm by 3 cm.
   Divide it into twelfths.
   Shade 5 twelfths.
   Shade a further 2 twelfths.
   How many twelfths are now shaded?

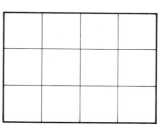

5 twelfths + 2 twelfths = $\boxed{?}$ twelfths

$$\frac{5}{12} + \frac{2}{12} = \frac{\boxed{?}}{12}$$

2. Draw a rectangle 4 cm by 2 cm.
   Divide it into eighths.
   Shade $\frac{3}{8}$ then shade a further $\frac{2}{8}$.
   How many eighths are now shaded?

$$\frac{3}{8} + \frac{2}{8} = \boxed{?}$$

Exercise 2

A 1. 4 pens + 5 pens   2. 4 cakes + 5 cakes

247

3. 4 tenths + 5 tenths

4. 3 sweets + 2 sweets

5. 3 marbles + 2 marbles

6. $\dfrac{3}{8} + \dfrac{2}{8}$

7. 4 ninths + 3 ninths

8. $\dfrac{4}{12} + \dfrac{3}{12}$

9. $\dfrac{7}{15} + \dfrac{4}{15}$

10. $\dfrac{5}{11} + \dfrac{4}{11}$

11. $\dfrac{11}{15} + \dfrac{2}{15}$

12. $\dfrac{2}{7} + \dfrac{4}{7}$

13. $\dfrac{5}{14} + \dfrac{6}{14}$

14. $\dfrac{1}{5} + \dfrac{2}{5}$

15. $\dfrac{4}{6} + \dfrac{1}{6}$

16. $\dfrac{5}{9} + \dfrac{3}{9}$

17. $\dfrac{4}{15} + \dfrac{4}{15}$

18. $\dfrac{3}{20} + \dfrac{14}{20}$

19. $\dfrac{6}{13} + \dfrac{4}{13}$

20. $\dfrac{7}{16} + \dfrac{6}{16}$

21. $\dfrac{14}{32} + \dfrac{13}{32}$

22. $\dfrac{23}{50} + \dfrac{24}{50}$

23. $\dfrac{64}{100} + \dfrac{17}{100}$

24. $\dfrac{8}{25} + \dfrac{4}{25}$

25. $\dfrac{23}{32} + \dfrac{6}{32}$

B Carry out these additions. Simplify your answers.

1. $\dfrac{1}{8} + \dfrac{3}{8}$

2. $\dfrac{2}{6} + \dfrac{1}{6}$

3. $\dfrac{3}{6} + \dfrac{1}{6}$

4. $\dfrac{3}{8} + \dfrac{3}{8}$

5. $\dfrac{2}{9} + \dfrac{1}{9}$

6. $\dfrac{3}{10} + \dfrac{3}{10}$

7. $\dfrac{7}{10} + \dfrac{1}{10}$

8. $\dfrac{5}{12} + \dfrac{1}{12}$

9. $\dfrac{5}{16} + \dfrac{3}{16}$

10. $\dfrac{4}{9} + \dfrac{2}{9}$

11. $\dfrac{7}{16} + \dfrac{5}{16}$

12. $\dfrac{4}{15} + \dfrac{2}{15}$

13. $\dfrac{5}{12} + \dfrac{3}{12}$

14. $\dfrac{9}{20} + \dfrac{6}{20}$

15. $\dfrac{3}{20} + \dfrac{5}{20}$

16. $\dfrac{4}{15} + \dfrac{6}{15}$

17. $\dfrac{7}{32} + \dfrac{9}{32}$

18. $\dfrac{13}{32} + \dfrac{11}{32}$

19. $\dfrac{3}{16} + \dfrac{11}{16}$

20. $\dfrac{7}{20} + \dfrac{9}{20}$

21. $\dfrac{12}{25} + \dfrac{8}{25}$ **23.** $\dfrac{3}{14} + \dfrac{9}{14}$ **25.** $\dfrac{7}{8} + \dfrac{1}{8}$ **27.** $\dfrac{11}{16} + \dfrac{5}{16}$

22. $\dfrac{8}{15} + \dfrac{4}{15}$ **24.** $\dfrac{3}{4} + \dfrac{1}{4}$ **26.** $\dfrac{7}{10} + \dfrac{3}{10}$ **28.** $\dfrac{5}{12} + \dfrac{7}{12}$

Exercise 3

A Copy and complete these sets of equivalent fractions:

1. $\left\{ \dfrac{1}{2}, \dfrac{2}{4}, \dfrac{3}{6}, \dfrac{4}{8}, \dfrac{5}{\boxed{?}}, \dfrac{\boxed{?}}{12}, \dfrac{\boxed{?}}{14}, \dfrac{\boxed{?}}{16}, \dfrac{9}{\boxed{?}}, \dfrac{\boxed{?}}{20} \right\}$

2. $\left\{ \dfrac{1}{3}, \dfrac{2}{6}, \dfrac{3}{\boxed{?}}, \dfrac{\boxed{?}}{12}, \dfrac{\boxed{?}}{15}, \dfrac{6}{\boxed{?}} \right\}$ **6.** $\left\{ \dfrac{1}{5}, \dfrac{2}{10}, \dfrac{\boxed{?}}{15}, \dfrac{4}{\boxed{?}} \right\}$

3. $\left\{ \dfrac{1}{4}, \dfrac{2}{8}, \dfrac{3}{\boxed{?}}, \dfrac{\boxed{?}}{16}, \dfrac{5}{\boxed{?}} \right\}$ **7.** $\left\{ \dfrac{1}{6}, \dfrac{2}{12}, \dfrac{\boxed{?}}{18} \right\}$

4. $\left\{ \dfrac{2}{3}, \dfrac{4}{6}, \dfrac{\boxed{?}}{9}, \dfrac{8}{\boxed{?}}, \dfrac{\boxed{?}}{15}, \dfrac{12}{\boxed{?}} \right\}$ **8.** $\left\{ \dfrac{1}{8}, \dfrac{2}{16}, \dfrac{3}{\boxed{?}}, \dfrac{\boxed{?}}{32} \right\}$

5. $\left\{ \dfrac{3}{4}, \dfrac{6}{8}, \dfrac{9}{\boxed{?}}, \dfrac{\boxed{?}}{16}, \dfrac{\boxed{?}}{20} \right\}$

B The above fractions may help you with these additions. Simplify your answers.

1. $\dfrac{1}{4} + \dfrac{1}{2}$ **5.** $\dfrac{1}{2} + \dfrac{7}{16}$ **9.** $\dfrac{4}{9} + \dfrac{1}{3}$ **13.** $\dfrac{1}{2} + \dfrac{3}{10}$

2. $\dfrac{3}{8} + \dfrac{1}{2}$ **6.** $\dfrac{5}{8} + \dfrac{3}{16}$ **10.** $\dfrac{2}{3} + \dfrac{2}{9}$ **14.** $\dfrac{1}{3} + \dfrac{1}{6}$

3. $\dfrac{1}{4} + \dfrac{3}{8}$ **7.** $\dfrac{3}{5} + \dfrac{1}{10}$ **11.** $\dfrac{3}{4} + \dfrac{1}{12}$ **15.** $\dfrac{2}{5} + \dfrac{4}{15}$

4. $\dfrac{5}{16} + \dfrac{1}{4}$ **8.** $\dfrac{1}{3} + \dfrac{1}{9}$ **12.** $\dfrac{1}{3} + \dfrac{5}{12}$ **16.** $\dfrac{2}{15} + \dfrac{2}{3}$

17. $\dfrac{7}{20} + \dfrac{1}{4}$ **21.** $\dfrac{3}{5} + \dfrac{9}{10}$ **25.** $\dfrac{7}{16} + \dfrac{5}{8}$ **29.** $\dfrac{5}{6} + \dfrac{2}{3}$

18. $\dfrac{3}{5} + \dfrac{3}{20}$ **22.** $\dfrac{2}{3} + \dfrac{4}{9}$ **26.** $\dfrac{7}{8} + \dfrac{11}{32}$ **30.** $\dfrac{4}{5} + \dfrac{9}{10}$

19. $\dfrac{1}{2} + \dfrac{3}{4}$ **23.** $\dfrac{7}{8} + \dfrac{3}{4}$ **27.** $\dfrac{3}{4} + \dfrac{7}{12}$

20. $\dfrac{5}{8} + \dfrac{7}{8}$ **24.** $\dfrac{3}{4} + \dfrac{5}{16}$ **28.** $\dfrac{5}{6} + \dfrac{7}{12}$

C Answer these. Simplify your answers.

1. (a) $\dfrac{1}{2} + \dfrac{2}{6}$ **4.** $\dfrac{1}{4} + \dfrac{2}{5}$ **10.** $\dfrac{3}{5} + \dfrac{5}{8}$ **16.** $\dfrac{1}{2} + \dfrac{5}{8} + \dfrac{3}{4}$

(b) $\dfrac{1}{2} + \dfrac{1}{3}$ **5.** $\dfrac{2}{3} + \dfrac{3}{5}$ **11.** $\dfrac{2}{3} + \dfrac{7}{8}$ **17.** $\dfrac{3}{4} + \dfrac{5}{6} + \dfrac{7}{12}$

2. (a) $\dfrac{1}{3} + \dfrac{3}{12}$ **6.** $\dfrac{4}{5} + \dfrac{1}{6}$ **12.** $\dfrac{2}{5} + \dfrac{2}{3}$ **18.** $\dfrac{5}{8} + \dfrac{1}{2} + \dfrac{5}{6}$

(b) $\dfrac{1}{3} + \dfrac{1}{4}$ **7.** $\dfrac{2}{3} + \dfrac{3}{4}$ **13.** $\dfrac{5}{6} + \dfrac{4}{9}$ **19.** $\dfrac{1}{6} + \dfrac{7}{10} + \dfrac{8}{15}$

3. (a) $\dfrac{5}{15} + \dfrac{2}{5}$ **8.** $\dfrac{1}{2} + \dfrac{2}{3}$ **14.** $\dfrac{3}{4} + \dfrac{7}{10}$ **20.** $\dfrac{1}{2} + \dfrac{2}{3} + \dfrac{3}{4}$

(b) $\dfrac{1}{3} + \dfrac{2}{5}$ **9.** $\dfrac{3}{4} + \dfrac{5}{6}$ **15.** $\dfrac{3}{10} + \dfrac{7}{8}$

Exercise 4

Answer these. Simplify your answers.

1. (a) $\frac{1}{2} + \frac{1}{8}$ **2.** (a) $\frac{5}{8} + \frac{1}{4}$ **3.** (a) $\frac{2}{5} + \frac{3}{10}$ **4.** (a) $\frac{3}{4} + \frac{5}{8}$

(b) $2\frac{1}{2} + 1\frac{1}{8}$ (b) $3\frac{5}{8} + 2\frac{1}{4}$ (b) $3\frac{2}{5} + 2\frac{3}{10}$ (b) $3\frac{3}{4} + 4\frac{5}{8}$

5. $3\frac{5}{6} + 6\frac{7}{12}$ **13.** (a) $\frac{1}{3} + \frac{2}{5}$ **17.** $1\frac{5}{6} + \frac{3}{8}$

6. $4\frac{7}{10} + 3\frac{2}{5}$ (b) $5\frac{1}{3} + 2\frac{2}{5}$ **18.** $7\frac{4}{5} + 3\frac{2}{3}$

7. $1\frac{1}{2} + 2\frac{9}{10}$ **14.** (a) $\frac{1}{4} + \frac{2}{3}$ **19.** $2\frac{3}{4} + 5\frac{4}{5}$

8. $2\frac{7}{16} + 1\frac{3}{4}$ (b) $2\frac{1}{4} + 6\frac{2}{3}$ **20.** $3\frac{7}{10} + 4\frac{2}{3}$

9. $3\frac{3}{8} + 4\frac{13}{16}$ **15.** (a) $\frac{1}{2} + \frac{4}{5}$ **21.** $5\frac{1}{4} + 3\frac{5}{6}$

10. $7\frac{2}{3} + 4\frac{5}{9}$ (b) $3\frac{1}{2} + 1\frac{4}{5}$ **22.** $6\frac{5}{8} + 1\frac{2}{3}$

11. $1\frac{9}{16} + 4\frac{11}{32}$ **16.** (a) $\frac{2}{5} + \frac{7}{8}$ **23.** $1\frac{3}{4} + 6\frac{9}{10}$

12. $3\frac{7}{32} + 5\frac{5}{8}$ (b) $5\frac{2}{5} + 4\frac{7}{8}$ **24.** $8\frac{11}{12} + 4\frac{5}{8}$

Exercise 5

A Carry out these subtractions:

1. 5 eighths – 2 eighths   **7.** $\frac{5}{7} - \frac{2}{7}$ **13.** $\frac{7}{10} - \frac{4}{10}$

2. 7 tenths – 6 tenths   **8.** $\frac{8}{9} - \frac{4}{9}$ **14.** $\frac{7}{10} - \frac{2}{5}$

3. 6 sevenths – 4 sevenths   **9.** $\frac{5}{6} - \frac{4}{6}$ **15.** $\frac{10}{12} - \frac{5}{12}$

4. 3 fifths – 1 fifth   **10.** $\frac{6}{8} - \frac{3}{8}$ **16.** $\frac{5}{6} - \frac{5}{12}$

5. 7 ninths – 3 ninths   **11.** $\frac{3}{4} - \frac{2}{4}$ **17.** $\frac{10}{12} - \frac{9}{12}$

6. 10 twelfths – 3 twelfths   **12.** $\frac{3}{4} - \frac{1}{2}$ **18.** $\frac{5}{6} - \frac{3}{4}$

B Carry out these subtractions. Simplify your answers.

1. $\frac{11}{12} - \frac{5}{12}$ **2.** $\frac{7}{8} - \frac{1}{8}$ **3.** $\frac{13}{16} - \frac{9}{16}$ **4.** $\frac{5}{6} - \frac{2}{6}$

5. $\dfrac{5}{6} - \dfrac{1}{3}$ **11.** $\dfrac{12}{16} - \dfrac{3}{16}$ **17.** $\dfrac{3}{5} - \dfrac{1}{10}$ **23.** $\dfrac{11}{12} - \dfrac{5}{8}$

6. $\dfrac{11}{12} - \dfrac{9}{12}$ **12.** $\dfrac{3}{4} - \dfrac{3}{16}$ **18.** $\dfrac{2}{3} - \dfrac{1}{2}$ **24.** $\dfrac{8}{9} - \dfrac{7}{15}$

7. $\dfrac{11}{12} - \dfrac{3}{4}$ **13.** $\dfrac{9}{12} - \dfrac{8}{12}$ **19.** $\dfrac{4}{5} - \dfrac{1}{2}$ **25.** $\dfrac{7}{9} - \dfrac{1}{6}$

8. $\dfrac{23}{24} - \dfrac{7}{24}$ **14.** $\dfrac{3}{4} - \dfrac{2}{3}$ **20.** $\dfrac{3}{4} - \dfrac{2}{5}$

9. $\dfrac{11}{16} - \dfrac{3}{16}$ **15.** $\dfrac{11}{12} - \dfrac{2}{3}$ **21.** $\dfrac{5}{6} - \dfrac{3}{8}$

10. $\dfrac{27}{32} - \dfrac{3}{32}$ **16.** $\dfrac{2}{3} - \dfrac{1}{6}$ **22.** $\dfrac{5}{6} - \dfrac{1}{4}$

C   Carry out these subtractions:

1. $1 - \dfrac{2}{3}$ **10.** $3 - \dfrac{4}{7}$ **19.** $8\dfrac{8}{9} - \dfrac{4}{9}$ **28.** $3\dfrac{11}{16} - 2\dfrac{4}{16}$

2. $1 - \dfrac{1}{8}$ **11.** $5 - \dfrac{13}{16}$ **20.** $6\dfrac{2}{3} - \dfrac{1}{3}$ **29.** $5\dfrac{31}{32} - 2\dfrac{22}{32}$

3. $1 - \dfrac{5}{9}$ **12.** $4 - \dfrac{25}{32}$ **21.** $5\dfrac{7}{9} - 2\dfrac{5}{9}$ **30.** $1\dfrac{28}{32} - 1\dfrac{3}{32}$

4. $1 - \dfrac{1}{4}$ **13.** $1\dfrac{6}{7} - \dfrac{2}{7}$ **22.** $8\dfrac{4}{5} - 1\dfrac{1}{5}$ **31.** $3\dfrac{13}{15} - 2\dfrac{6}{15}$

5. $1 - \dfrac{3}{10}$ **14.** $3\dfrac{9}{11} - \dfrac{7}{11}$ **23.** $7\dfrac{7}{9} - 7\dfrac{2}{9}$ **32.** $7\dfrac{17}{20} - 4\dfrac{8}{20}$

6. $3 - \dfrac{5}{6}$ **15.** $5\dfrac{4}{5} - \dfrac{1}{5}$ **24.** $5\dfrac{11}{12} - 2\dfrac{4}{12}$ **33.** $9\dfrac{21}{25} - 1\dfrac{12}{25}$

7. $2 - \dfrac{3}{4}$ **16.** $7\dfrac{7}{9} - \dfrac{2}{9}$ **25.** $6\dfrac{3}{5} - 4\dfrac{2}{5}$ **34.** $4\dfrac{14}{25} - 2\dfrac{6}{25}$

8. $4 - \dfrac{3}{5}$ **17.** $6\dfrac{4}{7} - \dfrac{3}{7}$ **26.** $4\dfrac{5}{8} - 1\dfrac{2}{8}$ **35.** $2\dfrac{51}{100} - 1\dfrac{28}{100}$

9. $7 - \dfrac{11}{12}$ **18.** $7\dfrac{5}{8} - \dfrac{5}{8}$ **27.** $2\dfrac{6}{7} - \dfrac{2}{7}$

Exercise 6

A   Carry out these subtractions. Simplify your answers.

1. $9\dfrac{7}{8} - \dfrac{3}{8}$ **3.** $6\dfrac{5}{6} - \dfrac{1}{6}$ **5.** $1\dfrac{7}{8} - \dfrac{5}{8}$ **7.** $5\dfrac{3}{4} - 2\dfrac{1}{4}$

2. $2\dfrac{3}{4} - \dfrac{1}{4}$ **4.** $5\dfrac{7}{10} - \dfrac{3}{10}$ **6.** $4\dfrac{7}{8} - 1\dfrac{3}{8}$ **8.** $6\dfrac{5}{6} - 3\dfrac{1}{6}$

9. $5\frac{7}{10} - 1\frac{3}{10}$ **12.** $7\frac{11}{12} - 2\frac{5}{12}$ **15.** $4\frac{5}{8} - 3\frac{3}{8}$ **18.** $4\frac{9}{10} - 1\frac{3}{10}$

10. $8\frac{7}{8} - 4\frac{5}{8}$ **13.** $8\frac{11}{16} - 2\frac{3}{16}$ **16.** $12\frac{7}{8} - 5\frac{1}{8}$ **19.** $10\frac{7}{12} - 7\frac{5}{12}$

11. $9\frac{7}{12} - 3\frac{7}{12}$ **14.** $5\frac{15}{16} - 1\frac{3}{16}$ **17.** $6\frac{13}{32} - 3\frac{5}{32}$ **20.** $6\frac{5}{9} - 4\frac{2}{9}$

B Carry out these subtractions. Simplify your answers.

1. $7\frac{3}{4} - 2\frac{2}{4}$ **6.** $4\frac{5}{6} - 1\frac{1}{3}$ **11.** $8\frac{5}{8} - 5\frac{5}{16}$ **16.** $4\frac{5}{6} - 1\frac{1}{2}$

2. $7\frac{3}{4} - 2\frac{1}{2}$ **7.** $12\frac{8}{10} - 4\frac{3}{10}$ **12.** $3\frac{7}{8} - 1\frac{3}{4}$ **17.** $5\frac{7}{12} - 3\frac{1}{4}$

3. $4\frac{5}{6} - 1\frac{4}{6}$ **8.** $12\frac{4}{5} - 4\frac{3}{10}$ **13.** $5\frac{1}{2} - 2\frac{1}{8}$ **18.** $3\frac{2}{3} - 1\frac{1}{12}$

4. $4\frac{5}{6} - 1\frac{2}{3}$ **9.** $7\frac{7}{9} - \frac{1}{3}$ **14.** $7\frac{13}{16} - 3\frac{1}{2}$ **19.** $6\frac{9}{20} - 5\frac{1}{5}$

5. $4\frac{5}{6} - 1\frac{2}{6}$ **10.** $5\frac{9}{16} - 2\frac{3}{8}$ **15.** $9\frac{15}{16} - 7\frac{1}{4}$ **20.** $4\frac{29}{32} - 1\frac{3}{8}$

C Carry out these subtractions. Simplify your answers.

1. $9\frac{4}{6} - 3\frac{3}{6}$ **9.** $12\frac{5}{8} - 7\frac{1}{3}$ **17.** $8\frac{3}{4} - 5\frac{2}{3}$ **25.** $3\frac{2}{3} - 1\frac{1}{5}$

2. $9\frac{2}{3} - 3\frac{1}{2}$ **10.** $9\frac{7}{10} - 2\frac{1}{3}$ **18.** $5\frac{3}{4} - 2\frac{2}{5}$ **26.** $4\frac{3}{4} - 3\frac{3}{10}$

3. $5\frac{6}{10} - 2\frac{5}{10}$ **11.** $7\frac{4}{5} - 4\frac{3}{4}$ **19.** $7\frac{3}{4} - 4\frac{1}{6}$ **27.** $8\frac{3}{5} - 5\frac{3}{10}$

4. $5\frac{3}{5} - 2\frac{1}{2}$ **12.** $6\frac{7}{8} - 4\frac{5}{12}$ **20.** $5\frac{5}{8} - 3\frac{1}{6}$ **28.** $2\frac{5}{6} - 2\frac{4}{9}$

5. $4\frac{10}{12} - 2\frac{3}{12}$ **13.** $3\frac{9}{10} - 1\frac{3}{4}$ **21.** $2\frac{2}{3} - 1\frac{3}{8}$ **29.** $3\frac{4}{5} - 1\frac{5}{12}$

6. $4\frac{5}{6} - 2\frac{1}{4}$ **14.** $9\frac{4}{5} - 2\frac{2}{3}$ **22.** $4\frac{4}{5} - 1\frac{3}{8}$ **30.** $7\frac{7}{10} - 4\frac{5}{12}$

7. $7\frac{20}{24} - 4\frac{9}{24}$ **15.** $5\frac{1}{2} - 1\frac{1}{5}$ **23.** $4\frac{4}{5} - 1\frac{1}{6}$

8. $7\frac{5}{6} - 4\frac{3}{8}$ **16.** $6\frac{2}{3} - 2\frac{1}{4}$ **24.** $5\frac{3}{4} - 1\frac{1}{6}$

Exercise 7

Carry out these subtractions:

1. $\frac{8}{5} - \frac{4}{5}$ **5.** $\frac{5}{4} - \frac{3}{4}$ **9.** $3\frac{4}{3} - \frac{2}{3}$ **13.** $2\frac{11}{8} - 1\frac{5}{8}$

2. $1\frac{3}{5} - \frac{4}{5}$ **6.** $1\frac{1}{4} - \frac{3}{4}$ **10.** $4\frac{1}{3} - \frac{2}{3}$ **14.** $3\frac{3}{8} - 1\frac{5}{8}$

3. $3\frac{8}{5} - \frac{4}{5}$ **7.** $4\frac{5}{4} - \frac{3}{4}$ **11.** $5\frac{6}{5} - 2\frac{4}{5}$ **15.** $7\frac{3}{5} - 2\frac{4}{5}$

4. $4\frac{3}{5} - \frac{4}{5}$ **8.** $5\frac{1}{4} - \frac{3}{4}$ **12.** $6\frac{1}{5} - 2\frac{4}{5}$ **16.** $4\frac{1}{8} - 3\frac{5}{8}$

17. $6\frac{4}{9} - 2\frac{7}{9}$

18. $4\frac{1}{6} - 1\frac{5}{6}$

19. $7\frac{5}{8} - 4\frac{7}{8}$

20. $5\frac{6}{4} - \frac{3}{4}$

21. $6\frac{2}{4} - \frac{3}{4}$

22. $6\frac{1}{2} - \frac{3}{4}$

23. $7\frac{1}{3} - \frac{5}{6}$

24. $4\frac{3}{8} - 2\frac{3}{4}$

25. $5\frac{1}{8} - 2\frac{1}{2}$

26. $4\frac{3}{16} - 3\frac{5}{8}$

27. $5\frac{9}{16} - 2\frac{3}{8}$

28. $7\frac{1}{8} - 4\frac{11}{16}$

29. $4\frac{1}{4} - 2\frac{2}{3}$

30. $3\frac{1}{3} - 1\frac{1}{2}$

31. $5\frac{1}{2} - 2\frac{3}{5}$

32. $7\frac{1}{5} - 3\frac{3}{4}$

33. $6\frac{5}{12} - 2\frac{3}{4}$

34. $4\frac{3}{8} - 1\frac{5}{6}$

35. $2\frac{2}{9} - 1\frac{5}{6}$

36. $9\frac{3}{8} - 5\frac{11}{12}$

37. $4\frac{5}{16} - 3\frac{11}{16}$

38. $4\frac{2}{3} - 2\frac{7}{8}$

39. $6\frac{3}{10} - 4\frac{3}{4}$

40. $5\frac{3}{8} - 3\frac{7}{10}$

Exercise 8

1. $\frac{3}{5}$ of my garden is lawn. The rest is used for vegetables. What fraction is used for vegetables?

2. Elizabeth bought $2\frac{1}{2}$ m of material. She then decided to buy a further $1\frac{3}{4}$ m. How many metres did she buy altogether?

3. A jug contained $\frac{11}{12}$ of a litre of milk. If I used $\frac{1}{3}$ of a litre, what fraction of a litre was left?

4. Sam spent $\frac{1}{4}$ of his money in one shop and $\frac{3}{8}$ in another. What fraction had he spent?

5. Sarah wanted a scarf $1\frac{1}{2}$ m in length. After knitting $\frac{9}{10}$ m, what fraction of a metre remained?

6. After using $1\frac{2}{5}$ kg of sultanas, a baker had $2\frac{3}{10}$ kg left. How many kilograms did he start with?

7. Pat walks $1\frac{5}{8}$ km each way to and from school each day. How far does she walk in five days?

8. I have a piece of wood that is 23 cm long. I cut off a piece that is $11\frac{7}{16}$ cm long. What length is left?

9. Is it possible to cut off two pieces of wood, one $12\frac{5}{16}$ cm long and the other $22\frac{3}{4}$ cm, from a piece that is 35 cm in length?

10. What is the total area of two fields, one that is $1\frac{1}{3}$ acres and the other $1\frac{2}{5}$ acres?

11. Mrs Jones needs $1\frac{3}{4}$ m of tape. If she cuts it off a length that is $3\frac{5}{6}$ m long, what length remains?

12. I need three lengths of wire, one $3\frac{1}{4}$ m, one $4\frac{2}{3}$ m and the third, $2\frac{5}{8}$ m. What total length is needed?

Exercise 9

1. Angela gave away $\frac{2}{3}$ of her sweets. If she had 7 sweets left, how many did she start with?

2. Jonathan broke $\frac{3}{4}$ of the eggs he was carrying. If he had 3 eggs left, how many did he have to start with?

3. Timothy lost $\frac{1}{6}$ of his money. If he lost £12, how much did he start with?

4. Peter ate $\frac{3}{5}$ of his sweets. If he had 6 sweets left, how many did he start with?

5. On a journey I used $\frac{3}{8}$ of the petrol in my petrol tank. I had 15 litres left. How much petrol did I have before starting my journey?

6. After travelling 140 km, I had travelled $\frac{7}{10}$ of my journey; how much further had I to go?

7. $\frac{2}{9}$ of a post is under the ground. If 40 cm is under the ground, how long is the post?

8. $\frac{1}{7}$ of the pupils in a class won an event in the school sports. If 24 pupils did not win, how many were in that class?

9. Jane used $\frac{4}{9}$ of the sheets from a box of stationery. If she had 45 sheets left, how many sheets were there to begin with?

10. Mary spent $\frac{5}{8}$ of her money. If she had £24 left, how much money did she have at first?

11. A shop sold $\frac{4}{7}$ of the biscuits on a shelf. If 56 packets were sold, how many packets were there to begin with?

12. In an election, J. Topps obtained $\frac{7}{10}$ of the votes. If she received 12 600 votes, what was the total number of votes cast?

Exercise 10

A 1. $4 \times \frac{1}{9}$ **5.** $3 \times \frac{2}{5}$ **9.** $3 \times \frac{7}{10}$ **13.** $7 \times \frac{3}{4}$

2. $4 \times \frac{2}{9}$ **6.** $3 \times \frac{4}{5}$ **10.** $7 \times \frac{9}{10}$ **14.** $5 \times \frac{7}{12}$

3. $4 \times \frac{4}{9}$ **7.** $6 \times \frac{3}{7}$ **11.** $3 \times \frac{5}{8}$ **15.** $7 \times \frac{5}{12}$

4. $3 \times \frac{1}{5}$ **8.** $5 \times \frac{1}{2}$ **12.** $5 \times \frac{3}{8}$ **16.** $8 \times \frac{6}{7}$

B   Work these out. Simplify your answers.

1. $6 \times \frac{1}{3}$ **5.** $6 \times \frac{3}{4}$ **9.** $5 \times \frac{3}{10}$ **13.** $10 \times \frac{13}{16}$

2. $6 \times \frac{2}{3}$ **6.** $4 \times \frac{3}{8}$ **10.** $2 \times \frac{7}{16}$ **14.** $10 \times \frac{5}{8}$

3. $4 \times \frac{3}{4}$ **7.** $4 \times \frac{7}{10}$ **11.** $8 \times \frac{11}{16}$ **15.** $6 \times \frac{8}{9}$

4. $8 \times \frac{3}{4}$ **8.** $3 \times \frac{5}{6}$ **12.** $12 \times \frac{5}{16}$ **16.** $8 \times \frac{7}{12}$

Exercise 11

Write these decimals correct to the nearest whole number:

1. 5.4	**13.** 56.4	**25.** 6.59	**37.** 46.51
2. 3.7	**14.** 23.1	**26.** 3.45	**38.** 2.803
3. 8.2	**15.** 69.2	**27.** 2.49	**39.** 1.916
4. 7.1	**16.** 59.7	**28.** 8.61	**40.** 13.267
5. 9.3	**17.** 46.6	**29.** 9.73	**41.** 48.198
6. 4.9	**18.** 81.3	**30.** 14.82	**42.** 37.821
7. 5.8	**19.** 75.9	**31.** 16.95	**43.** 5.496
8. 7.7	**20.** 99.8	**32.** 21.37	**44.** 8.999
9. 6.9	**21.** 4.75	**33.** 28.76	**45.** 73.389
10. 2.6	**22.** 8.26	**34.** 31.68	**46.** 51.707
11. 41.2	**23.** 1.84	**35.** 55.19	**47.** 46.256
12. 37.8	**24.** 7.66	**36.** 82.27	**48.** 70.652

Exercise 12

A   Estimate the answers to these additions:

e.g. $4.6 + 7.3 \approx 5 + 7 = \underline{\underline{12}}$

1. 5.4 + 2.6	**11.** 52.3 + 15.8	**21.** 2.81 + 5.38
2. 4.8 + 5.1	**12.** 29.1 + 41.3	**22.** 7.62 + 4.45
3. 6.9 + 2.8	**13.** 63.9 + 50.4	**23.** 9.17 + 8.53
4. 7.2 + 4.7	**14.** 84.2 + 32.6	**24.** 41.36 + 26.27
5. 8.7 + 2.9	**15.** 91.7 + 75.2	**25.** 37.87 + 9.74
6. 3.8 + 1.4	**16.** 46.4 + 41.9	**26.** 29.92 + 53.66
7. 6.3 + 9.1	**17.** 35.1 + 82.4	**27.** 271.48 + 46.19
8. 12.1 + 35.7	**18.** 23.6 + 6.8	**28.** 363.81 + 135.07
9. 43.6 + 24.2	**19.** 87.3 + 9.34	**29.** 794.25 + 27.70
10. 71.8 + 46.9	**20.** 18.7 + 2.96	**30.** 87.55 + 78.63

B Copy these and carry out the calculations:

1.
```
  7.6
+ 1.3
```

6.
```
  47.7
+ 21.5
```

11.
```
  49.3
+  9.8
```

16.
```
    6.28
  512.7
+  23.95
```

2.
```
  3.4
+ 4.8
```

7.
```
  63.8
+ 18.6
```

12.
```
  3.14
+ 2.69
```

17.
```
  263.5
   17.42
+  85.31
```

3.
```
  8.5
+ 5.9
```

8.
```
  54.2
+ 72.9
```

13.
```
  6.27
+ 1.08
```

18.
```
   46.83
   12.00
+ 275.4
```

4.
```
  32.6
+ 25.1
```

9.
```
  81.7
+ 12.4
```

14.
```
  84.61
   7.14
+ 47.35
```

19.
```
  637.46
+ 195.9
```

5.
```
  8.9
+ 5.0
```

10.
```
  8.6
+ 24.6
```

15.
```
  741.62
+  19.7
```

20.
```
   90.73
  105.08
+  84.6
```

C Carry out these calculations. Set them out in columns.

1. 8.3 + 1.4	**11.** 45.9 + 34.1	**21.** 5.4 + 8
2. 5.1 + 3.7	**12.** 72.3 + 21.9	**22.** 8.21 + 4.55 + 1.89
3. 6.7 + 2.2	**13.** 81.7 + 14.7	**23.** 27.3 + 466.21
4. 3.6 + 4.3	**14.** 93.8 + 82.6	**24.** 45.68 + 814.7
5. 2.9 + 4.1	**15.** 67.3 + 43.9	**25.** 357.4 + 83.38 + 9.9
6. 7.2 + 6.8	**16.** 34.2 + 99.4	**26.** 265 + 8.46 + 39.3
7. 8.3 + 4.9	**17.** 5.87 + 3.25	**27.** 9.76 + 28.4 + 607.2
8. 31.6 + 23.2	**18.** 12.09 + 9.64	**28.** 82.01 + 318.1 + 46
9. 52.7 + 19.2	**19.** 72.6 + 70.39	**29.** 7.5 + 80.16 + 218.93
10. 60.8 + 23.5	**20.** 125.1 + 65.91	**30.** 43.7 + 119.03 + 294.8

Exercise 13

1. Add one-tenth to each of these numbers:
   (*a*) 4.3   (*b*) 7.9   (*c*) 3.56   (*d*) 14.93   (*e*) 19.98

2. A rectangle measures 8.7 cm by 3.5 cm. Find its perimeter.

3. John bought three items costing £3.42, £4.76, and £1.81.
   Mary paid £2.97, £4.98, and £2.15 for three items.
   Which of them spent less than £10?

4. In a competition, for the 'A'-team, Jones scored 8.3 points, Kershaw
   scored 5.9 and Lawson scored 6.7.
   For the 'B'-team, Andrews scored 7.6, Brown scored 7.2 and Collins
   scored 6.3.
   Total the points for each team. Which team won?

5. The lengths of four pieces of wood are 1.26 m, 0.84 m, 1.65 m and
   1.47 m.
   What is the total length?

Exercise 14

Estimate the answers to these:

e.g. 1 $6.3 - 2.9 \approx 6 - 3 = \underline{\underline{3}}$

e.g. 2 $17.5 - 10.7 \approx 18 - 11 = \underline{\underline{7}}$

1. 7.6 – 3.7		**9.** 15.9 – 9.1		**17.** 28.5 – 19.3	
2. 8.2 – 2.9		**10.** 8.5 – 3.6		**18.** 47.9 – 8.4	
3. 9.8 – 1.2		**11.** 22.2 – 15.5		**19.** 51.3 – 29.02	
4. 6.1 – 3.4		**12.** 19.4 – 10.2		**20.** 49.61 – 38.4	
5. 8.6 – 5.8		**13.** 36.7 – 26.9		**21.** 23.86 – 11.48	
6. 10.3 – 4.1		**14.** 25.1 – 20.8		**22.** 35.9 – 20.71	
7. 14.4 – 7.3		**15.** 30.8 – 28.5		**23.** 38.02 – 31.6	
8. 12.7 – 8.6		**16.** 41.3 – 21.7		**24.** 59 – 38.99	

Exercise 15

Carry out these calculations. Set them out in columns.

1. 8.7 – 5.4	**13.** 37.2 – 24.1	**25.** 39.35 – 14.82
2. 9.2 – 2.3	**14.** 29.7 – 19.6	**26.** 50.74 – 31.67
3. 7.6 – 5.7	**15.** 41.5 – 23.8	**27.** 48.01 – 18.32
4. 5.4 – 3.9	**16.** 30.1 – 28.5	**28.** 43.28 – 29.4
5. 4.1 – 0.8	**17.** 54.0 – 37.4	**29.** 50.2 – 39.6
6. 8.3 – 5.0	**18.** 45 – 33.7	**30.** 74.3 – 26.49
7. 7.5 – 4.5	**19.** 61.9 – 49.0	**31.** 208.5 – 123.88
8. 12.9 – 7.3	**20.** 9.37 – 4.63	**32.** 5.64 – 0.87
9. 15.8 – 9.1	**21.** 7.14 – 2.95	**33.** 45.1 – 9.83
10. 9 – 4.5	**22.** 8.82 – 4.78	**34.** 467.2 – 130.94
11. 14 – 7.2	**23.** 6.03 – 5.69	**35.** 831.05 – 407.67
12. 19.8 – 12.9	**24.** 9.30 – 1.07	**36.** 700.34 – 216.74

Exercise 16

1. One length of wood measures 2.83 m while another measures 1.97 m. Find the difference in their lengths.

2. By how much is 12.86 less than 15.34?

3. From a piece of wire 26.8 m in length, pieces measuring 8.7 m, 4.9 m and 7.8 m are cut off. What length is left?

4. I bought two 4 m lengths of copper tubing. I cut 3.2 m off one length and 2.78 m off the other. The rest was waste. Calculate the total length of the waste.

5. I need three pieces of wood. The pieces must measure 1.37 m, 2.09 m and 1.76 m. What is the total length needed?

Exercise 17

Estimate the answers to these:

e.g. 1 $4.7 \times 8 \approx 5 \times 8 = \underline{\underline{40}}$

e.g. 2 $76.3 \div 4 \approx 80 \div 4 = \underline{\underline{20}}$

1. 6.1×4	**11.** $9.8 \div 5$	**21.** $53.8 \div 2$
2. 5.8×2	**12.** $27.9 \div 6$	**22.** 48.4×5
3. 5×7.3	**13.** 6×30.8	**23.** 2×80.4
4. 4×8.8	**14.** 31.7×8	**24.** $67.3 \div 7$
5. $5.6 \div 2$	**15.** $43.6 \div 8$	**25.** $58.1 \div 3$
6. $8.9 \div 3$	**16.** $19.9 \div 4$	**26.** 6×74.5
7. $9.2 \div 3$	**17.** 5×26.7	**27.** 23.9×9
8. 9.2×3	**18.** 47.9×4	**28.** $98.1 \div 4$
9. 4.1×7	**19.** 51.6×9	**29.** $76.3 \div 5$
10. $7.6 \div 4$	**20.** $66.6 \div 5$	**30.** 69.24×8

Exercise 18

Carry out these calculations:

1. 3.6×2	**13.** 24.3×2	**25.** 5.64×3
2. 7.1×6	**14.** 31.7×3	**26.** 6×7.99
3. 5×4.7	**15.** 40.6×9	**27.** 4×9.13
4. 4×2.9	**16.** 14.1×4	**28.** 4.07×7
5. 5.6×3	**17.** 5×36.2	**29.** 3×49.5
6. 8.2×7	**18.** 6×45.7	**30.** 3×4.95
7. 7.8×2	**19.** 2×59.1	**31.** 16.38×2
8. 3×9.3	**20.** 28.4×7	**32.** 5×54.26
9. 9×1.4	**21.** 32.9×8	**33.** 9×20.43
10. 5.3×8	**22.** 47.8×3	**34.** 7×1.008
11. 2.7×9	**23.** 19.7×5	**35.** 7.024×6
12. 4×6.5	**24.** 63.4×8	**36.** 3.625×3

Exercise 19

Carry out these calculations:

1. $4.8 \div 2$
2. $9.6 \div 3$
3. $7.2 \div 2$
4. $7.2 \div 3$
5. $8.5 \div 5$
6. $\dfrac{6.8}{2}$
7. $\dfrac{9.4}{2}$
8. $8.4 \div 3$
9. $26.8 \div 2$
10. $34.8 \div 4$
11. $47.7 \div 3$
12. $\dfrac{51.6}{6}$

13. $4.32 \div 2$
14. $5.94 \div 6$
15. $\dfrac{8.28}{9}$
16. $7.04 \div 8$
17. $\dfrac{6.79}{7}$
18. $9.24 \div 7$
19. $\dfrac{7.62}{6}$
20. $5.916 \div 2$
21. $\dfrac{8.424}{9}$
22. $61.25 \div 5$

23. $4.634 \div 7$
24. $7.086 \div 3$
25. $3.00 \div 4$
26. $5.000 \div 8$
27. $7 \div 8$
28. $1 \div 4$
29. $56.25 \div 9$
30. $9.801 \div 3$
31. $14.58 \div 6$
32. $20.616 \div 2$
33. $\dfrac{83.645}{5}$
34. $92.603 \div 7$
35. $232.65 \div 9$

Exercise 20

Here is a test. Check the answers. If an answer is wrong, copy the question and find the correct answer.

1.
$$\begin{array}{r} 72.6 \\ + 17.7 \\ \hline 89.13 \end{array}$$

2.
$$\begin{array}{r} 43.72 \\ - 14.28 \\ \hline 29.34 \end{array}$$

3.
$$\begin{array}{r} 6.182 \\ - 2.734 \\ \hline 3.448 \end{array}$$

4.
$$\begin{array}{r} 2.185 \\ \times \quad 3 \\ \hline 6.555 \end{array}$$

5.
$2\overline{)36.94}$ 1.847

6.
$3\overline{)17.34}$ 57.8

7.
$$\begin{array}{r} 84.57 \\ + 19.84 \\ \hline 104.41 \end{array}$$

8.
$$\begin{array}{r} 76.83 \\ - 16.94 \\ \hline 59.89 \end{array}$$

9.
$4\overline{)35.76}$ 8.94

10.
$$\begin{array}{r} 4.069 \\ \times \quad 4 \\ \hline 16.276 \end{array}$$

11.
$$\begin{array}{r} 83.7 \\ + 4.69 \\ \hline 130.6 \end{array}$$

12.
$6\overline{)4.236}$ 0.76

261

13. $\begin{array}{r} 31.93 \\ \times 5 \\ \hline 159.65 \end{array}$	18. $\begin{array}{r} 18.7 \\ - 8.94 \\ \hline 9.84 \end{array}$	23. $\begin{array}{r} 89 \\ + 27.62 \\ \hline 116.62 \end{array}$	28. $\begin{array}{r} 4.082 \\ 17.6 \\ + 8.89 \\ \hline 30.572 \end{array}$

14. $\begin{array}{r} 8.076 \\ - 2.192 \\ \hline 6.124 \end{array}$
19. $\begin{array}{r} 21.36 \\ 104.7 \\ + 2.98 \\ \hline 129.04 \end{array}$
24. $\begin{array}{r} 56 \\ + 24.83 \\ \hline 80.17 \end{array}$
29. $\begin{array}{r} 20.06 \\ \times 7 \\ \hline 140.42 \end{array}$

15. $\begin{array}{r} 45.302 \\ + 4.69 \\ \hline 49.992 \end{array}$
20. $7\overline{)19.628}$ with quotient 2.804
25. $\begin{array}{r} 61 \\ - 27.49 \\ \hline 33.51 \end{array}$
30. $7\overline{)142.8}$ with quotient 2.4

16. $\begin{array}{r} 71.64 \\ \times 3 \\ \hline 213.192 \end{array}$
21. $9\overline{)463.23}$ with quotient 51.47
26. $\begin{array}{r} 42.82 \\ \times 6 \\ \hline 25.692 \end{array}$

17. $\begin{array}{r} 709.63 \\ - 249.81 \\ \hline 469.82 \end{array}$
22. $\begin{array}{r} 4.634 \\ 21.89 \\ + 3.258 \\ \hline 10.081 \end{array}$
27. $9\overline{)10.467}$ with quotient 1.163

Exercise 21

A Answer these using a calculator:

1. 1.34 × 10
2. 8.67 × 10
3. 7.29 × 10
4. 10 × 8.46
5. 10 × 62.45

6. 54.91 × 10
7. 70.64 × 10
8. 2.837 × 10
9. 10 × 4.156
10. 10 × 5.038

11. 6.102 × 10
12. 2.304 × 10
13. 9.561 × 10
14. 10 × 3.916
15. 10 × 8.927

Write down a rule to explain how to multiply a decimal by 10.

B 1. Key in the number 4.167 on a calculator.

2. Multiply it by 10.

3. Multiply your answer by 10.

4. Multiply this answer by 10.

5. Write a sentence to explain what happens to your number each time it is multiplied by 10.

C Answer these using a calculator:

1. $42.6 \div 10$	**9.** $51.36 \div 10$
2. $39.4 \div 10$	**10.** $96.65 \div 10$
3. $86.9 \div 10$	**11.** $435.7 \div 10$
4. $463.2 \div 10$	**12.** $291.4 \div 10$
5. $196.5 \div 10$	**13.** $873.6 \div 10$
6. $354.8 \div 10$	**14.** $741.3 \div 10$
7. $43.97 \div 10$	**15.** $608.9 \div 10$
8. $60.72 \div 10$	

D **1.** Key in the number 769.2 on a calculator.

2. Divide it by 10.

3. Divide your answer by 10.

4. Divide this answer by 10.

5. Write a sentence to explain what happens to your number each time it is divided by 10.

E Answer these *without using a calculator*:

1. 53.6×10	**11.** 10×3.917
2. 8.214×10	**12.** 10×9.003
3. $42.1 \div 10$	**13.** $83.61 \div 10$
4. $93.67 \div 10$	**14.** $381.2 \div 10$
5. 10×34.86	**15.** 74.08×10
6. $541.8 \div 10$	**16.** 10×4.371
7. 10×1.903	**17.** $651.3 \div 10$
8. $12.85 \div 10$	**18.** $282.5 \div 10$
9. $764.8 \div 10$	**19.** 10×62.984
10. 25.72×10	**20.** $183.02 \div 10$

Exercise 22

A Answer these using a calculator:

1. 48.762 × 100	**6.** 6.5432 × 1000	**11.** 46.108 × 100
2. 3.917 × 100	**7.** 2.7951 × 1000	**12.** 1.7349 × 1000
3. 8.7063 × 100	**8.** 8.5034 × 1000	**13.** 3.1965 × 1000
4. 9.175 × 100	**9.** 9.1258 × 1000	**14.** 2.934 × 100
5. 7.4251 × 100	**10.** 12.637 × 100	**15.** 54.731 × 100

Write a sentence to explain what happens to a number when it is multiplied by 100.

Write a sentence to explain what happens to a number when it is multiplied by 1000.

B Answer these using a calculator:

1. 254.6 ÷ 100	**6.** 6052.3 ÷ 1000	**11.** 945.1 ÷ 100
2. 741.9 ÷ 100	**7.** 5381.7 ÷ 1000	**12.** 807.9 ÷ 100
3. 462.8 ÷ 100	**8.** 8146.2 ÷ 1000	**13.** 4791.4 ÷ 100
4. 9206.1 ÷ 100	**9.** 3892.6 ÷ 100	**14.** 5614.2 ÷ 1000
5. 1453.5 ÷ 100	**10.** 2903.4 ÷ 100	**15.** 7032.5 ÷ 1000

Write a sentence to explain what happens to a number when it is divided by 100.

Write a sentence to explain what happens to a number when it is divided by 1000.

C Answer these *without using a calculator:*

1. 2.916 × 100	**11.** 146.7 ÷ 100	**21.** 4183.9 ÷ 1000
2. 8.463 × 100	**12.** 9273.5 ÷ 100	**22.** 1.2964 × 100
3. 71.582 × 100	**13.** 9273.5 ÷ 1000	**23.** 3.4567 × 1000
4. 6.2354 × 1000	**14.** 81.062 × 100	**24.** 7584.2 ÷ 1000
5. 1.9547 × 1000	**15.** 638.44 ÷ 100	**25.** 3968.5 ÷ 1000
6. 354.7 ÷ 100	**16.** 2863.5 ÷ 1000	**26.** 312.74 ÷ 10
7. 893.6 ÷ 10	**17.** 45.826 × 100	**27.** 898.65 ÷ 100
8. 7614.2 ÷ 1000	**18.** 19.8713 × 1000	**28.** 72.046 × 100
9. 83.79 × 10	**19.** 4.8602 × 1000	**29.** 4.1793 × 1000
10. 83.79 ÷ 10	**20.** 8493.6 ÷ 1000	**30.** 1693.2 ÷ 1000

Exercise 23

A Answer these using a calculator:

1. (a) 4.265×3 **3.** (a) 7.391×5 **5.** (a) $8354.7 \div 3$
   (b) 4.265×30 (b) 7.391×50 (b) $8354.7 \div 30$
   (c) 4.265×300 (c) 7.391×500 (c) $8354.7 \div 300$
   (d) 4.265×3000 (d) 7.391×5000 (d) $8354.7 \div 3000$

2. (a) 5.867×4 **4.** (a) $6143.6 \div 2$ **6.** (a) $9247.8 \div 6$
   (b) 5.867×40 (b) $6143.6 \div 20$ (b) $9247.8 \div 60$
   (c) 5.867×400 (c) $6143.6 \div 200$ (c) $9247.8 \div 600$
   (d) 5.867×4000 (d) $6143.6 \div 2000$ (d) $9247.8 \div 6000$

B Answer these *without using a calculator:*

1. 4.293×200 **6.** $6173.6 \div 800$ **11.** $3649.8 \div 2000$
2. $7642.8 \div 400$ **7.** $92.54 \div 70$ **12.** 1.7063×3000
3. $9163.5 \div 5000$ **8.** 83.92×80 **13.** 28.612×5000
4. 1.6892×6000 **9.** $2568.6 \div 9000$ **14.** $9300.6 \div 600$
5. 3.0476×900 **10.** 5.1984×7000 **15.** 62.81×400

Exercise 24

A calorie is the unit that is used to tell us how much energy is produced by certain types of food.

We use energy every day even when we are sleeping.

An average adult uses:
    running   19.4 calories per minute
    swimming 11.2 calories per minute
    cycling   8.2 calories per minute
    walking   5.2 calories per minute
    sleeping   1.2 calories per minute

Work out the number of calories used by the following people:

1. A man who runs for 4 minutes.

2. Mrs Fish who enjoys a 30-minute swim.

3. Mr Plod who has a 2-hour walk in a morning.

4. Mrs Race who runs every day for 20 minutes.

5. Mr Walker who enjoys a 5-hour walk.

6. Mrs Tyrer who runs for 30 minutes, has a 20-minute swim then sleeps for 8 hours.

7. Mr Little has a short run that lasts 5 minutes, then walks for 10 minutes, then he has a 40-minute sleep.

8. Mrs Duckworth wakes up in the morning after 7 hours sleep. She then cycles to the swimming baths, a 10-minute journey. After a 40-minute swim, she cycles home, taking 12 minutes.

Exercise 25

A Estimate the answers:

e.g. $42.67 \times 384.9 \approx 40 \times 400 = \underline{16\ 000}$

1. 56.3×310.4 **6.** 26.3×81.7

2. 874.6×4.76 **7.** 9.4×436.9

3. 12.3×7.8 **8.** $408.2 \div 78.5$

4. $105.3 \div 3.9$ **9.** $365.7 \div 5.3$

5. $58.56 \div 3.2$ **10.** 62.9×19.4

B Answer these using a calculator:

1. (*a*) 539×287 **4.** (*a*) $2516 \div 68$
   (*b*) 53.9×2.87 (*b*) $251.6 \div 6.8$
   (*c*) 5.39×2.87 (*c*) $25.16 \div 6.8$

2. (*a*) 893×32 **5.** (*a*) $2491 \div 53$
   (*b*) 89.3×3.2 (*b*) $24.91 \div 5.3$
   (*c*) 8.93×3.2 (*c*) $249.1 \div 5.3$

3. (*a*) 354×461 **6.** (*a*) $4655 \div 19$
   (*b*) 35.4×4.61 (*b*) $465.5 \div 1.9$
   (*c*) 3.54×46.1 (*c*) $4.655 \div 1.9$

Look carefully at the three answers to each question. What do you notice?

C Answer these *without using a calculator*. As a check, estimate each answer.

1. 7.4 × 2.3
2. 41.6 × 3.1
3. 62.8 × 5.4
4. 1.8 × 9.26
5. 2.93 × 8.6

6. 92.04 ÷ 2.6
7. 421.4 ÷ 4.3
8. 63.58 ÷ 3.4
9. 233.7 ÷ 8.2
10. 98.88 ÷ 9.6

11. 1.3 × 5.71
12. 313.74 ÷ 6.3
13. 4.8 × 88.9
14. 70.4 × 9.5
15. 80.48 ÷ 1.6

Exercise 26

Try these on your calculator.
Watch what happens to some of the zeros.

1. [C] [0] [.] [2] [8] [6] [=]

2. [C] [.] [2] [8] [6] [=]

3. [C] [3] [.] [4] [5] [0] [0] [=]

4. [C] [6] [2] [.] [7] [0] [0] [0] [=]

5. [C] [0] [0] [5] [.] [6] [3] [=]

6. [C] [2] [9] [.] [0] [0] [5] [0] [=]

7. [C] [6] [7] [.] [0] [0] [=]

8. [C] [0] [0] [3] [.] [7] [0] [0] [=]

Exercise 27

A Use a calculator to help you with these:

1. 0.035 × 100
2. 0.064 32 × 1000
3. 0.183 × 10
4. 0.004 12 × 1000
5. 0.008 57 × 10 000
6. 5.82 × 100
7. 6.49 × 1000
8. 37.6 × 100
9. 90.7 × 1000
10. 8.36 × 10 000

11. 497 ÷ 10
12. 386 ÷ 100
13. 1462 ÷ 100
14. 29 ÷ 100
15. 3.75 ÷ 100
16. 47.62 ÷ 1000
17. 76.91 ÷ 100
18. 0.623 ÷ 10
19. 82.4 ÷ 1000
20. 95.84 ÷ 1000

B Answer these *without using a calculator:*

1. 0.076×100
2. $0.008\,21 \times 1000$
3. 0.065×10
4. 0.3146×1000
5. 0.0815×100
6. $48.9 \div 10$
7. $365 \div 100$
8. $23.8 \div 100$
9. $49.7 \div 1000$
10. $0.718 \div 10$

11. 0.037×30
12. 0.816×200
13. 0.0047×50
14. 0.0523×400
15. $0.067\,08 \times 6000$
16. $584 \div 20$
17. $37.62 \div 600$
18. $715.6 \div 400$
19. $6174 \div 3000$
20. $82.65 \div 5000$

Exercise 28

A Answer these using a calculator:

1. (*a*) 3×4
   (*b*) 0.3×0.4

2. (*a*) 2×8
   (*b*) 0.2×0.8

3. (*a*) 4×9
   (*b*) 0.4×0.09

4. (*a*) 7×5
   (*b*) 0.7×0.05

5. (*a*) 3×7
   (*b*) 0.03×0.7

6. (*a*) 8×6
   (*b*) 0.8×0.06

7. (*a*) 18×2
   (*b*) 1.8×0.2

8. (*a*) 9×53
   (*b*) 0.9×0.53

9. (*a*) 4×37
   (*b*) 0.4×0.037

10. (*a*) 62×8
    (*b*) 6.2×0.08

11. (*a*) 5×93
    (*b*) 0.05×0.93

12. (*a*) 16×7
    (*b*) 1.6×0.07

13. (*a*) 239×3
    (*b*) 23.9×0.3

14. (*a*) 6×584
    (*b*) 0.6×5.84

15. (*a*) 407×9
    (*b*) 0.407×0.09

Try to find a rule for finding the position of the decimal point when two decimals are multiplied.

B Answer these *without using a calculator:*

1. 0.2×0.7
2. 0.3×0.05
3. 0.04×0.08
4. 0.13×0.2
5. 0.41×0.03

6. 2.7×0.05
7. 0.4×3.6
8. 0.9×2.3
9. 0.06×7.8
10. 0.07×0.52

11. 61.8×0.3
12. 9.36×0.8
13. 0.561×0.6
14. 0.7×0.033
15. 6.92×0.04

C Answer these using a calculator:

1. (*a*) $0.86 \div 0.2$
   (*b*) $8.6 \div 2$

2. (*a*) $0.564 \div 0.3$
   (*b*) $5.64 \div 3$

3. (*a*) $4.25 \div 0.5$
   (*b*) $42.5 \div 5$

4. (*a*) $0.0348 \div 0.4$
   (*b*) $0.348 \div 4$

5. (*a*) $0.762 \div 0.03$
   (*b*) $76.2 \div 3$

6. (*a*) $0.0256 \div 0.08$
   (*b*) $2.56 \div 8$

7. (*a*) $0.0954 \div 0.06$
   (*b*) $9.54 \div 6$

8. (*a*) $0.0539 \div 0.007$
   (*b*) $53.9 \div 7$

9. (*a*) $0.621 \div 0.009$
   (*b*) $621 \div 9$

10. (*a*) $0.0174 \div 0.002$
    (*b*) $17.4 \div 2$

11. (*a*) $0.007\,05 \div 0.005$
    (*b*) $7.05 \div 5$

12. (*a*) $5.704 \div 0.08$
    (*b*) $570.4 \div 8$

D Answer these *without using a calculator:*

1. $0.75 \div 0.3$
2. $0.345 \div 0.5$
3. $8.56 \div 0.4$
4. $0.0294 \div 0.6$
5. $0.952 \div 0.07$
6. $0.0144 \div 0.09$
7. $0.0456 \div 0.06$
8. $0.0698 \div 0.002$

9. $0.368 \div 0.008$
10. $0.0252 \div 0.004$
11. $0.009\,24 \div 0.007$
12. $5.424 \div 0.03$
13. $83.61 \div 0.9$
14. $0.4605 \div 0.05$
15. $0.001\,392 \div 0.08$

Exercise 29

A Use a calculator to answer these:

1. (a) 64×59
   (b) 6.4×5.9

2. (a) 23×72
   (b) 2.3×0.72

3. (a) 892×17
   (b) 8.92×1.7
   (c) 0.892×1.7

4. (a) 956×32
   (b) 9.56×3.2
   (c) 95.6×3.2
   (d) 9.56×0.32

5. (a) 46×136
   (b) 0.46×1.36
   (c) 0.046×1.36

6. (a) 75×629
   (b) 0.75×6.29
   (c) 7.5×62.9

7. (a) 208×54
   (b) 2.08×0.54

8. (a) 82×361
   (b) 8.2×0.361

Look at the above questions and answers. Try to work out how to find the position of the decimal point.

B Answer these *without using a calculator:*

1. 4.2×7.4
2. 9.3×2.5
3. 1.8×0.34
4. 5.1×84.6
5. 60.7×4.8

6. 0.29×3.5
7. 54.2×0.73
8. 0.66×0.83
9. 0.91×1.24
10. 7.8×0.036

11. 0.52×0.028
12. 4.31×0.092
13. 87.6×0.0014
14. 0.38×61.8
15. 9.25×4.1

Exercise 30

1. Use $32.5 \times 8.64 = 280.8$ to help you to find the value of 325×0.0864.

2. Which gives the bigger answer:
   (a) 12×4 or $12 \div 4$?
   (b) 12×0.4 or $12 \div 0.4$?
   (c) 1.2×0.4 or $1.2 \div 0.4$?

3. A car travels 14.2 km on each litre of petrol.
   How far will it travel on 9ℓ?

4. Find the value of:

(a) 0.03×0.08 (c) 0.06×0.06 (e) $0.28 \div 0.007$

(b) 0.6×0.6 (d) 0.2×0.2 (f) $6.5 \div 0.05$

5. A car travels 306 miles on 8 gallons of petrol.
Find its petrol consumption in miles per gallon (m.p.g.).

6. A car uses 37 l of petrol in travelling 500 km.
How many litres does it use in travelling 100 km?

7. $3.7 \div 0.8 = 0.4625$ or 4.625 or 46.25 or 462.5.
Which is the correct answer?

8. On 1 l of petrol, a car can travel 14.5 km. Which calculation, 14.5×0.65 or $14.5 \div 0.65$, gives the distance the car will travel on $0.65\ l$ of petrol?

9. The cricketer, A. Batty, scored 351 runs in 6 innings, while I. Ball scored 467 runs in 8 innings.
Calculate their batting averages.
Who had the better batting average?

Exercise 31

In each of the following, the decimal point has not been given in the answer. Copy each question, and write the correct answer:

1. $0.7 \times 0.4 = 28$

2. $0.9 \times 0.2 = 18$

3. $43.8 \div 6 = 73$

4. $43.8 \div 0.6 = 73$

5. $43.8 \div 60 = 73$

6. $6.5 \times 0.7 = 455$

7. $3.1 \times 0.2 = 62$

8. $9.3 \times 5.6 = 5208$

9. $9.3 \times 56 = 5208$

10. $93 \times 5.6 = 5208$

11. $0.93 \times 5.6 = 5208$

12. $20.3 \div 3.5 = 58$

13. $0.203 \div 0.35 = 58$

14. $9.18 \div 2.7 = 34$

15. $9.18 \div 0.27 = 34$

16. $71.44 \div 4.7 = 152$

17. $7.144 \div 0.47 = 152$

18. $38.1 \times 2.2 = 8382$

19. $7.09 \times 1.93 = 136837$

20. $5.87 \times 3.12 = 183144$

21. $305.37 \div 2.9 = 1053$

22. $786.42 \div 0.51 = 1542$

23. $2.79 \times 82.6 = 230454$

24. $2.15 \times 401.3 = 862795$

25. $63.242 \div 20.6 = 307$

26. $0.6 \times 0.4 = 24$

27. $0.4 \times 0.2 = 8$

28. $4.2 \times 3 = 126$

29. $4.2 \times 0.3 = 126$

30. $0.42 \times 0.003 = 126$

31. $0.78 \times 0.69 = 5382$

32. $0.29 \times 0.31 = 899$

33. $0.401 \times 0.022 = 8822$

34. $58.86 \div 0.27 = 218$

35. $588.6 \div 27 = 218$

36. $5.886 \div 2.7 = 218$

37. $5.886 \div 0.027 = 218$

38. $98.94 \div 3.4 = 291$

39. $989.4 \div 3.4 = 291$

40. $989.4 \div 0.34 = 291$

41. $989.4 \div 0.0034 = 291$

42. $2869.94 \div 0.0782 = 367$

43. $0.05 \times 0.002 = 1$

44. $0.08 \times 0.09 = 72$

45. $65.2 \times 0.0037 = 24124$

46. $0.000\,92 \times 4.38 = 40296$

47. $0.0715 \times 0.861 = 615615$

48. $0.063\,36 \div 4.8 = 132$

49. $0.008\,817\,3 \div 0.101 = 873$

50. $0.914\,76 \div 2.52 = 363$

Exercise 32

Give the answers to these in three different ways:
(1) with a remainder, (2) as a common fraction, (3) as a decimal.

e.g. 1 $\quad 8\,\overline{)19} \quad \text{2 rem 3}$

e.g. 2 $\quad \dfrac{19}{8} = 2\dfrac{3}{8}$

e.g. 3 $\quad 8\,\overline{)19.^30^60^40} \quad \text{2. 3 7 5}$

1. $9 \div 2$

2. $15 \div 4$

3. $18 \div 5$

4. $21 \div 4$

5. $51 \div 8$

6. $43 \div 10$

7. $91 \div 20$

8. $77 \div 5$

9. $103 \div 8$

10. $253 \div 20$

Exercise 33

Give sensible answers to these problems (a decimal, or a common fraction, or a number with a remainder).

1. Share 9 bars of chocolate between 2 people (equal shares).

2. Share 9 cups between 2 people (equal shares).

3. 105 m of string is cut into 8 m lengths. How many pieces are obtained?

4. 105 m of string is cut into 8 equal lengths.
How long is each piece?

5. How many pupils can be given 4 books each out of a pile of 79 books?

6. 15 cakes are shared equally between 6 people. Work out what each person receives.

Exercise 34

1. Alan is 1.73 m tall while Brenda is 1.58 m tall. How much taller than Brenda is Alan?

2. The diagram shows a pipe. Its external diameter is 4.8 cm while its internal diameter is 3.9 cm. Find the thickness of the metal.

3. The perimeter of a triangle is 21.4 cm. Two of its sides measure 8.7 cm and 5.6 cm. Find the third side.

4. The product of two numbers is 9.92. One of the numbers is 0.8. Find the other number.

5. If 240 tea bags have a total mass of 750 g, find the mass of each tea bag.

6. A box of 50 tea bags of a special type of tea has a mass of 283 g. If each tea bag holds 3 g of tea, find the total mass of the packing.

7. A chess board is 30 cm square. If the 30 cm includes a 1 cm border, how big is each of the 64 small squares?

8. How many pieces of wire, each measuring 1.2 m, can be cut from a 20.4 m length?

9. When travelling by air, my luggage allowance is 20 kg. If my two cases have masses of 13.65 kg and 4.83 kg, how many kilograms of my allowance is not used?

10. A container full of sand has a mass of 0.365 kg. If the container has a volume of 200 cm^3 and if it has a mass of 85 g when empty, find the mass, in grams, of 1 cm^3 of sand.

Exercise 35

Without using calculating aids and without working these out, say which answers are definitely wrong:

1. $4.9 \times 3.8 = 186.2$

2. $3.7 \times 6.9 = 25.57$

3. 5.26 + 8.31 = 13.58

4. 82.4 + 69.5 = 151.9

5. 57.8 + 23.61 = 293.9

6. 10.81 ÷ 4.7 = 23

7. 32.6 × 5.9 = 192.34

8. 89.16 − 35.87 = 53.23

9. 4.2 × 9.8 = 41.18

10. 234.96 ÷ 8.7 = 26.7

11. 207 × 1.6 = 331.2

12. 27 × 51.3 = 138.51

13. 8.06 + 35.7 = 43.13

14. 908.4 − 21.73 = 886.67

15. 865.6 ÷ 1.6 = 54.1

16. 10.36 ÷ 2.8 = 3.9

17. 378.42 ÷ 5.3 = 7.14

18. 6.013 + 12.68 = 18.693

19. 11.02 × 0.29 = 38

20. 11.02 ÷ 0.29 = 38

Now check your answers using a calculator.

Exercise 36

A The number 56.043 is correct to 3 decimal places.
How many decimal places are there in each of these numbers?

1. 4.86

2. 83.5

3. 7.605

4. 812.97

5. 32.064

6. 194.1

7. 208.53

8. 97.802

9. 0.763

10. 0.007

11. 1.0083

12. 14.70

13. 821.930

14. 0.6300

15. 83.3070

16. 0.060 80

17. 0.011 700

18. 65.010

19. 2649.6

20. 19.004 00

B 1.

(*a*) Is 13.7 closer to 13 or to 14?

So 13.7 should be rounded to [?]

(*b*) Is 15.2 closer to 15 or to 16?

So 15.2 should be rounded to [?]

(*c*) Is 16.5 closer to 16 or to 17?
It is halfway, so we shall round it *up* to 17.
We shall agree to round *upwards* anything that is halfway.

2.

(*a*) Is 13.48 closer to 13.4 or 13.5?

So 13.48 should be rounded to [?]

(b) Is 13.63 closer to 13.6 or 13.7?

So 13.63 should be rounded to [?]

Note   In this question we are rounding to 1 decimal place.

(c) Round 13.36 to 1 decimal place.
(d) Round 13.24 to 1 decimal place.
(e) What is 13.57 correct to 1 decimal place?
(f) Write 13.69 correct to 1 decimal place.
(g) Write 13.45 correct to 1 decimal place.
(h) What is 46.28 correct to 1 decimal place?
(i) Write 72.86 correct to 1 decimal place.
(j) Write 52.15 correct to 1 decimal place.
(k) What is 28.75 correct to 1 decimal place?

Exercise 37

1.

34.27   34.28   34.29   34.30   34.31   34.32

(a) Is 34.286 closer to 34.28 or 34.29?

So 34.286 should be rounded to [?]

(b) Is 34.303 closer to 34.30 or to 34.31?

So 34.303 should be rounded to [?]

We are now rounding to 2 decimal places.
   34.286 = 34.29 correct to 2 decimal places,
and 34.303 = 34.30 correct to 2 decimal places.

2. Round these decimals to 2 decimal places:

(a) 4.362	(f) 326.834	(k) 1.438	(p) 7.815
(b) 52.487	(g) 597.566	(l) 8.3097	(q) 93.1149
(c) 19.316	(h) 9.673	(m) 70.8324	(r) 20.001
(d) 2.948	(i) 65.092	(n) 36.1432	(s) 58.199
(e) 68.291	(j) 88.609	(o) 47.375	(t) 84.998

3. Round each of these decimals to the number of decimal places stated:

(a) 37.38 to 1 d.p.   (b) 4.92 to 1 d.p.

(c) 8.567 to 2 d.p.   (o) 183.662 to 1 d.p.
(d) 71.231 to 2 d.p.   (p) 5.8371 to 2 d.p.
(e) 94.679 to 2 d.p.   (q) 89.5146 to 1 d.p.
(f) 50.7153 to 3 d.p.   (r) 2.0379 to 1 d.p.
(g) 69.0270 to 3 d.p.   (s) 41.7082 to 2 d.p.
(h) 6.3546 to 3 d.p.   (t) 7.1390 to 2 d.p.
(i) 4.874 to 2 d.p.   (u) 12.666 66 to 3 d.p.
(j) 23.458 to 2 d.p.   (v) 3.45 to 1 d.p.
(k) 1.7812 to 3 d.p.   (w) 92.825 to 2 d.p.
(l) 84.0009 to 3 d.p.   (x) 61.0925 to 3 d.p.
(m) 926.133 to 2 d.p.   (y) 5.498 to 2 d.p.
(n) 70.325 to 1 d.p.

Exercise 38

A Work these out using a calculator.
Give each answer correct to 2 decimal places.

1. $573 \div 125$
2. $661 \div 125$
3. $959 \div 250$
4. $978 \div 375$
5. $987 \div 500$
6. $\dfrac{2904}{750}$
7. $9.149 \div 875$
8. $45.38 \div 2.5$
9. $\dfrac{52.77}{7.5}$
10. $174 \div 62.5$

11. $15 \div 8$
12. $\dfrac{31}{40}$
13. $19 \div 3$
14. $\dfrac{73.2}{9}$
15. $17 \div 3$
16. $5 \div 16$
17. $75 \div 16$
18. $3 \div 8$

19. $\dfrac{5}{6}$
20. $\dfrac{3}{7}$
21. $5 \div 7$
22. $\dfrac{0.87}{0.16}$
23. $19.7 \div 1.2$
24. $95 \div 13$
25. $27.72 \div 7.5$

B Work these out *without using a calculator*.
Give each answer correct to 2 decimal places.

1. $12.16 \div 5$
2. $75.3 \div 50$
3. $30.58 \div 8$

4. $3.5 \div 4$
5. $\dfrac{2}{3}$

6. $\dfrac{4}{7}$
7. $21.9 \div 8$

Exercise 39

A Calculate the perimeter of each shape:

1.

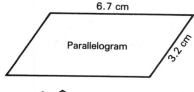

6.7 cm

Parallelogram

3.2 cm

2.

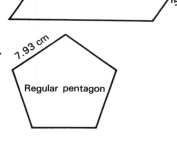

7.93 cm

Regular pentagon

3.

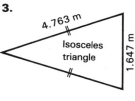

4.763 m

Isosceles triangle

1.647 m

B Find the length of the unknown sides of each shape:

1.

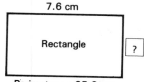

7.6 cm

Rectangle

?

Perimeter = 25.8 cm

2.

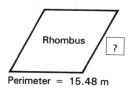

Rhombus

?

Perimeter = 15.48 m

3.

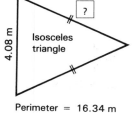

4.08 m

?

Isosceles triangle

Perimeter = 16.34 m

4.

?

Regular hexagon

Perimeter = 15.9 cm

5.

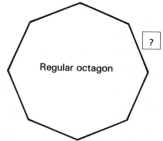

?

Regular octagon

Perimeter = 66.72 m

6.

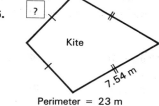

?

Kite

7.54 m

Perimeter = 23 m

277

C Solve these problems:

1. An equilateral triangle has a perimeter of 14.4 cm.
   Calculate the length of each side.

2. Each side of a regular hexagon is 9.56 m.
   Calculate its perimeter.

3. A parallelogram has a perimeter of 34.2 cm. Two of its sides each measure 6.5 cm.
   Find its other two sides.

4. Each side of a regular octagon is 7.29 m. A regular hexagon has the same size perimeter as this octagon.
   Calculate the length of each side of this hexagon.

5. The breadth of a rectangle is one-quarter of its length. If it is 5.192 m long, calculate its perimeter.

12 Plane and Solid Shapes

The Elements of Euclid

Meet Mr Polly:

1. What is the shape of Mr Polly's body?
2. What is the shape of his head?

3. his mouth?	**9.** left arm?	**15.** left foot?
4. his nose?	**10.** right hand?	**16.** his ears?
5. his right eye?	**11.** left hand?	**17.** middle button?
6. his left eye?	**12.** right leg?	**18.** bottom button?
7. neck?	**13.** left leg?	**19.** top button?
8. right arm?	**14.** right foot?	**20.** his hat?

Exercise 2

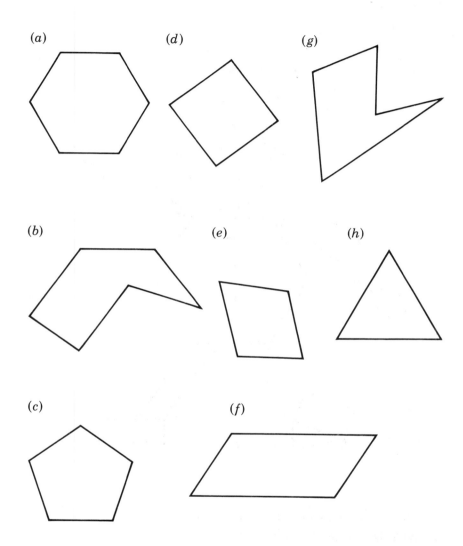

(a)

(d)

(g)

(b)

(e)

(h)

(c)

(f)

1. Which of these polygons are regular polygons?

2. Which of these polygons are convex?

3. Which of these polygons are both regular and convex?

Exercise 3

1. Look at parallelogram ABCD:
   (a) Which side is opposite side BC?
   (b) Which angle is opposite angle D?
   (c) Which angle is opposite angle DCB?

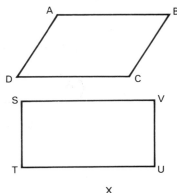

2. Look at rectangle STUV:
   (a) Which side is opposite side TU?
   (b) Which angle is opposite Ŝ?
   (c) Which angle is opposite ∠SVU?

3. Look at kite WXYZ:
   (a) Which side is opposite side XY?
   (b) Which side is the same length as side WX?
   (c) Which angle has the same size as ∠WXY?
   (d) Which sides are adjacent to side ZY?

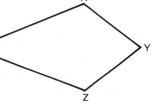

Exercise 4 **M**

Make, out of **paper** or **card**, four **quadrilaterals** the same as this:

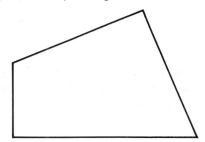

Put all four together to make:

1. a square
2. a trapezium
3. a parallelogram
4. a pentagon
5. an octagon
6. two squares (one inside the other)
7. two rectangles (one inside the other)

Exercise 5

Use geo-strips (geometric strips), or make your own from flat ice-lolly sticks or card. (If you make your own, make a few of several different sizes.)

You will also need paper fasteners and some pieces of fine elastic.

Make:

1. a square.
   Is it always a square, or could it be a rhombus?

2. a rectangle.
   Is it always a rectangle, or could it be a parallelogram?

3. a kite.
   Is it always a kite?

4. a trapezium.
   Is it always a trapezium?

Make diagonals for each quadrilateral out of elastic.
Note what happens to the diagonals as each quadrilateral changes shape.

Exercise 6

1. Draw a square (be careful and accurate). The side may be of any length. Label the four vertices A, B, C, D in that order.
   Now draw both diagonals. Label the point at which the diagonals cross as X.
   Measure:
   (*a*) AC   (*b*) AX   (*c*) CX   (*d*) BD   (*e*) DX   (*f*) BX
   What do you notice about lengths:
   (*g*) AC and BD?   (*i*) BX and DX?
   (*h*) AX and CX?   (*j*) Measure angle AXB?

2. Carefully construct a rectangle. Label the four vertices A, B, C, D as for the square and answer the same questions as in question 1.

3. Repeat question 1, but this time draw a parallelogram.

4. Repeat question 1 for a rhombus.

5. Repeat question 1 for a kite.

6. Repeat question 1 for a trapezium.

7. If both diagonals of a quadrilateral are of equal length, what sort of quadrilateral could it be?

8. The diagonals of a quadrilateral bisect each other. What could it be?

9. The diagonals of a quadrilateral meet at right-angles. What could it be?

10. The diagonals of a quadrilateral bisect each other at right-angles. What could it be?

Exercise 7

1. Make a neat drawing of the rectangle in fig. 1.

Fig. 1

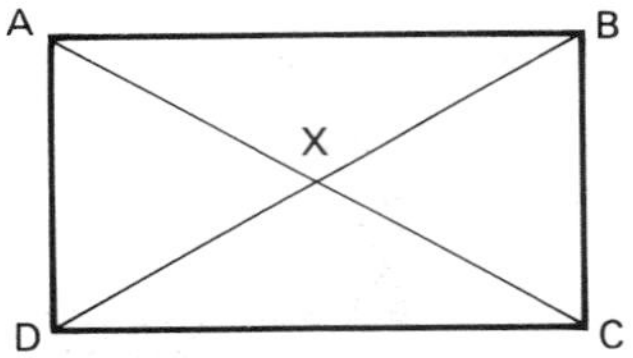

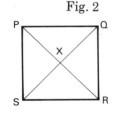

Copy and complete:

(a) AB = CD   (c) AC = ?

(b) BC = ?   (d) AX = ? = ? = DX

2. Draw a square, PQRS (fig. 2).
Let X be the centre of this square.

Fig. 2

(a) PQ = ? = ? = SP

(b) PX = ? = RX = ?

(c) PR is perpendicular to ?

3. Draw a parallelogram, WXYZ (fig. 3).

(a) WX = ?   (b) WZ = ?

(c) Does any length equal WO? If so, state it.

(d) Does WY = XZ?

(e) Does XO = OZ?

Fig. 3

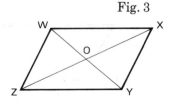

4. Draw a rhombus, KLMN (fig. 4).

   (*a*) Does KP = MP?

   (*b*) Does KP = NP?

   (*c*) Does KM = LN?

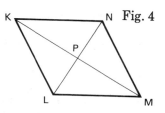

Fig. 4

5. Draw a kite, EFGH (fig. 5).

   (*a*) Does FQ = HQ?

   (*b*) Does EQ = GQ?

   (*c*) Name a side equal to FG.

   (*d*) Name an angle equal to angle HGQ.

   (*e*) Name an angle equal to angle FEQ.

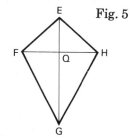

Fig. 5

Exercise 8

1. Construct parallelograms from this information:

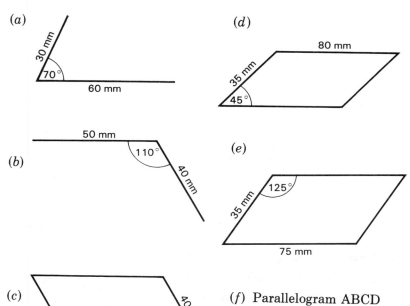

(*a*) 30 mm / 70° / 60 mm

(*b*) 50 mm / 110° / 40 mm

(*c*) 120° / 65 mm / 40 mm

(*d*) 80 mm / 35 mm / 45°

(*e*) 35 mm / 125° / 75 mm

(*f*) Parallelogram ABCD where AB = 52 mm angle BAD = 65° and BD = 39 mm.

285

(g) Parallelogram JKLM where JK = 63 mm, ∠ JML = 105° and KL = 34 mm.

(h) Parallelogram WXYZ where WX = 55 mm, ∠ WXY = 90° and XY = 37 mm.

(i) A parallelogram where the diagonals are 90 mm and 60 mm long. An angle between the diagonals is 115°.

(j) Parallelogram PQRS where PQ = 54 mm, diagonal PR = 50 mm and diagonal QS = 72 mm.

(k) Parallelogram EFGH where EF = FG = 42 mm and where ∠ EFG = 69°.

2. Construct rectangles from this information:

(a) (b)

(c) Rectangle with sides of 52 mm and 30 mm.

(d) Rectangle with diagonals of 65 mm. An angle between the diagonals is 57°.

(e) Rectangle with diagonals of 49 mm. One pair of opposite sides is 44 mm in length.

3. Construct a square with sides of 45 mm.

4. Construct a rhombus with sides of 38 mm, where one of its angles is 115°.

5. Construct a rhombus with sides of 44 mm, where its angles are right-angles. What other name does this shape have?

6. Construct a kite with sides of 67 mm and 31 mm when the angle between these sides is 123°.

7. Construct a kite with sides of 72 mm and 34 mm if its long diagonal is 87 mm in length.

8. Construct a kite where both diagonals are 54 mm long if one diagonal is cut so that its two parts are 42 mm and 12 mm long.

9. The angle between the two short sides of a kite is 134°. If its short sides are 20 mm long and its long diagonal is 62 mm, construct the kite.

10. Construct a kite with diagonals of length 58 mm and 28 mm if these diagonals bisect each other.

Exercise 9

Construct these on squared paper (or graph paper):

1. Construct a square with diagonals that are 40 mm long.

2. Construct a rhombus with diagonals of 60 mm and 40 mm.

3. Construct a rectangle where both diagonals are 48 mm long, and cut each other at right-angles.

4. The diagonals of a kite are 75 mm and 38 mm long. Construct the kite where the long diagonal is cut into two parts such that one part is twice as long as the other part.

Exercise 10

1. Which statement is always true for a rectangle?
   (*a*) The diagonals cross at right-angles.
   (*b*) All the sides are equal.
   (*c*) The diagonals are equal.
   (*d*) Only one of the diagonals is bisected.

2. Which statement is always true for a rhombus?
   (*a*) The diagonals are equal.
   (*b*) The angles are all right-angles.
   (*c*) The diagonals are perpendicular to each other.

3. Which statement is always true for a parallelogram ?
   (*a*) The diagonals are equal.
   (*b*) Opposite angles are equal.
   (*c*) All the angles are equal.

1. Which pairs of lines could be diagonals of a square?

(a)    (c)

(b) 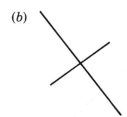   (d)   (e)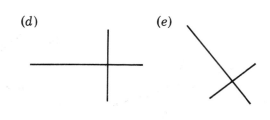

2. Which pairs of lines could be diagonals of a rectangle?

(a) 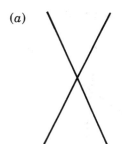   (c)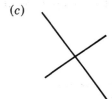

(b) 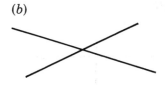   (d)

(e)

3. Which pairs of lines could be diagonals of a parallelogram?

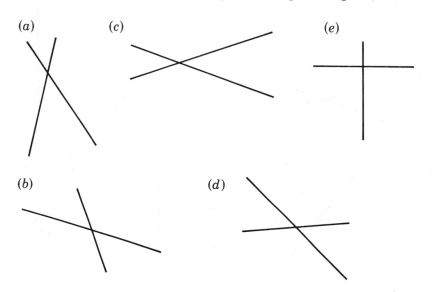

(a) (c) (e)

(b) (d)

4. Which pairs of lines could be diagonals of a rhombus?

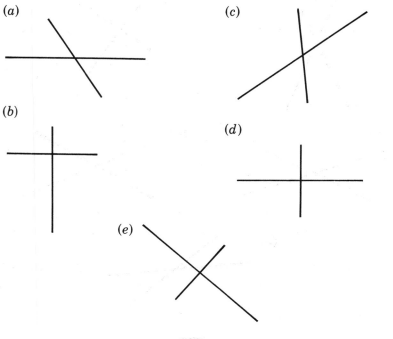

(a) (c)

(b) (d)

(e)

5. Which pairs of lines could be diagonals of a kite?

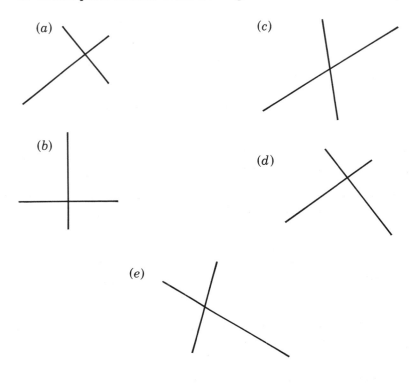

(a)

(c)

(b)

(d)

(e)

Exercise 12

Use a large sheet of paper.
It can be any shape.
Make sure that its edges are NOT straight.

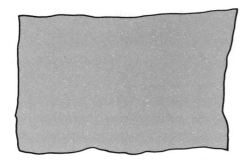

1. By folding the paper (nothing else is allowed) make a rectangle.
2. Use another piece of paper to fold a square.
3. Use another piece to fold a rhombus.
4. Use another piece to fold a kite.
Rule lines on your correct folds.

A **1.** Draw a rectangle that is not a square.

    2. A rhombus has at least one angle that is a right-angle. What is its special name?

    3. A rectangle has diagonals that are perpendicular to each other. What sort of rectangle is it?

    4. The diagonals of a quadrilateral bisect each other, but not at right-angles. What sort of quadrilateral could it be?

    5. A quadrilateral has diagonals of different lengths. If the diagonals bisect each other at right-angles, what sort of quadrilateral could it be?

B Copy these sentences. Complete each one by filling in the missing name of the quadrilateral.

    1. A parallelogram containing right-angles is a ⬚?⬚

    2. A parallelogram with equal diagonals is a ⬚?⬚

    3. A rhombus containing right-angles is a ⬚?⬚

C Copy these sentences. Complete each one by filling in a special property in place of the question mark.

    1. A rhombus is a parallelogram with ⬚?⬚

    2. A square is a rectangle with ⬚?⬚

D **1.** Are the properties of a parallelogram also true for a rectangle?

    2. Are the properties of a rectangle also true for a parallelogram?

    3. Are the properties of a rectangle also true for a square?

    4. Are the properties of a square also true for a rectangle?

    5. Are the properties of a kite also true for a square?

Exercise 14   To Construct a Regular Hexagon

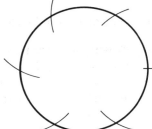

1. Set your pair of compasses to the same radius as the side of the hexagon.

2. Draw a circle.

3. Mark a point on its circumference.

4. With centre at that point, draw an arc to cut the circle. (Keep the same radius throughout.)

5. With centre at the new point, draw another arc to cut the circle.

6. Repeat until you reach your starting point (5 arcs).

7. Join all 6 points in order.

Exercise 15

1. (*a*) Draw a circle (radius about 30 mm).
   Draw a radius.
   Draw an angle of 45° at the centre of your circle (your radius should be one arm of this angle).
   Make the other arm into a second radius.
   Now from this new radius, draw another angle of 45° at the centre of your circle.
   Continue doing this until you reach the first radius again.
   (*b*) How many 45° angles have you drawn?
   (*c*) Why did you obtain that number of angles?
   (*d*) Join, in order, the points at which these radii meet the circumference.
   (*e*) What sort of polygon have you drawn?

2. (*a*) Draw another circle with the same radius as before.
   (*b*) What angle do you need to draw at the centre to make a hexagon?
   (*c*) Draw a hexagon using this method.

3. (*a*) Draw another circle.

(*b*) What is the name of the polygon you would obtain if you were to draw angles of 72° at the centre?

(*c*) Draw this polygon.

4. What angle would you use to make a decagon?

5. Say whether or not you would obtain a polygon if you were to draw these angles at the centre of your circle:

(*a*) 90°   (*c*) 20°   (*e*) 15°   (*g*) 40°

(*b*) 50°   (*d*) 30°   (*f*) 75°   (*h*) 24°

Exercise 16   **M**

1. Draw these polygons (they do not need to be regular):

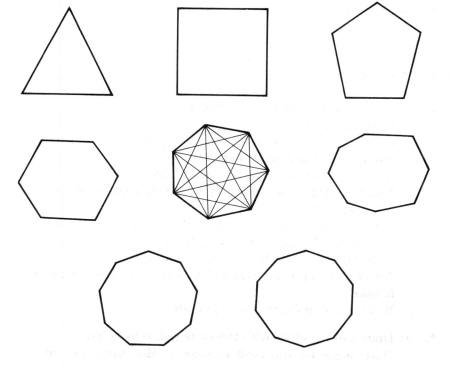

2. Draw in all the diagonals for each polygon (the diagonals of the heptagon have been drawn).

3. Copy and complete this table:

Name of polygon	Number of edges, n	Number of diagonals	$n - 3$	$n(n - 3)$
triangle	3	0	0	0
square	4	2	1	4
pentagon				
hexagon				
heptagon	7		4	28
octagon				
nonagon	9			
decagon	10			

4. Compare the number of diagonals with the numbers in the $n(n - 3)$ column.

5. How many diagonals has a 20-sided polygon?

Exercise 17 Polygons and Rigidity

Use geo-strips (geometric strips). You will also need paper fasteners.

1. Make a triangle. Is a triangle a rigid shape?

2. Make a quadrilateral.
Its shape changes so it cannot be rigid.
Use another piece of geo-strip to make your quadrilateral rigid.

3. Make a pentagon. Is it rigid?
By using some more pieces of geo-strip, make your pentagon rigid.

4. Make a hexagon. Is it rigid?
By using some more pieces of geo-strip, make your hexagon rigid.

5. Make any other polygon. Make it rigid using more geo-strips.

6. Write down what you noticed about how to make any polygon rigid.

Exercise 18

Collect pictures and drawings from magazines to show how a triangle is used to make a structure rigid.

For example, pictures of bridges, pylons, cranes, and some furniture show the importance of the triangle.

Exercise 19 M

Carefully copy these polygons.

Make at least six of each out of thin card or paper.
The radius of the circumscribed circle, r, is given.

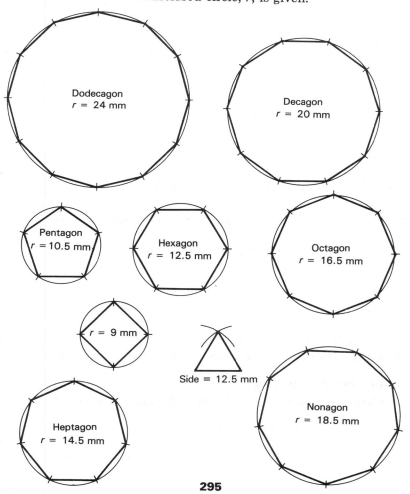

Dodecagon
$r = 24$ mm

Decagon
$r = 20$ mm

Pentagon
$r = 10.5$ mm

Hexagon
$r = 12.5$ mm

Octagon
$r = 16.5$ mm

$r = 9$ mm

Side = 12.5 mm

Nonagon
$r = 18.5$ mm

Heptagon
$r = 14.5$ mm

Exercise 20

Here is a tiling (or tessellation) used by bees. Bees form hexagons in making their honeycombs.

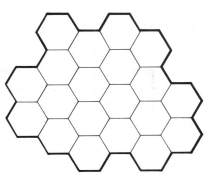

We say that a shape *tessellates* if we can fit a lot of them together without any overlap and without gaps. So, regular hexagons tessellate.

To help you with these questions you need a set of polygons made of card or plastic (sometimes called 'discovery shapes' or 'geometric shapes'). You can make your own by tracing or copying those on p. 295.

1. Which other regular polygons will tessellate on their own?
   Test:
   - (*a*) equilateral triangles
   - (*b*) squares
   - (*c*) pentagons
   - (*d*) heptagons
   - (*e*) octagons
   - (*f*) nonagons
   - (*g*) decagons
   - (*h*) dodecagons

2. Will any triangle tessellate?
   Test your answer by making twenty to thirty identical triangles and trying to make them tessellate.
   Either stick your triangles in your book or make a drawing of the tiling pattern.

3. (*a*) Will a rectangle tessellate?
   (*b*) Will any parallelogram tessellate?
   (*c*) Will any trapezium tessellate?
   (*d*) Will any kite tessellate?
   (*e*) Will any quadrilateral tessellate?
   Show your answers in your book, either by drawing or by sticking the quadrilaterals in your book.

Exercise 21

Try to explain why all triangles or all quadrilaterals should tessellate.

Exercise 22

Shapes such as these tessellate:

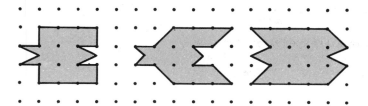

Such shapes can be found printed on fabrics and wallpapers:

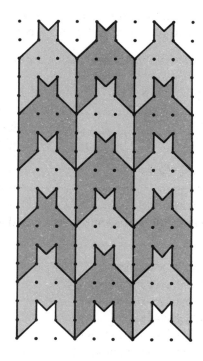

1. Copy one of these shapes and use dotty paper (or squared paper) to show how it tessellates. (You may find it easier to cut out your shapes before trying to see if they tessellate.)

2. Make a tessellating pattern of your own.
   You will need to invent a shape (such as these) that will tessellate.

Exercise 23

Tessellations can be formed by offsetting shapes:

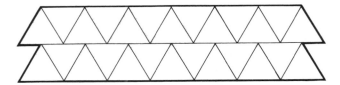

1. Try to make a pattern of your own where the shapes are offset.

2. Try to make such a pattern using squares.

3. Try to make such a pattern using hexagons.

Exercise 24

Bricks are laid to form a tessellating pattern.
Here are some different ways of laying bricks:

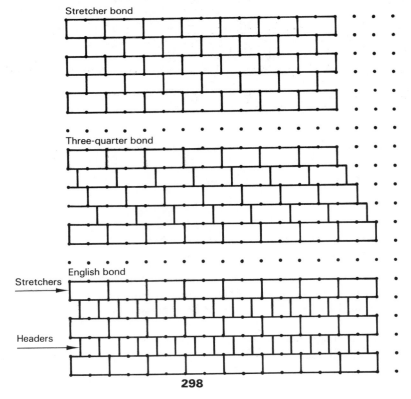

Stretcher bond

Three-quarter bond

English bond

Stretchers

Headers

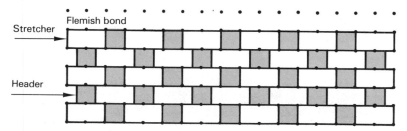

Flemish bond

Stretcher →

Header →

Lengthwise bricks are called *stretchers*. Bricks laid across the thickness of a wall are called *headers*.

1. Copy these into your graph book or on to dotty paper.
2. Which of the bonds uses the least number of bricks?
3. Which of the bonds uses the most headers?

Exercise 25

1. Try to make a tessellation using octagons.
   It does not work. There are gaps.
   However, the gaps can be filled using squares.

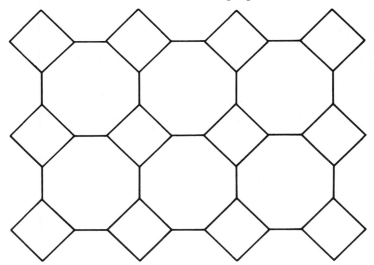

   Copy this tessellation.

2. Try to find some more tessellations that need two polygons.

3. Try to find some tessellations that need three polygons.
   Find one that uses a dodecagon.

299

The Pyramids

The Egyptian pyramids were built as burial places for their pharaohs. They were built from about 2680 BC onwards.

The Great Pyramid at Giza, near Cairo, is one of the Seven Wonders of the World. It is about 140 m high and has a square base where each side is 230 m long (made to an accuracy of 3 cm). Its base area would hold about 7 or 8 football pitches.

It was built with simple hand tools. A Greek, Herodotus, wrote in the fifth century BC that it probably took 100 000 workers about 20 years to build it. Over two million blocks of stone were used. Most had masses between 2 and 3 tonnes, although some were considerably larger.

The pyramids were built so that their four faces pointed north, south, east and west. The shafts were probably used for ventilation but one interesting theory states that they were designed so that rays from the stars could shine into the burial chamber.

Because the pharaohs were buried together with their most valuable treasures, the entrances were blocked up and false passages and rooms were built.

Here are some drawings of solids. (It would be useful to see some models of these.)

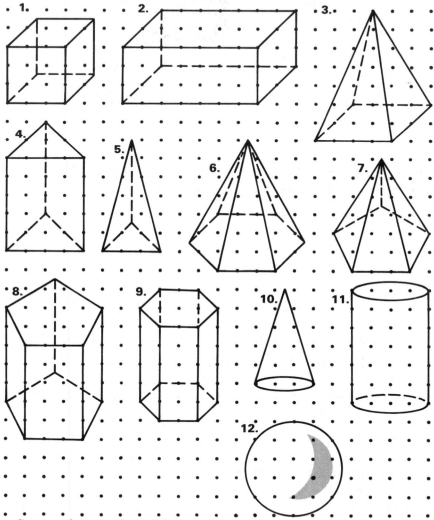

Copy and name the solids (use dotty paper).

Choose the names from this set: {cube, cuboid, triangular prism, pentagonal prism, hexagonal prism, cylinder, triangular pyramid, square pyramid, pentagonal pyramid, hexagonal pyramid, cone, sphere}

It is quite easy to draw cuboids on dotty paper.
(The dots should form triangles and should be used the right way up.)

This is right: This is wrong:

Parts of cuboids have been drawn below.
Copy them on dotty paper.
Complete the cuboids.

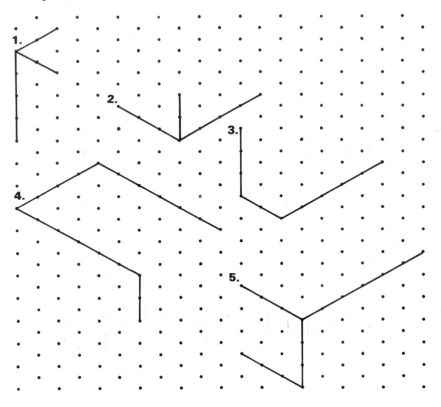

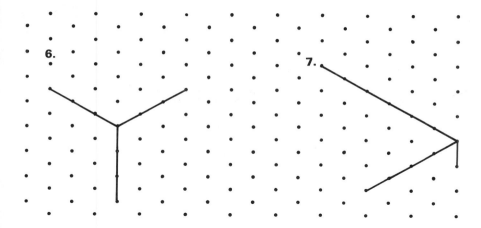

6.

7.

Exercise 28

What is the smallest number of cubes that could be used to make each of these shapes?
Build each shape with cubes to check your answers.

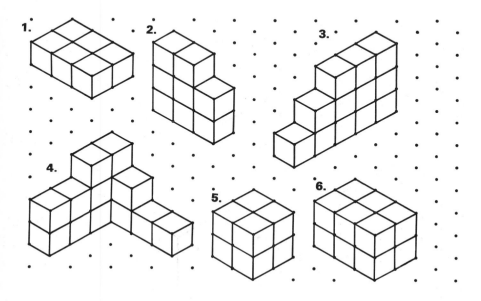

1.

2.

3.

4.

5.

6.

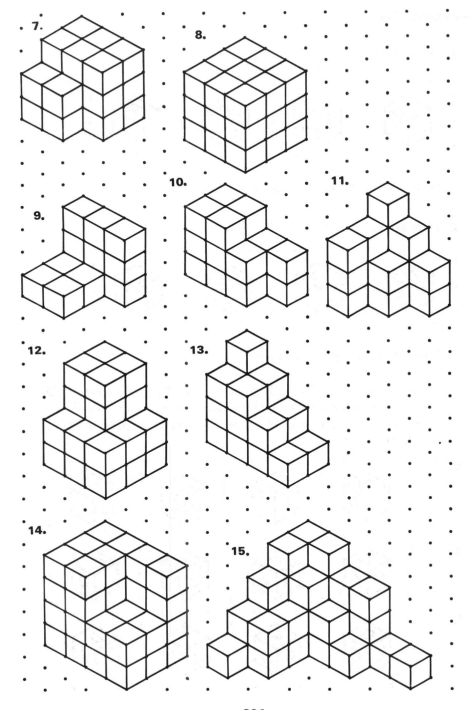

Exercise 29

1. Here are four views of the same cube:

Work out which letter is opposite which.

2. Here are four views of another cube:

Which letter is opposite which?

In questions 3, 4 and 5, sketch the four cubes. On your sketches, fill in the letter missing from the blank face. The letter must be shown in the way it would be marked on the cube (use dotty paper for your sketches).

3.

4.

5.

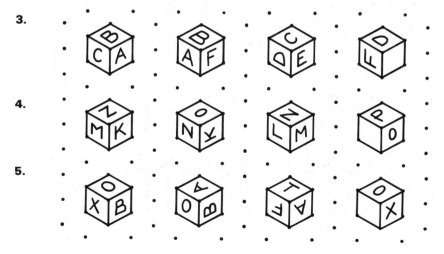

Exercise 30

Build each of these with cubes.
Add an extra cube where the shading is.
Draw some of the final shapes on dotty paper.

e.g.

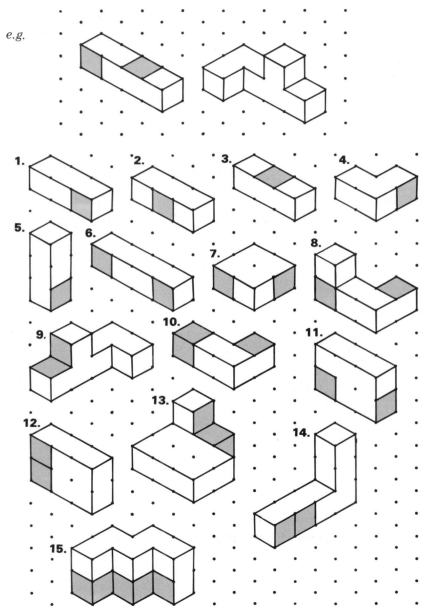

1.

2.

3.

4.

5.

6.

7.

8.

9.

10.

11.

12.

13.

14.

15.

A *polyhedron* (plural — 'polyhedra') is a solid that has plane (i.e. flat) faces. A cylinder is not a polyhedron, because it has a curved face.

A cube is shown.
One *face* is shaded.

This is an *edge.* ⟶

The corners are called *vertices*.
Each corner is called a *vertex*.

Leonhard Euler (1707–83), a Swiss mathematician, discovered a formula relating the number of faces, edges, and vertices of any polyhedron.

Copy and complete this table, then try to find the formula:

Polyhedron	Number of faces, F	Number of vertices, V	Number of edges, E	$F + V$
cuboid			12	14
square pyramid				
triangular prism				
triangular pyramid		4		
pentagonal prism				
pentagonal pyramid				
hexagonal prism	8			
hexagonal pyramid				

Exercise 32

1. Name four sports where a spherical ball is used.

2. Name a sport where a ball that is not shaped like a sphere is used.

3. Make a drawing to show how a cone is used in everyday life.

4. Show how cylinders are used in everyday life.

5. Make a drawing to show how a triangular prism is used in everyday life.

6. Give two examples where a cuboid is used in everyday life.

Exercise 33

1. Which two of these four patterns will fold to make a cube?

(*a*)   (*b*)   (*c*)   (*d*)

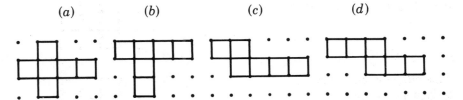

Make each of them out of squared paper, and fold them to see if they work.

A pattern (or shape) that can be folded to make a solid is called a *net*.

The two shapes in question 1 that fold into a cube are called *nets of a cube*.

2. Try to find some more nets of a cube. (There are, in fact, eleven.) To make a cube, we need to put some tabs on some of the edges of some of the squares in the net.

3. Here is a net of a cube showing the tabs.
Copy this net on squared paper.
Cut it out.
Stick down the tabs to make a cube.
(Your cube need not to be the same size as this.)

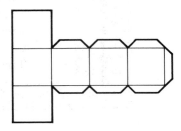

Exercise 34

Collect as many different-shaped cardboard containers as you can.

Cut along some of the edges so that they unfold to make a net.

Draw the nets in your exercise book.
Do not forget to give the names of the solids.
(e.g. 'net of a triangular prism'.)

Exercise 35

This shape is a net of an open box made with square faces (it folds into a box).

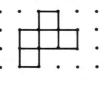

This shape is not a net.
It does not work.

Try to find some different nets of an open box with square faces.
Draw them on squared paper.

Exercise 36

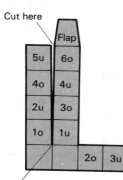

Make this pattern out of squared paper.
Fold the edges of each square downwards.
Now start to plait a cube.
On this diagram 1o folds over the top of 1u (o means 'over' and u means 'under'). 2u folds down, then 2o folds over the top.
Continue doing this until you reach the flap.
The flap simply tucks in.

Exercise 37

1. Here is a net of a triangular prism.
   Copy this net, but make your copy larger.
   (Make each rectangular face 8 cm long and
   4 cm wide.)
   Make your copy on paper (or thin card).
   Put flaps on it. Cut out the net.
   Fold it to make a triangular prism.

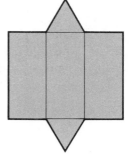

2. Draw a net of a square pyramid (any size).
   Use paper (or thin card). Put flaps on it.
   Cut it out. Fold it to make a square pyramid.

Exercise 38

Draw the net of a cone without its circular base (i.e. an open cone).

Exercise 39

A rectangular box (a cuboid) is 8 cm long, 6 cm wide and 4 cm high.

Here is one possible
net of this box drawn
to one-quarter of its
true size.

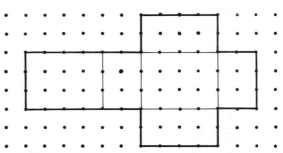

1. Draw two other different nets of this box (both should be one-quarter of the true size).

2. On squared (or dotty) paper draw a half-size net of a box that measures 10 cm by 8 cm by 2 cm.

Exercise 40

Make a model of a building such as a church.

If you make a church, you will probably need to make cuboids, a triangular prism, and a pyramid.

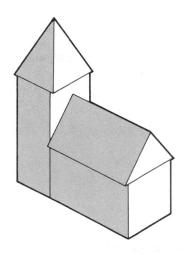

Exercise 41

1. Is it possible to draw a straight line on:
   (a) a cube?   (c) a sphere?   (e) a square pyramid?
   (b) a cylinder?   (d) a cone?

2. Which of these patterns, when cut out, will fold to give a cube?

(a)

(d)

(b)

(e)

(c)

3. The drawings show two solids that were made from straws (pipe cleaners were used at the vertices to join the straws together).

(a)

(b)

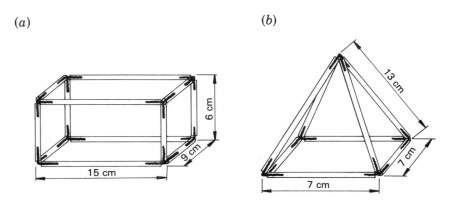

What is the total length of the straws used for each solid?

4. Name any solid that has:
   (a) six plane faces
   (b) no edges, no vertices
   (c) five plane faces
   (d) two plane faces, one curved face, two curved edges, no vertices

5. The eight vertices of this cuboid are labelled A, B, C, D, E, F, G and H.
   (a) Which three edges are the same length as edge AE?
   (b) Which edges are parallel to edge AB?
   (c) Which edges are parallel to edge FG?
   (d) Which face is parallel to face AEFB?

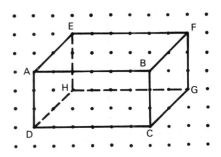

Here are two different views of a square pyramid.

The second view shows what the square pyramid looks like from above.

A view of something from above is called a *plan*.

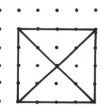

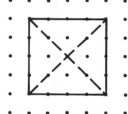

This drawing shows what a square pyramid looks like from below.

The lines shown by dashes stand for the edges of the pyramid that cannot be seen (they are 'hidden' edges).

Check them by looking at a square pyramid from different directions. (It may be useful to make one.)

Draw two different views of each of these solids:

1. triangular prism

2. cylinder

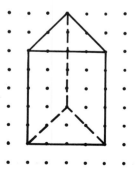

13 Area

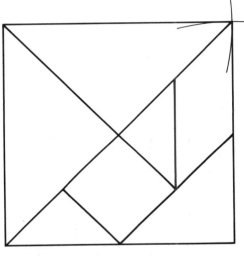

Carefully copy this tangram on to a piece of card. You may use any drawing instruments to help you.

The sides of your square should measure 6 cm.

Cut out each of the seven pieces.

Now using all seven pieces each time, make shapes or pictures as shown below. (Draw around each piece.)

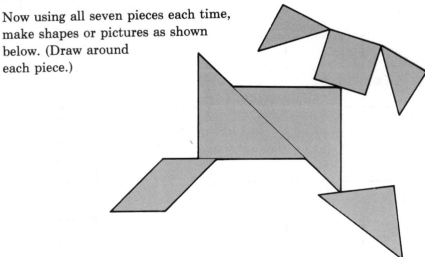

For each shape (or picture) that you make, say whether it is bigger than, smaller than, or the same size as the square.

Exercise 2

For each question, use all the seven tangram pieces of Exercise 1. Draw around your pieces to show each answer.

1. Make a rectangle.

2. Make a parallelogram.

3. Make a right-angled triangle.

4. Make a right-angled trapezium.

5. Make an isosceles trapezium.

6. What can you say about the areas of all the shapes you have made?

Exercise 3

Find the area of each of these shapes:

Exercise 4

Answer these on one-centimetre-squared paper, or on graph paper.

1. Draw a shape of your own that has an area of 14 cm².
2. Draw a shape that has an area of 20 cm².
3. Draw a shape that has an area of 16 cm².

Exercise 5

Which of these shapes has the largest area?

1.   **2.**   **3.**   **4.**

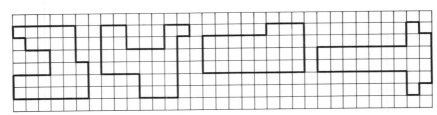

Note that we can use other-sized squares than one-centimetre squares.

Exercise 6

Find the area of each of these rectangles:

1.

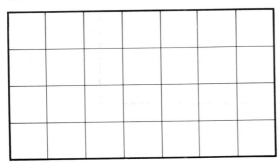

2.

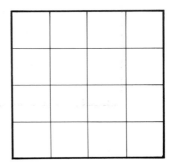

3.

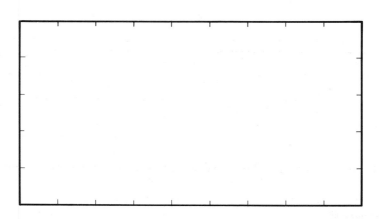

4.

5.

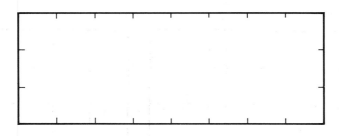

Exercise 7   Match the Areas

This is a game for 2 players.

Three sets of special cards are needed —see p. 319.

There should be 48 green cards divided into centimetre squares.

There should be 50 red and 50 blue cards. The red and blue cards should be identical in size. (They can be any size — 5 cm by 3 cm is suggested.) These cards should show the areas of the green cards. The extra two cards can have any areas written on them.

1. The green cards are mixed up then placed face downwards in one pile.

2. The red cards are given to one player and the blue to the other.

3. The first player turns over the top green card so that both players can see the squares.

4. Both players try to find one of their cards (the red or the blue) that shows the area. The first player to find the correct answer card places the answer beside the green card. He or she then wins that green card and places it, together with the answer card, beside him or her.

5. The second player now turns over the next green card so that both players can see the squares.

6. Step 4 is repeated until all the green cards have been turned over.

7. The winner is the person who wins the greatest number of green cards.

The green set of cards (48 cards)

These should measure (all units are cm):

10 × 10	9 × 9	8 × 8	7 × 7	6 × 6	5 × 5	4 × 4
10 × 9	9 × 8	8 × 7	7 × 6	6 × 5	5 × 4	4 × 3
10 × 8	9 × 7	8 × 6	7 × 5	6 × 4	5 × 3	4 × 2
10 × 7	9 × 6	8 × 5	7 × 4	6 × 3	5 × 2	
10 × 6	9 × 5	8 × 4	7 × 3	6 × 2	5 × 1	
10 × 5	9 × 4	8 × 3	7 × 2	6 × 1		
10 × 4	9 × 3	8 × 2	7 × 1			
10 × 3	9 × 2	8 × 1				
10 × 2	9 × 1					
10 × 1						

The green set of cards should be divided into square centimetres.
For example, this is
the 4 × 3 card:

The red and blue cards (50 of each) show the areas of the green cards.

100	81	64	49	36	25	16
90	72	56	42	30	20	12
80	63	48	35	24	15	8
70	54	40	28	18	10	
60	45	32	21	12	5	
50	36	24	14	6		
40	27	16	7			
30	18	8				
20	9	56				
10	54					

For example, there will be a
red card *and* a blue card like this:

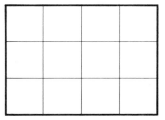

12cm²

Exercise 8

Find the area of each of these rectangles (take care with your units):

1.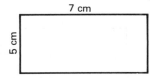

5.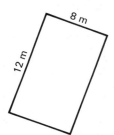

2.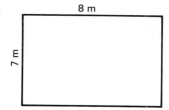

6.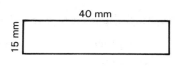

3.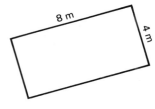

7.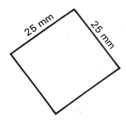

4.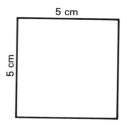

8.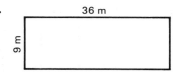

Exercise 9

1. Find the area of the rectangle in the middle:

8 m

2. Find the area of the missing piece:

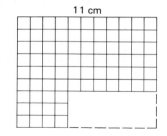

11 cm

3. Find the area of each of these rectangles:

	Length	Breadth
(a)	9 cm	4 cm
(b)	10 m	6 m
(c)	7 m	3 m
(d)	11 m	8 m
(e)	12 cm	7 cm
(f)	16 m	9 m
(g)	20 m	13 m
(h)	30 mm	18 mm
(i)	35 cm	35 cm
(j)	23 m	8 m

Exercise 10

Find the area of each of these shapes:

1.

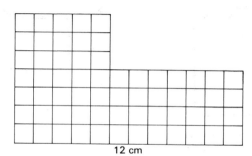

12 cm

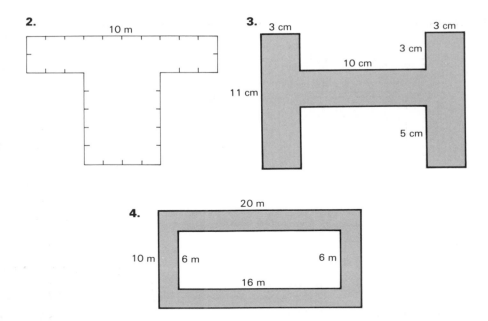

2. 10 m

3. 3 cm   3 cm   3 cm   10 cm   11 cm   5 cm

4. 20 m   10 m   6 m   6 m   16 m

Exercise 11

Find the area of each of these rectangles. Try to find a pattern.

1.

(a)	(b)		(c)			(d)				(e)					

2.

(p)	(q)		(r)			(s)				(t)					

3.

(v)	(w)		(x)			(y)				(z)					

Exercise 12

Calculate the area of each shaded border:

1.

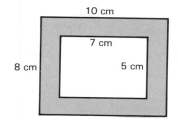

3.

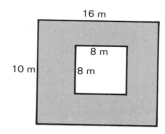

2.

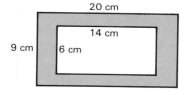

4.

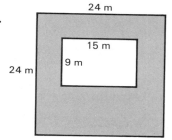

5. Find the area of a border, 2 cm wide, around the outside of this rectangle:

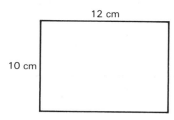

6. Find the area of a border, 2 cm wide, that is inside this rectangle.

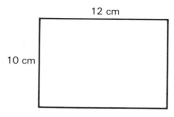

7. A picture measures 40 cm by 30 cm. A frame, 2 cm wide, surrounds this picture.
Calculate the area of the frame.

8. A garden measures 30 m by 14 m. A rectangular lawn is sown to measure 25 m by 10 m.
Calculate the area of the border.

Exercise 13

1. Find the area of a rectangle of length 12 cm and breadth 9 cm.

2. Find the area of a square of side 11 cm.

3. A rectangular room measures 6 m by 4 m.
Find its area.

4. Find the area of a rectangular lawn that is 25 m long and 9 m wide.

5. The perimeter of a square is 36 cm.
Find its area.

6. A rectangle of length 11 cm has a perimeter of 36 cm.
Find its area.

7. A football pitch measures 90 m by 70 m.
Calculate its area.

8. Find the area of the top of a small box that is 50 mm long and 35 mm wide.

9. I have some 15 mm square tiles which I use to tile a part of a bathroom wall measuring 2.1 m by 1.2 m.
How many tiles must I have used?

10. If I want to pave a patio measuring 9 m by 6 m, using paving stones that are 600 mm square, how many paving stones do I need?

11. I have 50 paving stones that are 500 mm square. If I use them to pave an area that is 6 m by 3 m, how many more 500 mm square paving stones will I need to finish the job?

12. How much paint do I need to paint one side of a garage door measuring 4 m by 3 m and both sides of nine doors measuring 2 m by 1 m, if 3 ℓ of paint will cover an area of 32 m². ($\frac{1}{2}$ ℓ tins of paint can be bought.)

Exercise 14

1. My lawn is rectangular and measures 34 m by 24 m. A path 2 m wide surrounds this lawn.
(*a*) Calculate the area of this path.
(*b*) If I decide to treat this path with weedkiller, and if one packet of weedkiller is needed for 34 m² of path, how many packets must I buy?

2. I wish to seed a lawn which is 13 m long and 8 m wide. If I need 80 g of grass seed for 1 m² of lawn, how many grams do I need altogether? If each box of grass seed holds 500 g, how many boxes do I need?

Exercise 15

1. Cut out any size of rectangle from a piece of graph paper. Make sure it measures a whole number of centimetres along each side.
This rectangle is 10 squares by 8 squares (it is not full-size).
(*a*) What is the area of your rectangle?
(*b*) What is its perimeter?

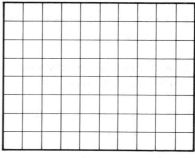

2. Now cut out part of your rectangle. (Cut out a corner.)
(*a*) What is the area of the shape remaining?
(*b*) What is its perimeter?

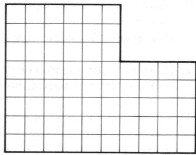

3. Now cut out another corner.
(a) What is the area of the shape remaining?
(b) What is its perimeter?

4. Cut out another corner and find the area and the perimeter of the remaining shape.

5. Do this for the last corner.

6. Make a table as shown. (Two answers have been filled in for this rectangle. Your answers may be different.)

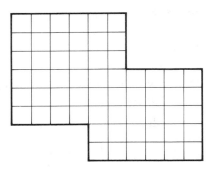

Figure	Area of shape	Perimeter of shape
1	80 cm^2	36 cm
2		
3		
4		
5		

Exercise 16

1. Draw, on one-centimetre-squared paper, as many rectangles as you can that have a perimeter of 20 cm and have sides that measure a whole number of centimetres. Here is one possible rectangle:

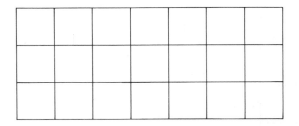

2. Find the area of each of your rectangles.

3. Which rectangle has the greatest possible area?

326

Exercise 17

Copy and complete the given table showing the possible number of rectangles that can be drawn having the given perimeter.

Each edge of the rectangles must measure a whole number of centimetres.

For example, there are 3 rectangles that have a perimeter of 12 cm (5 cm by 1 cm, 4 cm by 2 cm and 3 cm by 3 cm).

Perimeter	Number of rectangles
4 cm	
6 cm	
8 cm	
10 cm	
12 cm	3
14 cm	
16 cm	
18 cm	

Exercise 18

The length of a rectangle is given by $l = (x + 3)$ cm, while its breadth is given by $b = (x + 2)$ cm.

1. Copy and complete this table:

x	Area, A
0	6 cm^2
1	
2	
3	
4	42 cm^2
5	
6	
7	

2. By looking at the pattern in the table, find area A when $x = 8$.

3. Now plot a graph of A against x.
Use a scale of 1 cm to $\frac{1}{2}$ cm on the x-axis
(i.e. 2 cm represents 1 cm).
On the A-axis, let 1 cm represent 5 cm^2.

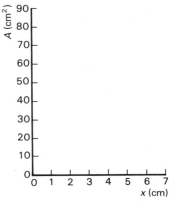

4. Make out another table.
This time, the table should show x and l:

x	l
0	3 cm
1	
2	
3	
4	
5	8 cm
6	
7	

5. Plot a graph of l against x. Use a scale of 1 cm to $\frac{1}{2}$ cm on both axes (i.e. 2 cm to 1 cm).

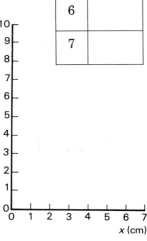

Exercise 19

Find the missing length in each of these rectangles:

1.

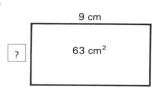

2.

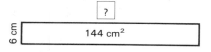

3.

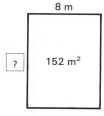

4.

5.

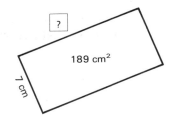

6.

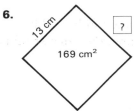

7.

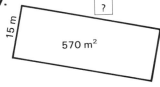

8.

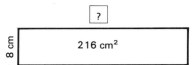

329

Exercise 20

Copy and complete this table for the given rectangles:

	Length	Breadth	Area
1.	7 cm	6 cm	?
2.	9 m	?	54 m²
3.	?	5 m	60 m²
4.	12 cm	?	120 cm²
5.	14 cm	9 cm	?
6.	30 m	?	210 m²
7.	?	8 cm	120 cm²
8.	?	16 m	544 m²
9.	42 m	26 m	?
10.	21 cm	?	399 cm²

Exercise 21

The shape below can be used to make a box without a lid — just fold along the broken lines.

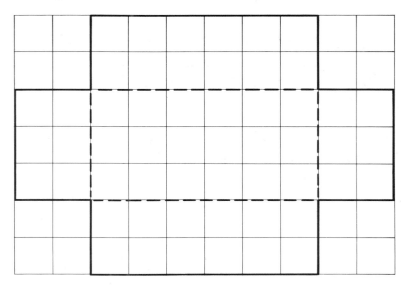

330

1. What would the length of the box be?

2. What would its breadth be?

3. Find its height in centimetres?

4. If this box were made from card, what area of card would be needed?

5. On one-centimetre-squared paper, draw the shape you would need to cut out to make a box without a lid, of length 5 cm, breadth 4 cm and height 3 cm.
   The area found is the *surface area* of the box.

Exercise 22

On squared paper, draw the net of a box with a lid, if the box measures 6 cm long, 4 cm wide and 3 cm high.

Calculate the surface area of this cuboid.

Exercise 23

Draw these cuboids on dotty paper (triangular).
Draw their nets on squared paper.
Calculate their surface areas.

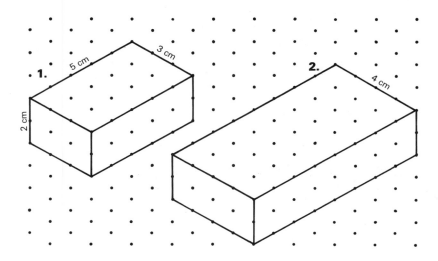

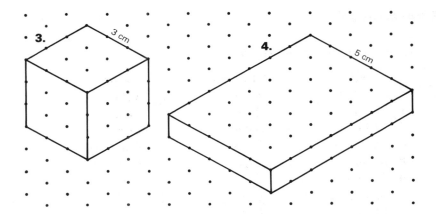

3. 3 cm

4. 5 cm

Exercise 24

This is the net of a house.
Make the house, but make it such that all lengths are twice as long as those in this net.

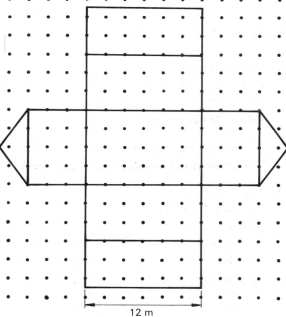

12 m

If the house is 12 m long, find:
1. the floor area
2. the perimeter of the house
3. the height of the house
4. the area of the roof
5. the total area of the four walls

Exercise 25

Calculate the surface area of each of these cuboids:

	Length	Breadth	Height
1.	5 cm	4 cm	2 cm
2.	7 cm	3 cm	2 cm
3.	9 cm	5 cm	1 cm
4.	8 cm	5 cm	3 cm
5.	10 cm	6 cm	4 cm
6.	4 cm	2 cm	1 cm
7.	8 cm	5 cm	2 cm
8.	12 cm	6 cm	3 cm
9.	9 cm	7 cm	5 cm
10.	8 cm	8 cm	4 cm

Exercise 26

1. Here is a net of a cube. Find its total surface area if each edge is 3.2 cm long. Calculate its perimeter.

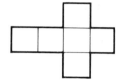

2. A room is 5 m long, 4 m wide and 2.4 m high. Calculate its total surface area (ignore doors and windows).

3. The net of a folder is shown. The two shaded flaps are both 3 cm wide. Calculate:
  (a) the total surface area of the folder
  (b) the area of cartridge paper that is wasted in making the folder

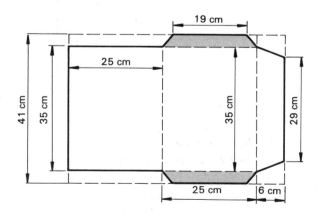

333

Exercise 27

Find the area of each of these shapes:

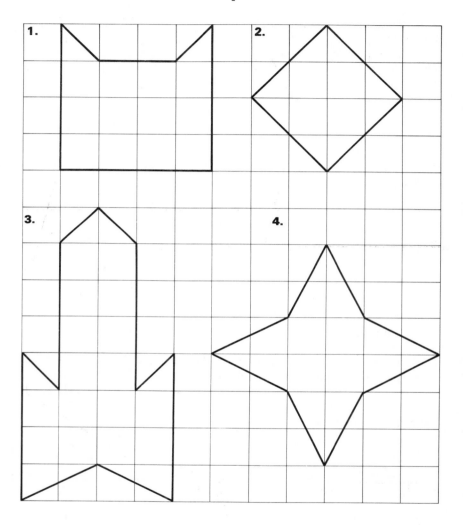

5. On one-centimetre-squared paper, trace around your hand.
Now find the area of the front of your hand by counting squares.

Exercise 28

Find the area of each of these parallelograms:

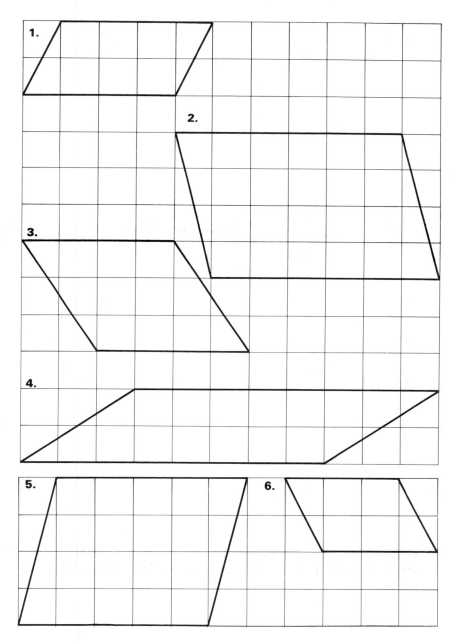

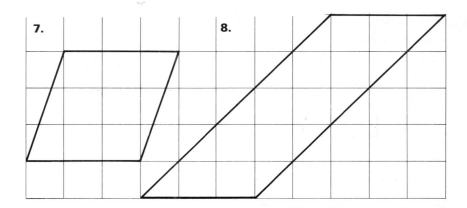

7. **8.**

Exercise 29

Calculate the area of each of these parallelograms:

1.

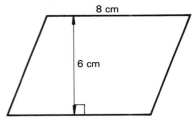

8 cm

6 cm

4.

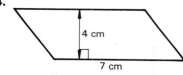

4 cm

7 cm

2.

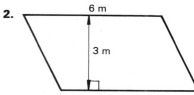

6 m

3 m

5.

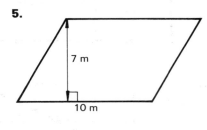

7 m

10 m

3.

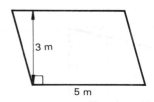

3 m

5 m

6.

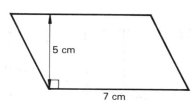

5 cm

7 cm

7.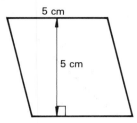

5 cm

5 cm

8.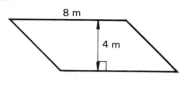

8 m

4 m

9. Base of parallelogram = 9 cm
perpendicular height = 6 cm

10. Base of parallelogram = 17 m
perpendicular height = 9 m

Exercise 30

Find the area of each of these triangles:

1.

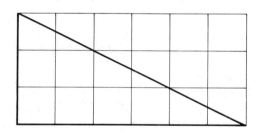

2.

3.

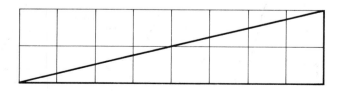

4.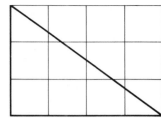

5.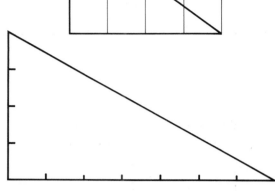

6.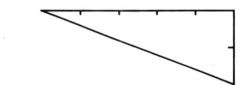

7.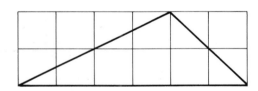

8.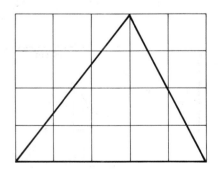

9. 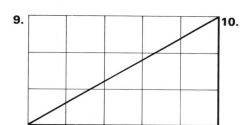 **10.**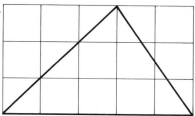

Exercise 31

Calculate the area of each of these triangles:

1.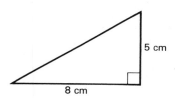

5 cm

8 cm

2.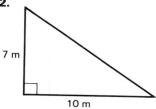

7 m

10 m

3.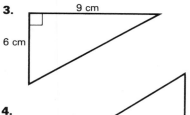

9 cm

6 cm

4.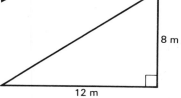

8 m

12 m

5.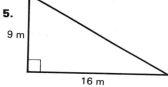

9 m

16 m

6.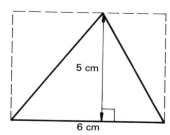

5 cm

6 cm

7.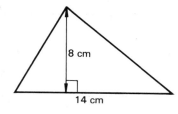

8 cm

14 cm

8.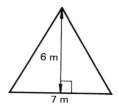

6 m

7 m

9.

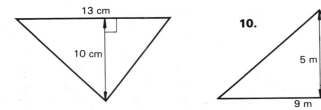

13 cm

10 cm

10.

5 m

9 m

Exercise 32

A In each question, by measuring and calculating, find out which shapes have the same area:

1. (*a*)   (*b*)   (*c*)   (*d*)

2. (*a*)   (*b*)   (*c*)   (*d*)

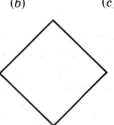
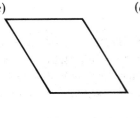

3. (*a*)   (*b*)   (*c*)   (*d*)

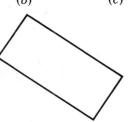

B In each question, find which shapes have the same area:

1. (a)   (b)   (c)   (d)

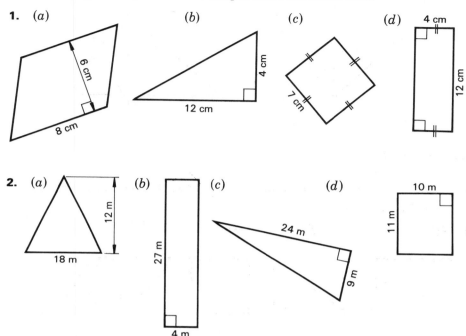

2. (a)   (b)   (c)   (d)

Exercise 33 M

Copy each of the following shapes. The sizes need not be exact. If a side is marked or labelled, draw, in a different colour, the height that is perpendicular to that side. If, however, a perpendicular height is given, then draw a side to which it is perpendicular, in a different colour.

1.

3.

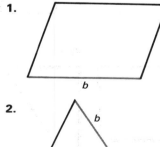

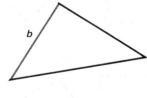

2.

4.

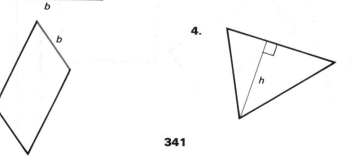

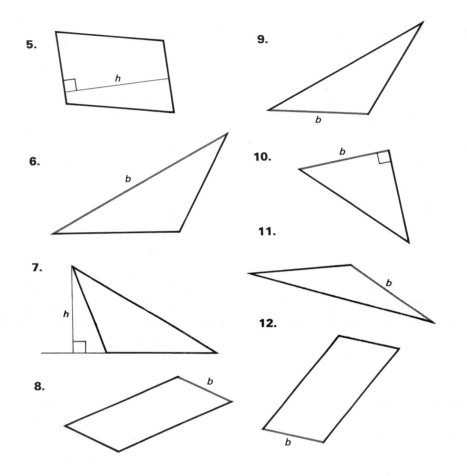

5.

6.

7.

8.

9.

10.

11.

12.

Exercise 34

Find the area of each of these shapes:

1.
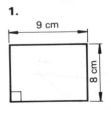
9 cm

8 cm

2.
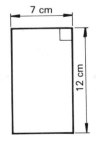
7 cm

12 cm

3.
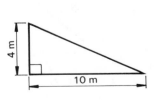
4 m

10 m

4.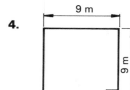

9 m

9 m

9.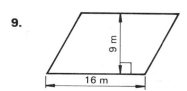

9 m

16 m

5.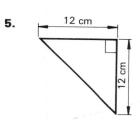

12 cm

12 cm

10.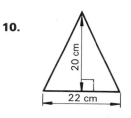

20 cm

22 cm

6.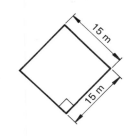

15 m

15 m

11.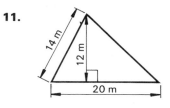

14 m

12 m

20 m

7.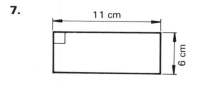

11 cm

6 cm

12.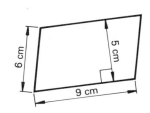

6 cm

5 cm

9 cm

8.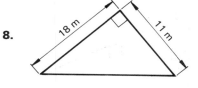

18 m

11 m

13.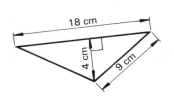

18 cm

4 cm

9 cm

343

14.

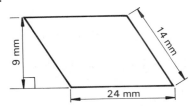

9 mm
14 mm
24 mm

18.

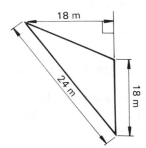

18 m
24 m
18 m

15.

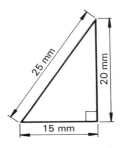

25 mm
20 mm
15 mm

19.

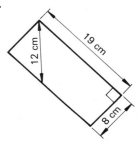

12 cm
19 cm
8 cm

16.

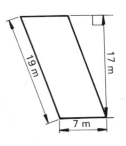

19 m
17 m
7 m

20.

17 mm
21 mm
32 mm

17.

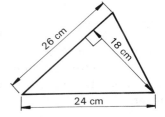

26 cm
18 cm
24 cm

Exercise 35

1. Calculate the area of a rectangle measuring 8.6 cm by 7 cm.

2. A rectangle is 6.9 cm long and 4.7 cm wide. Find its area.

3. There are two bedrooms in a house.
   Bedroom 1 is 4 m long and 3.43 m wide. Bedroom 2 is 3.7 m square. Which is the larger bedroom?

4. A rectangle is 7 cm long. It has an area of 22.33 cm².
   Find its width.

5. A football pitch is 110 m by 72.4 m. Find its area.

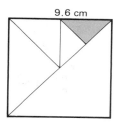

6. (a) What fraction of the square in fig. 1 is shaded?
   (b) Calculate the shaded area.

7. The floor of a room has an area of 16.32 m². If the room is 4 m wide, calculate its length.

Fig. 1

8. A parallelogram has a base of 6.3 cm and a perpendicular height of 5.2 cm.
   Find its area.

9. Calculate the area of the given triangle in fig. 2.

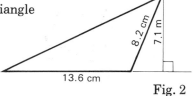

10. A rectangle of length 6.4 cm has the same area as a square of side 5.6 cm.
    Calculate the breadth of the rectangle.

Fig. 2

11. A parallelogram has the same size base and the same area as a rectangle. If they both have a base of 8.4 m and the perpendicular height of the parallelogram is 5.87 m, find the breadth of the rectangle. Give reasons for your answer.

12. A right-angled triangle has sides measuring 4.5 cm, 10.8 cm and 11.7 cm.
    Calculate its area.

Use a calculator to help with these:

1. A rectangle measures 12.6 cm by 9.4 cm.
   Find its area.

2. Find the area of the top of a matchbox that is 4.1 cm long and 3.2 cm wide.

3. Find the total area of grass needed to turf a lawn that measures 27.6 m by 15.3 m.

4. A lawn 19.2 m long and 13.7 m wide is surrounded by rose beds that are 1.9 m wide, as shown in fig. 1.
   Calculate the area of the rose beds.

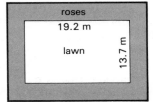

Fig. 1

5. A garden that is 21.8 m long is enclosed by a fence of length 78.2 m. Calculate the area of this garden.

6. A carpet measuring 4.5 m by 3.7 m is placed on the floor of a room that is 5.6 m long and 4.2 m wide.
   Calculate the area of the floor not covered by the carpet.

7. Calculate the area of the parallelogram in fig. 2.

8. Calculate the area of a triangle with a base of 7.49 m and perpendicular height 4.8 m.

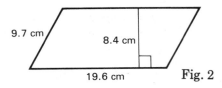

Fig. 2

9. Construct a parallelogram having two of its sides measuring 6 cm and 4.5 cm. One of its diagonals is 5.8 cm long. Draw its diagonals to form four triangles.
   Do the four triangles have the same area? Give a reason.
   Check your answer by measuring and calculating.

10. A square has an area of 69.2224 m². Try to find the length of its sides.

14 Algebra

Exercise 1

1. (*a*) What is the sum of 5 and 8?
(*b*) What is the sum of x and y?

2. (*a*) What number is 4 more than 7?
(*b*) What number is 4 more than c?
(*c*) What number is a more than c?

3. (*a*) Subtract 3 from 9.   (*c*) Subtract g from h.
(*b*) Subtract 3 from h.

4. (*a*) What must be added to 12 to give 23?
(*b*) What must be added to 12 to give p?
(*c*) What must be added to t to give 23?
(*d*) What must be added to t to give p?

5. (*a*) Write down the number that is 7 more than 12.
(*b*) Write down the number that is 7 more than m.
(*c*) Write down the number that is n more than 12.
(*d*) Write down the number that is n more than m.

6. (*a*) By how many is 41 bigger than 18?
(*b*) By how many is 41 bigger than d?
(*c*) By how many is f bigger than 18?
(*d*) By how many is f bigger than d?

7. (*a*) 24 minus 15.   (*c*) w minus 15.
(*b*) 24 minus l.   (*d*) w minus l.

8. (*a*) What number is 14 less than 37?
(*b*) What number is u less than v?

9. (*a*) What number is obtained if 47 is decreased by 29?
(*b*) What number is obtained if q is decreased by h?
(*c*) What number is obtained if q is increased by h?

Exercise 2

Write in algebraic form:

1. a plus b
2. c minus d
3. e minus 7
4. 3 times g
5. h times 4
6. the sum of k and 2
7. the product of 5 and l
8. the product of m and n
9. 17 take t
10. u take v
11. w divided by 5
12. x divided by y
13. 8 less than z
14. t less than u
15. 4 more than b
16. k more than l
17. d increased by p
18. e decreased by q

Exercise 3

Write in algebraic form where letters are used:

1. (a) James has 8 books while Ann has 11 books. How many have they altogether?
   (b) Susan has p books while Alan has 4 books. How many have they altogether?

2. (a) If I ran 150 metres and walked 90 metres, how far had I travelled altogether?
   (b) If I ran r metres and walked w metres, how far had I travelled altogether?

3. (a) In a test, Richard got 18 more marks than Alan. If Alan got 57 marks, how many did Richard get?
   (b) In a test, Richard got m more marks than Alan. If Alan got g marks, how many did Richard get?

4. (a) In another test, Jane got 14 more marks than Deborah. If Jane got 45, how many did Deborah get?
   (b) In a test, Jane got j more marks than Deborah. If Jane got t marks, how many did Deborah get?

5. (a) If Bill has twice as many marbles as Tom, and if Tom has 18 marbles, how many has Bill got?
   (b) If Bill has twice as many marbles as Tom, and if Tom has m marbles, how many has Bill got?

(c) If Bill has n times as many marbles as Tom, and if Tom has m marbles, how many has Bill got?

6. (a) If Janet has 14 sweets, and if she has twice as many as Andrea, how many has Andrea got?

   (b) If Janet has j sweets, and if she has twice as many as Andrea, how many has Andrea got?

   (c) If Janet has j sweets, and if she has k times as many as Andrea, how many has Andrea got?

Exercise 4

How many terms are there in each of these expressions?

1. $a + b - c$
2. $3a - 4 + 2d - 2e$
3. $5c - 3pq - ac$
4. $3 \times p + 4 \times q - 8$
5. $5 \times c + 4 - 2 \times d \times e$
6. $8lmn - 2$
7. $5xyz$
8. $3jk - 3 \times 2 + 4 \times l \times m$

9. $7m - n + pqr$
10. $4 \times s \times t - 3 \times 2 \times q$
11. $7 \times 4 \times 3 \times 5$
12. $8 - 7 + 3 + 9 - 6$
13. $2u - 13mn + 9t$
14. $18 - 7kt$
15. $h \times 2 + 6$
16. $4x - 8y + 3z$

Exercise 5

Copy and complete to make true sentences:

1. $3 + 3 = 2 \times 3$
   $6 + 6 = 2 \times \boxed{?}$
   $7 + 7 = 2 \times \boxed{?}$
   $9 + 9 = \boxed{?} \times 9$
   $n + n = \boxed{?} \times n$

2. $2 + 2 + 2 = 3 \times 2$
   $5 + 5 + 5 = 3 \times \boxed{?}$
   $7 + 7 + 7 = 3 \times \boxed{?}$
   $8 + 8 + 8 = \boxed{?} \times 8$
   $d + d + d = \boxed{?} \times d$

3. $3 + 3 + 3 + 3 = 4 \times \boxed{?}$
   $5 + 5 + 5 + 5 = \boxed{?} \times 5$
   $6 + 6 + 6 + 6 = 4 \times \boxed{?}$
   $f + f + f + f = \boxed{?} \times f$
   $p + p + p + p = 4 \times \boxed{?}$

4. $6 + 6 + 6 + 6 + 6 = \boxed{?} \times 6$
   $e + e + e + e + e = \boxed{?} \times e$
   $t + t + t = \boxed{?} \times t$
   $m + m + m + m = 4 \times \boxed{?}$
   $c + c + c + c + c + c = \boxed{?} \times \boxed{?}$

5. $8 - 8 = \boxed{?}$

$3 - 3 = \boxed{?}$

$5 - 5 = \boxed{?}$

$n - n = \boxed{?}$

$x - x = \boxed{?}$

$3u - 3u = \boxed{?}$

6. $4 \div 4 = \boxed{?}$

$9 \div 9 = \boxed{?}$

$10 \div 10 = \boxed{?}$

$g \div g = \boxed{?}$

$y \div y = \boxed{?}$

$5k \div 5k = \boxed{?}$

Exercise 6

Simplify:

1. $d + d + d + d + d$

2. $x + x + x$

3. $n + n + n + n + n + n + n + n$

4. $4k + 3k$

5. $2v + 7v$

6. $3t + 6t + 8t$

7. $5l + 7l + 2l + 3l$

8. $4c + 9c + c + 5c$

9. $7g + g + 4g + 2g + 8g$

10. $4h + 2h + 3h + 6h$

11. $4 + 2 + 3 + 6$

12. $x + e + x + x + e + e + e + x + x$

13. $m + a + a + a + m + a + a + a$

14. $2f + 4f + 5p + 3f + 4p + 4f$

15. $3q + 6t + 7t + 4q + 5q + 3t$

16. $4y + 2y + 3u + y + 4u$

17. $5k + k + 7l + 2k + l$

18. $7g + h + 4h + 5g + h$

19. $5x + 3y + 2y + z + 4x + 7z + y$

20. $7d + 2d + 9 + 4d + 8$

21. $8 + 5e + 7e + 7 + 2 + e + 1$

22. $9p + 9 + 6 + 3q + 5 + 4p + 2 + 2q$

23. $4m + 3n + 7 + 2m + 3n + 9 + 5m$

24. $4 + 19 + 2u + 3 + 7w + 7$

25. $2b + 4t + 6b + 10 + t + 8 + 9b + 1 + 6t$

Exercise 7

Find the *perimeter* of each of the following shapes. Simplify your answer where possible.

1.

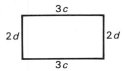

2.

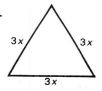

3.

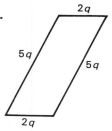

4.

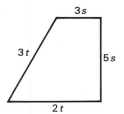

5.

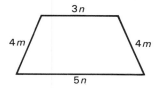

6.

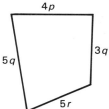

7.

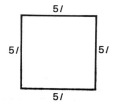

8.

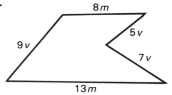

9.

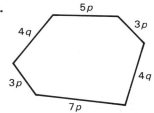

10.

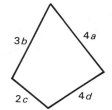

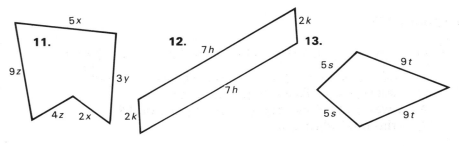

11. 5x, 9z, 3y, 4z, 2x

12. 2k, 7h, 7h, 2k

13. 5s, 9t, 5s, 9t

Exercise 8

Simplify:

1. $5m - 3m$
2. $16t - 9t$
3. $18a - 5a$
4. $23y - 5y - 9y$
5. $18w - 3w - 2w$
6. $14d - d$
7. $17f - f$
8. $21h - 5h - h$
9. $16e + 3e - 7e$
10. $18z - 7z + 5z$
11. $14n + 6n - 3n + 5n - 7n$

12. $19b - 7b + 8b - 3b - b$
13. $21v - 18v - 3v$
14. $15g + 8g - 3g - g - 10g$
15. $k + 5k - 2k + 7k$
16. $3q - 2q + 19q - q$
17. $19l - 7l + 8l + 2l - 3l$
18. $7u + 14u - 9u - 2u - 6u$
19. $15x - 15x + 3x - 2x$
20. $6n + 7n + 8n - 9n - 10n$
21. $6v + 7v - 8v + 9v - 10v$
22. $14d - 7d + d + 5d - 2d$

Exercise 9

Where possible, simplify the following. If no shorter form is possible, write 'NO SHORTER FORM'.

1. $5m + 3n + 4m + 2n$
2. $4p + 6q - 2q + 3p$
3. $7t - 2t + 6u - 3u$
4. $7x + 8y - 2x - 3x$
5. $4v + 9 - 3v - 2 + 2v$
6. $8k + 7l - 2l - k + 4l$
7. $3f + 8g + 2f + 7h + 4h$
8. $5k + 2b + 6d - 2k$
9. $14x + 5y - 5x + 2z$
10. $17h - 2h + 3k + l + 4k$
11. $8p + 4m + 2n$
12. $7v + 8w - 2v - 8w$

13. $8d + 3d + 5e - 7d - e$
14. $3h + 5 + 6g - h - 3 + 4g$
15. $18t + 7u - 18t + 3u$
16. $4t + 7u - t - 7u - 3t$
17. $7x + 7y + 7x - 7y$
18. $15 + 6e - 7 - 3e + 2$
19. $12n + 7m - n - m + 3n$
20. $14h + 7k + 8h + 7 - 2k$
21. $18 + 3m + 8n + 5p$
22. $16p + 8q - 5q - 3p - 3q$
23. $15z + 9$
24. $19y + 8x - 5y + 2x + 4x$

Exercise 10

Write the following in a shorter form and simplify your answers:

1. Richard got $5x$ house points on Monday, $7x$ on Tuesday, $2x$ on Wednesday, $8x$ on Thursday and $4x$ on Friday.
What was his total number of points for the week?
Find this total when $x = 3$.

2. Andrew had $12k$ jelly babies. He gave $4k$ away, ate $5k$, bought a further $3k$, then ate $2k$.
How many did he have left?
Find the number he had left when $k = 4$.

3. Susan had $7t$ pence. She spent $5t$ pence, earned $8t$ pence, was given $9t$ pence, then spent $10t$ pence.
How much did Susan have left?
Find this amount of money when $t = 8$.

4. Mrs Allen had $4f$ apples and $6h$ bananas. On Monday, her family ate $3h$ bananas. On Tuesday they ate $3f$ apples but she bought another $2f$ apples and $4h$ bananas.
What did she have left?
If $f = 3$ and $h = 2$, find the number of apples and bananas that were left.

5. Janet had $6w$ eggs. She used $4w$ for baking, bought $7w$ more but her brothers then ate $2w$ of them. How many were left?
How many were left if $w = 4$?

6. Steven had $12d$ marbles and $8e$ conkers. He gave $3e$ conkers away, won $3d$ marbles, collected $5e$ conkers, then lost $7d$ marbles.
What did he have left?
When $d = 8$ and $e = 3$ how many marbles did he have left?
How many conkers did he have left?

Exercise 11

1. If $a = 4$ and $b = 8$, find the value of   (a) ab,   (b) ba.
What do you notice about the two answers?

2. If $x = 12$ and $y = 3$, find the value of   (a) xy,   (b) yx.
What do you notice about the two answers?

3. If $t = 2$ and $u = 7$, find the value of (a) $3tu$, (b) $3ut$.
What do you notice about the two answers?

4. If $p = 6$ and $q = 4$, find the value of (a) $5pq$, (b) $5qp$.
What do you notice about the two answers?

5. If $m = 2$ and $v = 3$, find the value of
(a) $3mv + 5mv$, (b) $8mv$.
What do you notice about the two answers?

6. If $c = 4$ and $d = 5$, find the value of (a) $6cd + 3cd$, (b) $9cd$.
What do you notice about the two answers?

7. If $l = 7$ and $m = 3$, find the value of (a) $4lm + 2ml$, (b) $6lm$.
What do you notice about the two answers?

Exercise 12

Where possible, write each of these expressions in a shorter form by
collecting like terms. If no shorter form is possible, write 'NO
SHORTER FORM'.

1. $3ad + 7ad$

2. $2pq + 5pq + 4pq$

3. $7xy - 2xy + 4xy$

4. $2tk + 5kt$

5. $7uw - 3wu$

6. $8ef - 3ef + 6fe$

7. $2mu + 4kc + 5mu$

8. $7ab - 2ba + 4cd - 2cd$

9. $6ax - 2xa + 3cx + 2xc$

10. $8be + 9 - 2eb - 7$

11. $4um + 2mu + 3mw + 5uw$

12. $5yz + 6xz + 2xy$

13. $9bc - cb + ac + 6cb$

14. $12 + 9vy - 2vy - 7 + 3xy$

15. $5nit + 7tin + 2int + 3itn$

16. $8mve + 2mev - 5mve$

17. $2a + 3ad + 7ade$

18. $12sut - 9ust + 6tun$

19. $8pvc + 2pv + 5vc$

20. $9sag + 2gas + 7ga - 6sag - ag$

Note that $\quad 4x + 4x + 4x = \underline{\underline{12x}}$

and that $\qquad 3 \times 4x = \underline{\underline{12x}}$

Note also that $\qquad 3 \times 4x = 3 \times 4 \times x$

$$= 12 \times x$$

$$= \underline{\underline{12x}}$$

Exercise 13

Simplify:

1. $3 \times 4c$
2. $5 \times 3d$
3. $7 \times 2e$
4. $4 \times 8x$
5. $9 \times 5t$
6. $8 \times 4a$
7. $6 \times 3f$
8. $2 \times 9h$
9. $9 \times 2n$
10. $5 \times 7u$
11. $8 \times 7m$
12. $2 \times 3k$
13. $7 \times 4g$
14. $9 \times 8l$
15. $7 \times 8p$
16. $6 \times 4d$
17. $8 \times 7d$
18. $5 \times 9b$
19. 8×6
20. 6×8
21. $5 \times 4b$
22. $4b \times 5$
23. $3t \times 4$
24. $2m \times 3$
25. $6k \times 2$
26. $9g \times 7$
27. $4x \times 6$
28. $3 \times 12c$
29. $4 \times 7f$
30. $10y \times 3$

Exercise 14

Simplify:

1. $2 \times d$
2. $c \times d$
3. $3 \times 4 \times e$
4. $3 \times e \times f$
5. $4 \times 2 \times g \times h$
6. $5 \times k \times 3$
7. $6 \times l \times 2$
8. $m \times 6$
9. $4 \times n \times 3 \times p$
10. $7 \times q \times t \times 2$
11. $u \times 6 \times 8$
12. $3 \times 2 \times v$
13. $3 \times 2v$
14. $4 \times 7w$
15. $8 \times 3x$
16. $4y \times 6$
17. $7 \times c \times d$
18. $7 \times cd$
19. $7 \times abc$
20. $4 \times 3de$
21. $f \times 2g$
22. $4p \times 3q$
23. $7g \times 8h$
24. $2k \times 9l$
25. $3mn \times 3p$
26. $4 \times 2q \times 3t$
27. $7v \times 3 \times 2w$
28. $8x \times 3y \times z$
29. $4ab \times 7c$
30. $2d \times 6e \times 7$

Exercise 15   A Secret Code

a	b	c	d	e	f	g	h	i	j	k	l	m
1	2	3	4	5	6	7	8	9	10	11	12	13

n	o	p	q	r	s	t	u	v	w	x	y	z
14	15	16	17	18	19	20	21	22	23	24	25	26

This is how the code works:

e.g. $h + k$
$\quad = 8 + 11$ (since $h = 8$ and $k = 11$)
$\quad = 19$
$\quad = \underline{\underline{s}}$ (from the table, $s = 19$)

Answer all of these questions. Each answer is a letter.

All the letters, written down one after the other, will give a sentence. Find the sentence.

1. $d + s$

2. $v - q$

3. $2f$

4. $e + g$

5. $y - u$

6. $5c$

7. $t - f$

8. $j \div 2$

9. $t + e$

10. $z - k$

11. $3g$

12. $\frac{1}{2}p$

13. $y - x$

14. $t + b$

15. $l - g$

16. $r \div 3$

17. $3e$

18. $b + s$

19. $r - d$

20. $r - n$

21. $10b$

22. $q - i$

23. $p - g$

24. $c + p$

25. $z \div 2$

26. $y \div 5$

27. $e + n$

28. $f + m$

29. $x - w$

30. $2p - y$

31. $\dfrac{t}{d}$

Exercise 16

Copy and complete the following. In each case, write the areas of the smallest rectangles inside them.

Also, remove the brackets and compare the answers with the areas of the rectangles.

1. (*a*)

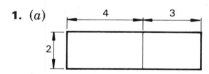

    (*b*) $2(4 + 3) = \boxed{?}$

4. (*a*)

    (*b*) $3(x + 4) = \boxed{?}$

2. (*a*)

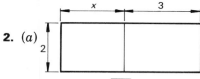

    (*b*) $2(x + 3) = \boxed{?}$

5. (*a*)

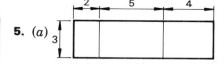

    (*b*) $3(2 + 5 + 4) = \boxed{?}$

3. (*a*)

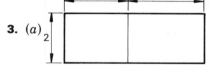

    (*b*) $2(x + y) = \boxed{?}$

6. (*a*)

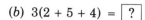

    (*b*) $3(x + y + z) = \boxed{?}$

Exercise 17

Multiply out:

1. $5(3 + 6)$	**11.** $7(g - 4)$	**21.** $10(5x - 3y - 7z)$
2. $4(5 - 2)$	**12.** $5(3 + a)$	**22.** $8(7c + 2d + e)$
3. $7(2 + 8)$	**13.** $2(7 - b)$	**23.** $7(7f - g + h)$
4. $2(5 + 9)$	**14.** $4(2h + 1)$	**24.** $4(9i - 3j)$
5. $6(13 - 5)$	**15.** $6(j + 3)$	**25.** $3(4k + 2l)$
6. $2(3a + 2)$	**16.** $2(3k + 2m)$	**26.** $9(7m - 4n + 8p)$
7. $3(c - 4)$	**17.** $5(3l - n)$	**27.** $11(q - r)$
8. $5(2d - 3)$	**18.** $7(2p - q + 3r)$	**28.** $12(s - 4t + 2u)$
9. $9(5e + 1)$	**19.** $6(3s + 2t + 5u)$	**29.** $3(v - 4w - 3u + 7)$
10. $6(4f + 3)$	**20.** $12(v - w)$	**30.** $7(9x - 4 + 6y - 8z)$

Exercise 18

Multiply out:

1. $4(3x - 2)$

2. $\dfrac{(8d + 6)}{2}$

3. $\frac{1}{2}(4p - 10)$

4. $(2m + 3) \times 3$

5. $\frac{1}{3}(12h + 9)$

6. $\dfrac{10k - 25}{5}$

7. $3(7a + 1)$

8. $2(12c - 3)$

9. $7(a - 2c + 4e)$

10. $\dfrac{(12x + 16y - 8z)}{4}$

11. $(6l - m + 2n) \times 4$

12. $\dfrac{(18f - 12g + 15h)}{3}$

Exercise 19

Simplify each of the following by multiplying out the brackets and then collecting like terms where possible:

1. $5(3p - 7)$
2. $3(2a + 3d)$
3. $7(q - 3s + 2t)$
4. $2(x + 3) + 3(x + 1)$
5. $6(n + 2) + 2(4n + 3)$
6. $5(3c + 7) + 3(c + 5)$
7. $4(2u + 1) + 2(4u + 5)$
8. $7(m + 2n) + 2(2m + n)$
9. $6(3 + 4e) + 5(3e + 2)$
10. $4(4t + 7) + 2(6 + t)$

11. $7(3y + 5) + 2(4y - 6)$
12. $3(9 + 8z) + 4(2 - 5z)$
13. $5(3f + 4) + 3(1 - 4f)$
14. $2(6l + 7) + 3(5l - 4)$
15. $4(7v + 5) + 5(6 + v)$
16. $9(1 + 3g) + 6(2 - 4g)$
17. $8(3k + 7) + 5(2k - 9)$
18. $5(w + 3) + 2(2w + 1)$
19. $4(8x + 3) + 6(x - 2)$
20. $6(4x + 3) + 8(2 - 3x)$

15 Order of Precedence

A Find the value of:

1. (*a*) 2 lots of seven
   (*b*) 2×7

2. (*a*) 3 lots of 9
   (*b*) 3×9

3. (*a*) 5 lots of 6
   (*b*) 5×6

4. 4 added to 3 lots of five

5. (*a*) 9 added to 4 lots of 8
   (*b*) 9 added to $\quad 4 \times 8$
   (*c*) 9 $\quad + \quad 4 \times 8$

6. (*a*) 6 lots of 1 + 8 lots of 2
   (*b*) $\quad 6 \quad + \quad 8 \times 2$

7. (*a*) 4 lots of 1 added to 3 lots of 5
   (*b*) $\quad 4 \times 1 \quad + \quad 3 \times 5$
   (*c*) $\quad 4 \quad + \quad 3 \times 5$

8. $7 + 5 \times 4$
9. $12 + 7 \times 2$
10. 4 lots of 7 added to 6
11. $3 \times 9 + 8$
12. $2 + 8 \times 7$
13. $15 - 4 \times 2$
14. $36 - 12 \times 2$
15. 11 take 12 divided by 4
16. $19 - 12 \div 4$
17. $16 + 15 \div 3$
18. $4 \times 7 + 6$
19. $4 \times 8 - 5$
20. $12 - 9 \div 3$
21. $6 + 8 \div 2$
22. $11 - 8 \div 2$
23. $17 + 3 \times 8$
24. $6 \times 7 + 9$

B Find the value of:

1. (*a*) 2 lots of 4 + 3 lots of 5
   (*b*) $\quad 2 \times 4 \quad + \quad 3 \times 5$

2. (*a*) 3 lots of 6 + 2 lots of 3
   (*b*) $\quad 3 \times 6 \quad + \quad 2 \times 3$

3. (*a*) 4 lots of 5 − 3 lots of 2
   (*b*) $\quad 4 \times 5 \quad - \quad 3 \times 2$

4. (*a*) 5 lots of 7 − 2 lots of 6
   (*b*) $\quad 5 \times 7 \quad - \quad 2 \times 6$

5. (a) 8 lots of 2 + 7 lots of 4

    (b) 8×2 + 7×4

6. $4 \times 6 + 2 \times 7$

7. $7 \times 6 - 3 \times 8$

8. $9 \times 2 + 6 \times 4$

9. $5 \times 4 + 3 \times 7$

10. $6 \times 6 - 5 \times 3$

11. $9 \times 5 - 7 \times 2$

12. $5 \times 8 + 9 \times 4$

13. $7 \times 5 + 6 \times 7$

14. $9 \times 7 - 8 \times 4$

15. $8 \times 7 - 5 \times 9$

Exercise 2

A Find the value of:

1. (a) $6 \times 3 + 8$

    (b) $14 \div 2 + 6$

2. (a) $20 - \quad 3 \times 4$

    (b) $15 - 12 \div 3$

3. (a) $8 \times 5 + 5 \times 6$

    (b) $8 \div 2$ added to $6 \div 3$

    (c) $8 \div 2 \quad + \quad 6 \div 3$

4. $9 \times 6 - 4 \times 7$

5. $6 \div 2 + 15 \div 5$

6. $4 \times 9 + 12 \div 2$

7. $18 \div 6 + 3 \times 9$

8. $28 \div 4 + 7 \times 7$

9. $9 \times 8 - 7 \times 3$

10. $8 \times 3 - 20 \div 5$

11. $7 \times 9 - 36 \div 4$

12. $5 \times 5 + 42 \div 6$

13. $2 \times 8 + 50 \div 5$

14. $56 \div 7 - 2 \times 2$

15. $81 \div 9 - 3 \times 3$

16. $54 \div 6 + 6 \times 5$

17. $9 \times 9 + 6 \times 8$

18. $56 \div 8 + 7 \times 8$

19. $8 \times 9 - 48 \div 6$

20. $63 \div 7 - 42 \div 7$

B Use your calculator to help you with these. If your calculator has brackets (parentheses) then use them. Compare the answers obtained in each part of each question.

1. (a) $4 \times (8 + 3)$

    (b) $4 \times 8 + 3$

    (c) $4 \times 8 + 4 \times 3$

    (d) 4×11

2. (a) $7 \times (5 + 9)$

    (b) $7 \times 5 + 9$

    (c) $7 \times 5 + 7 \times 9$

    (d) 7×14

3. (a) $8 \times (9 - 3)$

    (b) $8 \times 9 - 3$

    (c) $8 \times 9 - 8 \times 3$

    (d) 8×6

4. (a) $48 \div (6 + 2)$

    (b) $48 \div 6 + 2$

    (c) $48 \div 6 + 48 \div 2$

    (d) $48 \div 8$

C Work these out *without using a calculator*:

1. $3 \times (4 + 2)$
2. $5 \times (6 + 4)$
3. $8 \times (7 - 3)$
4. $4 \times (9 - 1)$
5. $7 \times (12 - 5)$

6. $36 \div (4 + 5)$
7. $40 \div (10 - 2)$
8. $(12 + 6) \div 3$
9. $(7 + 2) \times 7$
10. $(15 - 3) \div 2$

11. $56 \div (19 - 12)$
12. $52 \div (6 + 7)$
13. $(42 + 18) \div 12$
14. $(29 - 23) \times 8$
15. $9 \times (14 - 7)$

Exercise 3

Say whether each statement is true or false:

1. $6 + 8 \times 2 = (6 + 8) \times 2$
2. $12 \div 4 + 8 = 12 + 8 \div 4$
3. $9 - 4 \times 2 = 9 \times 2 - 4$
4. $5 + 3 \times 7 = 5 + (3 \times 7)$
5. $14 - 2 \times 4 = 2 \times 4 - 14$
6. $14 + 2 \times 4 = 2 \times 4 + 14$
7. $4 \times (7 + 2) = 4 \times 7 + 2$
8. $5 \times (9 - 3) = 5 \times 9 - 3$
9. $7 \times 4 + 6 = 4 \times 7 + 6$
10. $3 + 7 \times 6 = 10 \times 6$

11. $3 \times (8 - 5) = 3 \times 8 - 3 \times 5$
12. $19 - 4 \times 2 = 15 \times 2$
13. $28 - 8 \div 2 = 28 \div 4$
14. $16 \div 4 + 4 = 16 \div 8$
15. $7 \times (3 + 2) = 7 \times 5$
16. $60 \div (10 + 2) = 60 \div 10 + 60 \div 2$
17. $(24 + 18) \div 6 = 24 \div 6 + 18 \div 6$
18. $(4 + 6) \times 9 = 4 \times 9 + 6 \times 9$
19. $(15 - 9) \times 3 = 6 \times 3$
20. $7 \times 9 - 7 \times 4 = 7 \times (9 - 4)$

Exercise 4

Find the value of:

1. (a) 4 lots of 3 + 2 lots of 3
   (b) 6 lots of 3
   (c) 6×3

2. (a) 9 lots of 7 − 5 lots of 7
   (b) 4 lots of 7
   (c) 4×7

3. (a) 3 lots of 5 + 4 lots of 5
   (b) $3 \times 5 \quad + \quad 4 \times 5$
   (c) 7×5

4. (a) 8 lots of 9 − 3 lots of 9
   (b) 5×9

5. 7 lots of 8 + 3 lots of 8
6. 15 lots of 7 − 5 lots of 7
7. $14 \times 9 - 4 \times 9$
8. $4 \times 6 + 5 \times 6$
9. $19 \times 8 - 11 \times 8$
10. $13 \times 7 + 7 \times 7$
11. $16 \times 5 - 12 \times 5$
12. $14 \times 2 + 16 \times 2$
13. $7 \times 29 + 3 \times 29$
14. $19 \times 7 - 7 \times 9$
15. $46 \times 91 + 54 \times 91$

Exercise 5

Try this on your calculator:

$$\boxed{3}\ \boxed{+}\ \boxed{2}\ \boxed{\times}\ \boxed{7}\ \boxed{=}$$

If your calculator shows the answer 17, then it sorts out the order of calculating for you,

since

$$3 + 2 \times 7$$
$$= 3 + 14$$
$$= \underline{\underline{17}}$$

$3 + 2 \times 7 \neq 35$ so if your calculator gives the answer 35, the answer is wrong.

You then need to work out the answer in a different way.

We use $3 + 2 \times 7 = 2 \times 7 + 3$ since 3 add 2 lots of 7 = 2 lots of 7 add 3.

So $\boxed{2}\ \boxed{\times}\ \boxed{7}\ \boxed{+}\ \boxed{3}\ \boxed{=}$ gives 17 (the correct answer).

Try it on your calculator.

Use your calculator to answer these:

1. $4 \times 8 + 9$	**11.** $7 + 12 \div 3$	**21.** $24 \div 6 + 5$
2. $3 + 7 \times 2$	**12.** $30 - 10 \times 3$	**22.** $30 \div 5 + 10$
3. $12 \div 4 + 6$	**13.** $16 + 5 \times 8$	**23.** $8 \times 9 - 12$
4. $9 - 2 \times 3$	**14.** $45 \div 5 + 4$	**24.** $10 + 8 \times 7$
5. $14 - 8 \div 4$	**15.** $4 \times 9 - 5$	**25.** $18 - 4 \div 2$
6. $15 + 3 \times 9$	**16.** $32 - 2 \times 7$	**26.** $54 \div 6 + 4 \times 7$
7. $6 \times 10 - 20$	**17.** $56 \div 8 - 7$	**27.** $5 \times 8 - 3 \times 7$
8. $5 \times 7 + 12$	**18.** $4 + 24 \div 8$	**28.** $72 \div 6 - 8 \div 4$
9. $42 \div 7 - 3$	**19.** $44 - 9 \div 3$	**29.** $9 \times 7 + 8$
10. $47 - 4 \times 9$	**20.** $6 \times 8 + 23$	**30.** $8 \times 9 + 12 \div 6$

Exercise 6

If $x = 7$, what is the value of:

1. $4x$ **2.** $5x$ **3.** $2x$

4. $6x$	**13.** $2x + 5$	**22.** $9x - 2x$
5. $3x$	**14.** $5 + 2x$	**23.** $5x + 4x$
6. $3x + 2$	**15.** $11 - x$	**24.** $x + 8x$
7. $3x - 5$	**16.** $23 - 2x$	**25.** $x + 7x$
8. $4x + 5$	**17.** $4x - 8$	**26.** $3x - x$
9. $5x - 1$	**18.** $17 + 3x$	**27.** $(x + 5) \div 3$
10. $x - 3$	**19.** $7x$	**28.** $4(2x - 9)$
11. $x + 6$	**20.** $3x + 4x$	**29.** $3x + 4 \times 3$
12. $6 + x$	**21.** $6x + x$	**30.** $(6x - 2) \div 5$

Exercise 7

If $a = 4$, $b = 6$, $c = 0$, $d = 1$, $e = 7$ and $f = 9$, find the value of:

1. $b + e$	**11.** $a + 2e$	**21.** bac
2. $a + c$	**12.** $3a + d$	**22.** $3ae$
3. $3e$	**13.** $3b + 2f$	**23.** $2bd$
4. $7f$	**14.** $4e - 3a$	**24.** $2fb + 8$
5. $e - a$	**15.** $a + e + f$	**25.** $3be - 14$
6. $2b + 3$	**16.** $f + b - d$	**26.** $100 - ef$
7. $6a + f$	**17.** $e + 2a - f$	**27.** $2ab + 3b$
8. $5e - b$	**18.** ab	**28.** $5ab$
9. $14 - 2a$	**19.** fe	**29.** $2ab + 3a$
10. $4 + 3f$	**20.** fab	**30.** $5a + b$

Exercise 8

Find the value of each of the following expressions:

1. (a) $2x + 1$
   (b) $2(x + 1)$ when $x = 6$
   (c) $2x + 2$

2. (a) $3y + 2$
   (b) $3(y + 2)$ when $y = 5$
   (c) $3y + 6$

3. (a) $12 - 4d$
   (b) $2(6 - 2d)$ when $d = 2$
   (c) $4(3 - d)$

4. (a) $4p - 3$
   (b) $4(p - 3)$
   (c) $4p - 12$ when $p = 7$
   (d) $2(2p - 6)$
   (e) $4p - 6$

5. (a) $\frac{1}{2}c + 8$
   (b) $\frac{1}{2}(c + 8)$ when $c = 4$
   (c) $\frac{1}{2}c + 4$

6. (a) $2m + n$
(b) $2(m + n)$ when $m = 7$
(c) $2m + 2n$ and $n = 4$

7. (a) $3x - y$
(b) $3(x - y)$ when $x = 6$
(c) $3x - 3y$ and $y = 2$

8. (a) $6k + t$
(b) $2(3k + t)$ when $k = 4$
(c) $6k + 2t$ and $t = 3$

9. (a) $8u + 3l$
(b) $4(2u + 3l)$ when $u = 3$
(c) $8u + 12l$ and $l = 5$

10. (a) $4h - 2g$
(b) $4(h - 2g)$ when $h = 8$
(c) $4h - 8g$ and $g = 3$

11. (a) $2pq$
(b) $2(p \times q)$ when $p = 4$
(c) $2p \times 2q$ and $q = 6$

12. (a) $x \times y \times z$ when $x = 3$
(b) $x \times (y \times z)$ $y = 4$
(c) $xy \times xz$ and $z = 6$

13. (a) $4(d \div e)$
(b) $4d \div 4e$ when $d = 6$
(c) $4d \div e$ and $e = 2$

14. (a) $4(d + e)$
(b) $4d + 4e$ when $d = 6$
(c) $4d + e$ and $e = 2$

15. (a) $4(d - e)$
(b) $4d - 4e$ when $d = 6$
(c) $4d - e$ and $e = 2$

Exercise 9

Here are some formulae that are used in maths and science:

1. The formula $P = 4l$ gives the perimeter of a square.
Find P when $l = 8$.

2. Use the formula $P = 6l$ to find P when $l = 12$.

3. $A = lb$ gives the area of a rectangle.
Find A when $l = 9$ and $b = 8$.

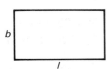

4. $P = 2l + 2b$ gives the perimeter of a rectangle.
Find P if $l = 9$ and $b = 8$.

5. $P = 2(l + b)$ is another formula that gives the perimeter of a rectangle.
Use it to find P when $l = 9$ and $b = 8$. Check your answer with question 4.

6. $v = \dfrac{s}{t}$ tells you how fast you are travelling (your velocity) if you

travel a distance s in a time t.
Find v if $s = 216$ and if $t = 3$.

7. $D = \dfrac{M}{V}$ gives the density of a solid.
Find D if $M = 750$ and $V = 150$.

8. Another formula used in science is $R = \dfrac{V}{I}$. It comes from Ohm's law.
Use it to find R when $I = 3$ and $V = 240$.

9. $A = bh$ gives the area of a parallelogram.
Find A when $b = 12$ and $h = 9$.

10. The formula that gives the circumference of a circle is $C = \pi d$
(the Greek letter π is pronounced 'pie').
Find C if $\pi = 3$ and $d = 43$.

Exercise 10

Here are some more maths and science formulae:

1. The science formula $pV = K$ is known as Boyle's law. Find K if
$p = 15$ and $V = 300$.

2. Use the formula $E = IR$ to find E when $I = 5$ and $R = 48$.

3. Use $C = 2\pi r$ to find C if $\pi = 3$ and $r = 25$.

4. $S = 90(2n - 4)$ gives the sum of the angles of a polygon.
Find S when $n = 8$.

5. $F = ma$ is another science formula.
Find F when $m = 57$ and $a = 10$.

6. A formula for calculating the volume of a prism is $V = Ah$.
Use it to find V if $A = 64$ and $h = 7$.

7. Another science formula is $P = mgh$.
Find P if $m = 74$, $g = 10$ and $h = 4$.

8. Use $v = u + at$ to find v when $u = 15$, $a = 10$ and $t = 7$.

9. The area of a rhombus, A, can be found using $A = \frac{1}{2}Dd$.
Find A when $D = 18$ and $d = 12$.

10. $I = \dfrac{Prn}{100}$ can be used to calculate interest.
Calculate I when $P = 800$, $r = 7$ and $n = 3$.

11. Use $S = \dfrac{n}{2}(a + l)$ to find S when $n = 7$, $a = 5$ and $l = 19$.

12. $A = \frac{1}{2}(a + b)h$ gives the area of a trapezium.
Find A when $a = 7$, $b = 15$ and $h = 6$.

13. Find l using $l = a + (n - 1)d$ if $a = 12$, $n = 9$ and $d = 6$.

14. $F = mg - ma$. Find F if $m = 4$, $g = 10$ and $a = 7$.

15. $F = \frac{9}{5}C + 32$ gives the temperature in degrees Fahrenheit if the
temperature in degrees Celsius is given.
Calculate F when $C = 45$.

Exercise 11

1. Use $P = 4l$ to find P when $l = 5.8$

2. If $A = bh$, find A when $b = 4.7$ and $h = 3$.

3. Use $R = \dfrac{V}{I}$ to find R when $V = 13.8$ and $I = 3$.

4. If $D = \dfrac{M}{V}$, find D when $M = 74.8$ and $V = 4$.

5. Use $C = \pi d$ to find C when $\pi = 3.14$ and $d = 7$.

6. Use $F = ma$ to find F when $m = 8$ and $a = 9.81$.

7. Use $A = \frac{1}{2}Dd$ to find A when $D = 12$ and $d = 6.9$.

8. If $R = r_1 + r_2$, find R when $r_1 = 5.84$ and $r_2 = 2.79$.

9. Use $F = \frac{9}{5}C + 32$ to find F when $C = 36.5$.

10. Use $v = u + at$ to find v when $u = 50$, $a = 9.8$ and $t = 4$.

Exercise 12

If $v = 8$, $w = 6$, $x = 3$, $y = 7$ and $z = 2$, find the value of:

1. $3w$

2. $x + y - z$

3. $y + 3v$

4. $4y - w$

5. $8z + 2x$

6. wx

7. $3yz$

8. $2wz + 9$

9. $5xz - v$

10. $3vx - 6y$

11. $2x + 2y$

12. $2(x + y)$

13. $6(w + z)$

14. $8(v - x)$

15. $v \div z$

16. $\dfrac{w}{x}$

17. $\dfrac{wv}{12}$

18. $4y - \dfrac{v}{2}$

19. $8x + (w \div 2)$

20. $2v - (w + y)$

21. $w + 3y$

22. $w + 3 \times y$

23. $(w + 3) \times y$

24. $4(y - 3)$

25. $4y - 12$

26. $5(v + x)$

27. $5v + 5x$

28. $7(2w - z)$

29. $14w - 7z$

30. $x(v + 2z - y)$

Exercise 13

1. If $x * y$ means $2x - y$, find the value of:
(a) $3 * 2$ (c) $1 * 2$ (e) $9 * 4$ (g) $7 * 0$
(b) $2 * 1$ (d) $7 * 3$ (f) $12 * 2$ (h) $8 * 8$

2. If $a * b$ means $5a + 2b$, find the value of:
(a) $6 * 3$ (c) $9 * 2$ (e) $11 * 5$ (g) $8 * 6$
(b) $3 * 3$ (d) $12 * 4$ (f) $7 * 1$ (h) $16 * 7$

3. If $p * q$ means $\dfrac{(p + q)}{2}$, find the value of:

(a) $8 * 6$ (c) $8 * 10$ (e) $6 * 14$ (g) $12 * 18$
(b) $2 * 12$ (d) $4 * 4$ (f) $16 * 10$ (h) $26 * 18$

4. If $v * w$ means $4v - 5w$, find the value of:
(a) $7 * 4$ (c) $12 * 6$ (e) $10 * 1$ (g) $12 * 8$
(b) $9 * 2$ (d) $3 * 2$ (f) $5 * 4$ (h) $10 * 8$

16 Directed Numbers

Exercise 1

A Write down the temperature, in degrees Celsius (°C), shown on each of these thermometers:

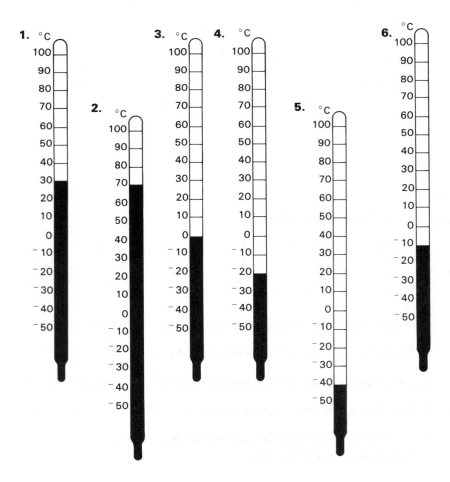

B 1. Is 30 °C warmer than 10 °C?

2. Is ⁻30 °C warmer than ⁻10 °C?

3. Is ⁻10 °C warmer than 20 °C?

4. Is ⁻15 °C colder than 15 °C?

5. Which is warmer, ⁻20 °C or 10 °C?

6. Which is warmer, ⁻8 °C or 16 °C?

7. Which is colder, ⁻25 °C or 45 °C?

8. Which is colder, 0 °C or ⁻13 °C?

9. Which is warmer, 29 °C or ⁻24 °C?

10. Which is colder, 3 °C or ⁻9 °C?

11. Write these temperatures in order, from coldest to hottest:
    18 °C   ⁻12 °C   ⁻23 °C   32 °C   9 °C   ⁻19 °C

12. Write these temperatures in order, from hottest to coldest:
    ⁻9 °C   14 °C   36 °C   ⁻21 °C   ⁻18 °C   6 °C

C Here is a list of temperatures:

⁻2 °C,	7 °C,	⁻7 °C,	0 °C,	⁻4 °C,	3 °C,
⁻9 °C,	⁻23 °C,	14 °C,	⁻13 °C,	12 °C,	20 °C,
⁻18 °C,	8 °C,	⁻10 °C,	17 °C,	⁻15 °C,	⁻32 °C.

1. Which is the fourth highest temperature in the above list?

2. Find the sixth lowest temperature in the list.

3. From the list, find the temperature that is just less than ⁻14 °C.

4. Which temperature is just greater than ⁻5 °C?

5. List the temperatures that are colder than ⁻10 °C.
   Choose from the above list.

Exercise 2

Copy each of these number lines and fill in the missing numbers:

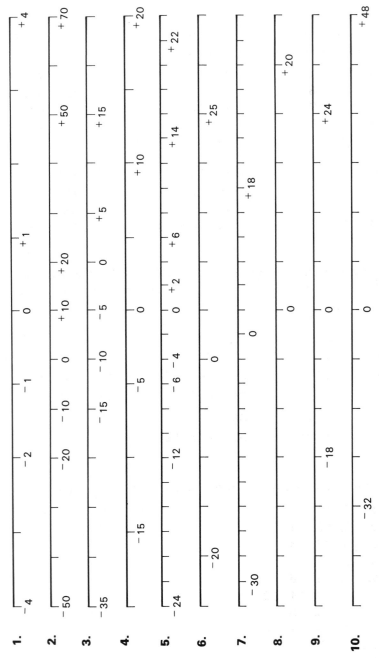

1. −4   −2   −1   0   +1   +4
2. −50   −20   −10   0   +10   +20   +50   +70
3. −35   −15   −10   0   +5   +15   +20
4. −15   −5   0   +5   +10   +15   +20
5. −24   −12   −6   −4   0   +2   +6   +14   +22
6. −20   0   +25
7. −30   0   +18
8. 0   +20
9. −18   0   +24
10. −32   0   +48

Exercise 3

A Copy each of the following statements and say whether it is true or false. (You may use a number line.)

1. $^+4 > {}^+1$	**11.** $^-8 > {}^-3$	**21.** $^-2 < 0$
2. $^+3 < {}^+8$	**12.** $^-2 < {}^-7$	**22.** $^+5 < {}^+7$
3. $^+5 > {}^+7$	**13.** $^-6 > {}^-4$	**23.** $^+6 > {}^+2$
4. $^+6 < {}^-8$	**14.** $^-7 > {}^-8$	**24.** $^+7 > {}^-5$
5. $^+2 > {}^-7$	**15.** $0 > {}^-4$	**25.** $^+4 < {}^-7$
6. $^-9 < {}^-4$	**16.** $^-1 < {}^-6$	**26.** $^+1 < 0$
7. $^-7 > {}^-3$	**17.** $^-5 < {}^-4$	**27.** $^-2 < {}^-5$
8. $^-1 > {}^-2$	**18.** $^-7 > {}^-1$	**28.** $^+6 > 0$
9. $^-4 < {}^+2$	**19.** $0 < {}^+5$	**29.** $^-2 > {}^-9$
10. $^+1 < {}^-6$	**20.** $^+6 > {}^-8$	**30.** $^-1 < {}^-12$

B Copy the following, but in place of each question mark, use the sign < (less than) or > (greater than) to make each statement correct:

1. $^+5 \boxed{?} {}^+2$	**8.** $^+1 \boxed{?} {}^-1$	**15.** $^-5 \boxed{?} {}^-6$
2. $^-4 \boxed{?} {}^+3$	**9.** $^-2 \boxed{?} {}^+4$	**16.** $^-2 \boxed{?} {}^-7$
3. $^-2 \boxed{?} {}^-7$	**10.** $0 \boxed{?} {}^-3$	**17.** $8 \boxed{?} {}^-1$
4. $^+2 \boxed{?} {}^-5$	**11.** $^-5 \boxed{?} {}^-2$	**18.** $^-3 \boxed{?} 7$
5. $^-6 \boxed{?} {}^-4$	**12.** $^+4 \boxed{?} {}^+2$	**19.** $^-2 \boxed{?} {}^-6$
6. $^-1 \boxed{?} 0$	**13.** $^-4 \boxed{?} {}^-2$	**20.** $^-10 \boxed{?} {}^-5$
7. $^-7 \boxed{?} {}^-10$	**14.** $^-4 \boxed{?} {}^+2$	

C Write these numbers in order of size, putting the smallest first:

1. $^+2, \ ^+5, \ ^+1$
2. $^+3, \ ^-6, \ ^-1$
3. $^-3, \ ^-7, \ ^-4$
4. $^-2, \ ^-8, \ ^-1$
5. $^+5, \ ^-3, \ ^-6$
6. $^-2, \ ^-6, \ ^+4, \ ^+2$
7. $^+7, \ ^-6, \ ^-8, \ ^-1$
8. $^-2, \ 0, \ ^+2, \ ^-4$
9. $^-3, \ ^-7, \ ^-4, \ ^-1$
10. $^+5, \ ^-3, \ 0, \ ^-8, \ ^+1$

Exercise 4

1. An aeroplane flying at a height of 2500 m falls to a height of 800 m. What height has it lost?

2. A man had £60 in his bank account. If he then wrote a cheque for £90, how much overdrawn would he be?

3. Mrs Brown is overdrawn by £50. If she spends a further £70, by how much would she now be overdrawn?

4. Mr Green's bank account is overdrawn by £80. How much must he deposit to have a credit of £60?

5. Mrs Black has £75 in her bank account. She spends £60, deposits £20 in the bank, then spends a further £40. By how much is she overdrawn?

6. Mr White has £42 in his bank account. He spends £65, deposits £45 in the bank, then spends a further £59. By how much is he overdrawn?

7. A submarine is at a depth of 1280 m. If it now dives a further 490 m, what is its new depth?

8. A submarine dives from a depth of 1970 m to a depth of 2680 m. By how many more metres has it dived?

9. In the football league, two teams had the same number of points. If team A had scored 41 goals but had 46 goals scored against them, while team B had 37 goals for them and 32 goals against them, which team should be higher in the league? Why?

10. In a competition, Ann gained 46 points but lost 37. Bill gained 45 but lost 29. Charles gained 51 and lost 63. Deborah gained 37 and lost 19. Eileen gained 34 but lost 50. Sort these five people into order on 'point difference'. (Compare points gained with points lost for each person.)

Exercise 5

Use this number line to help you to answer these questions:

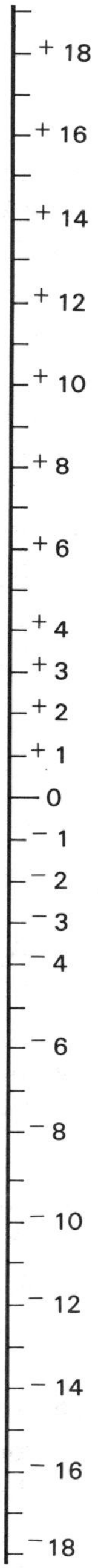

+ 18
+ 16
+ 14
+ 12
+ 10
+ 8
+ 6
+ 4
+ 3
+ 2
+ 1
0
− 1
− 2
− 3
− 4
− 6
− 8
− 10
− 12
− 14
− 16
− 18

1. $6 + 2$
2. $^{+}5 + 8$
3. $^{+}3 + 6$
4. $^{-}3 + 6$
5. $0 + 15$
6. $^{-}4 + 13$
7. $^{-}1 + 7$
8. $8 - 1$
9. $^{+}13 - 5$
10. $8 - 5$
11. $5 - 8$
12. $3 - 11$
13. $2 - 2$
14. $^{+}2 - 15$
15. $3 - 15$
16. $7 - 2$
17. $^{-}7 - 2$
18. $5 + 6$
19. $^{-}5 - 6$
20. $3 + 7$
21. $^{-}3 + 7$
22. $^{-}7 + 3$
23. $7 - 3$
24. $3 - 7$
25. $^{-}3 - 7$
26. $^{-}7 - 3$
27. $5 + 8 - 3$
28. $8 - 2 + 4$
29. $11 - 5 - 3$
30. $^{-}4 + 7 + 2$
31. $6 + 1 - 11$
32. $4 - 5 - 6$
33. $^{-}5 + 2 + 9$
34. $^{-}9 + 1 + 4$
35. $^{-}10 + 3 - 2$
36. $17 - 9 + 9$
37. $^{-}4 + 8 + 4$
38. $^{-}8 + 8 + 13 - 1$
39. $^{-}12 - 7 + 2 + 12$
40. $^{-}13 - 8 + 13 + 11$

Copy and complete:

	Previous temperature	Temperature change	New temperature
1.	8 °C	⁺6 °C	
2.	15 °C	⁻7 °C	
3.	6 °C		23 °C
4.		⁺9 °C	12 °C
5.	27 °C		11 °C
6.	⁻5 °C	⁺16 °C	
7.	⁻7 °C		4 °C
8.	⁻2 °C	⁻4 °C	
9.	⁻9 °C		16 °C
10.	8 °C	⁻9 °C	
11.	2 °C	⁻13 °C	
12.	⁻3 °C		⁻8 °C
13.		⁺13 °C	4 °C
14.		⁻8 °C	5 °C
15.		⁻12 °C	⁻3 °C
16.		⁻4 °C	⁻6 °C
17.	⁻14 °C		⁻5 °C
18.	0 °C		⁻9 °C
19.	11 °C	⁻24 °C	
20.		⁺15 °C	0 °C
21.	⁻5 °C	⁺5 °C	
22.	⁻7 °C		7 °C
23.		⁻9 °C	0 °C
24.	9 °C		⁻9 °C
25.	17 °C		4 °C

Exercise 7

Copy these. By finding a pattern, fill in the missing answers.

1. $^+4 + {}^+3 = {}^+7$
$\quad$ $^+4 + {}^+2 =$ ⬚?
$\quad$ $^+4 + {}^+1 =$ ⬚?
$\quad$ $^+4 + 0 =$ ⬚?
$\quad$ $^+4 + {}^-1 =$ ⬚?
$\quad$ $^+4 + {}^-2 = {}^+2$
$\quad$ $^+4 + {}^-3 =$ ⬚?
$\quad$ $^+4 + {}^-4 =$ ⬚?
$\quad$ $^+4 + {}^-5 =$ ⬚?
$\quad$ $^+4 + {}^-6 =$ ⬚?
$\quad$ $^+4 + {}^-7 =$ ⬚?

2. $^-4 + {}^+7 = {}^+3$
$\quad$ $^-4 + {}^+6 = {}^+2$
$\quad$ $^-4 + {}^+5 =$ ⬚?
$\quad$ $^-4 + {}^+4 = 0$
$\quad$ $^-4 + {}^+3 =$ ⬚?
$\quad$ $^-4 + {}^+2 =$ ⬚?
$\quad$ $^-4 + {}^+1 =$ ⬚?
$\quad$ $^-4 + 0 = {}^-4$
$\quad$ $^-4 + {}^-1 =$ ⬚?
$\quad$ $^-4 + {}^-2 =$ ⬚?
$\quad$ $^-4 + {}^-3 =$ ⬚?

Exercise 8

In a certain school, the pupils were given merit marks for good work or good behaviour and were given de-merit marks for poor work or bad behaviour.

The pupils were given cards with merit marks or de-merit marks on them.

The cards looked like this:

$\boxed{^+3}$ is worth 3 merit marks $\qquad$ $\boxed{^-2}$ is worth 2 de-merit marks

e.g. 1 $\;$ If John got $\boxed{^+5}$ and $\boxed{^-3}$ he would have 2 marks altogether, since $\boxed{^+5}$ and $\boxed{^-3}$ is the same as $\boxed{^+2}$.
$\qquad$ We would write $\boxed{^+5} + \boxed{^-3} = \boxed{^+2}$.

e.g. 2 $\;$ $\boxed{^+2} + \boxed{^-3} = \boxed{^-1}$.

Work out these:

1. $\boxed{^+3} + \boxed{^+2}$

2. $\boxed{^+6} + \boxed{^-2}$

3. $\boxed{^+2} + \boxed{^-2}$

4. $\boxed{^+7} + \boxed{^-3}$

5. $\boxed{^+6} + \boxed{^+7}$

6. $\boxed{^+2} + \boxed{^+5} + \boxed{^+4}$

375

7. $^+6$ + $^+4$ + $^-3$

8. $^+7$ + $^-2$ + $^-3$

9. $^+4$ + $^-3$ + $^+2$

10. $^+6$ + $^+2$ + $^-3$ + $^+4$

11. $^+5$ + $^-3$

12. $^-3$ + $^+5$

13. $^-6$ + $^+9$

14. $^+3$ + $^-7$

15. $^-5$ + $^+2$

16. $^+3$ + $^-5$ + $^+4$

17. $^+6$ + $^+1$ + $^-9$

18. $^-3$ + $^+7$ + $^-2$

19. $^-5$ + $^+3$ + $^+8$

20. $^-4$ + $^+6$ + $^-5$

Exercise 9

4↑ means 'a journey 4 places up'.

3↓ means 'a journey 3 places down'.

5↑ + 2↓ can be read as 'a journey 5 places up *followed by* a journey 2 places down'.

e.g. 1   5↑ + 2↓ = $^+3$

e.g. 2   3↓ + 2↑ = $^-1$

Answer these questions. Use the number line.

1. 4↑ + 3↑

2. 7↑ + 2↓

3. 8↑ + 6↓

4. 10↑ + 2↑

5. 3↑ + 7↓

6. 5↑ + 9↓

7. 3↓ + 8↑

8. 9↓ + 4↑

9. 4↓ + 4↑

10. 8↑ + 8↓

11. 7↑ + 4↓

12. 7↓ + 4↑

13. 7↑ + 4↑

14. 7↓ + 4↓

15. 9↑ + 2↓

16. 2↓ + 9↑

17. 2↑ + 9↓

18. 9↓ + 2↑

19. 9↑ + 2↑

20. 9↓ + 2↓

21. 5↑ + 5↓

22. 5↑ + 5↑

23. 5↓ + 5↓

24. 13↑ + 6↓

25. 6↑ + 4↓

26. 16↑ + 14↓

27. 9↑ + 5↓

28. 10↑ + 6↓

29. 8↑ + 4↓

30. 7↑ + 6↑ + 2↓

31. 4↑ + 5↓ + 2↑

32. 3↓ + 7↑ + 2↑

33. 9↓ + 3↓ + 5↑

34. 14↑ + 9↓ + 5↓

35. 7↓ + 7↑ + 6↑

36. 8↓ + 4↑ + 3↑ + 4↓

+12
+10
+8
+6
+4
+3
+2
+1
0
−1
−2
−3
−4
−6
−8
−10
−12

Exercise 10

M

This nomogram can be used for addition.

You need to use a ruler.

Try to see how it works.

Use the nomogram to help you to answer these questions:

1. 4 + 4
2. 7 + 7
3. 2 + 2
4. 9 + 9
5. 8 + 4
6. 4 + 8
7. 6 + 2
8. 2 + 6
9. 4 + 0
10. 0 + 8
11. 5 + 2
12. 9 + 4
13. 6 + $^-$2
14. 9 + $^-$3
15. 7 + $^-$1
16. 8 + $^-$5
17. 8 + $^-$4
18. $^-$4 + 8
19. $^-$2 + 4
20. 7 + $^-$7
21. $^-$5 + 5
22. 3 + $^-$7
23. 1 + $^-$9
24. $^-$5 + 3
25. $^-$6 + 0
26. $^-$3 + $^-$5
27. $^-$2 + $^-$6
28. $^-$6 + $^-$1
29. $^-$8 + $^-$6
30. $^-$9 + $^-$7

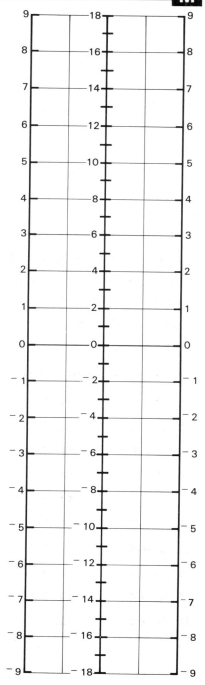

377

Exercise 11 *'Snap'* (A directed Numbers Game)

You need a set of cards such as those shown below:

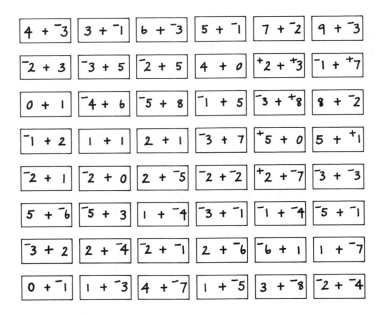

1. The cards are put together and shuffled.

2. They are then shared between the players (2, 3 or 4 players is suggested).

3. The game is then like the ordinary game of 'snap'.
   The players take it in turns to put one card on top of another, face up, forming a pile of cards.
   If a card is played that has the same total as the previous card, then the first person to call 'snap' wins the pile of cards on the table.

4. The game continues until one person has won all the cards.

Exercise 12

A Find the value of:

1. $3 + 5$	**18.** $^-4 + 7$	**35.** $^-3 + ^-4$
2. $^+7 + 6$	**19.** $4 + ^-7$	**36.** $4 + ^-9$
3. $2 + ^+4$	**20.** $^-4 + ^-7$	**37.** $^-9 + 4$
4. $^+5 + ^+7$	**21.** $4 + ^+7$	**38.** $4 + ^+9$
5. $^-6 + 9$	**22.** $9 + ^-2$	**39.** $^-4 + ^-9$
6. $^-8 + 3$	**23.** $^-9 + 2$	**40.** $^-2 + ^-4$
7. $^-7 + ^+2$	**24.** $^-9 + ^-2$	**41.** $2 + ^+4$
8. $^-9 + ^+11$	**25.** $^+9 + ^+2$	**42.** $^-5 + 3 + ^-6$
9. $6 + ^-2$	**26.** $^-1 + ^-1$	**43.** $5 + ^-3 + 6$
10. $9 + ^-4$	**27.** $7 + ^-3$	**44.** $^-12 + 12$
11. $^+8 + ^-3$	**28.** $6 + ^-11$	**45.** $^-13 + ^-9 + ^+8$
12. $^+4 + ^-7$	**29.** $^+1 + ^-5$	**46.** $13 + ^-9 + ^-8$
13. $^-6 + 8$	**30.** $^-3 + ^+8$	**47.** $14 + ^-14 + ^-2$
14. $^-6 + ^-8$	**31.** $^-5 + 12$	**48.** $0 + ^-7$
15. $^-4 + ^-3$	**32.** $^-13 + 4$	**49.** $^-6 + ^-12 + ^+7$
16. $^-2 + ^-5$	**33.** $^-11 + ^+8$	**50.** $^-8 + ^-8$
17. $^-10 + ^-6$	**34.** $^-3 + 4$	

B Find the value of:

1. $4 + 6$	**15.** $(-5) + (-7)$	**28.** $(-16) + 16$
2. $(+3) + 5$	**16.** $7 + (-5)$	**29.** $(-4) + (-11) + (+9)$
3. $7 + (+1)$	**17.** $(-7) + 5$	**30.** $(-12) + 6 + (-1)$
4. $(+2) + (+5)$	**18.** $(-3) + 9$	**31.** $12 + (-6) + 1$
5. $(-3) + 7$	**19.** $3 + (-9)$	**32.** $(-9) + (-9)$
6. $(-9) + 4$	**20.** $(-3) + (-9)$	**33.** $7 + (-7) + (-12)$
7. $(-2) + (+8)$	**21.** $3 + (+9)$	**34.** $16 + (-6)$
8. $(-7) + (+3)$	**22.** $(-6) + 6$	**35.** $(-3) + (+7) + (-4)$
9. $8 + (-5)$	**23.** $(-6) + (-6)$	**36.** $(-12) + (+5) + (-3)$
10. $4 + (-9)$	**24.** $6 + (+6)$	**37.** $(-1) + 0 + (-7) + 6$
11. $(+12) + (-7)$	**25.** $(-3) + 0$	**38.** $12 + (-15) + (-5)$
12. $(+3) + (-10)$	**26.** $(-9) + (-4)$	**39.** $(-7) + (-7)$
13. $(-5) + 8$	**27.** $0 + (-4)$	**40.** $(-5) + (-5)$
14. $(-7) + (-5)$		

Exercise 13

Find the missing numbers that make each statement correct:

1. $5 + \boxed{?} = 9$
2. $^-6 + \boxed{?} = 4$
3. $\boxed{?} + ^-2 = 5$
4. $\boxed{?} + ^-2 = ^-5$
5. $6 + \boxed{?} = 0$
6. $8 + \boxed{?} = 2$
7. $10 + \boxed{?} = ^+6$
8. $\boxed{?} + 3 = 2$
9. $\boxed{?} + ^+7 = 4$
10. $^-4 + \boxed{?} = ^-2$

11. $\boxed{?} + ^-2 = ^+6$
12. $^-8 + \boxed{?} = ^-6$
13. $\boxed{?} + ^-5 = ^-1$
14. $\boxed{?} + ^-4 = ^-8$
15. $5 + \boxed{?} = 2$
16. $2 + \boxed{?} = ^-7$
17. $\boxed{?} + ^-5 = ^-8$
18. $^-11 + \boxed{?} = ^-12$
19. $\boxed{?} + ^+10 = 0$
20. $\boxed{?} + ^-6 = 12$

17 **Functions**

Find the numbers that should be written in the empty circles:

1. (9) —$+7$→ ( )

2. (14) —-5→ ( )

3. (7) —$\times 4$→ ( )

4. ( ) —$\times 8$→ (48)

5. ( ) —-9→ (23)

6. (18) —$\div 2$→ ( )

7. ( ) —$+12$→ (24)

8. (8) —$\times 7$→ ( )

9. ( ) —$\times 9$→ (63)

10. (14) —$+15$→ ( )

11. ( ) —$+23$→ (52)

12. (33) —-14→ ( )

13. ( ) —-17→ (33)

14. (42) —$\div 6$→ ( )

15. ( ) —$\div 8$→ (8)

16. (17) —$\times 2$→ ( )

17. ( ) —-27→ (12)

18. ( ) —$\times 6$→ (42)

19. (37) —$+19$→ ( )

20. ( ) —-19→ (41)

381

Exercise 2

M

Find the numbers that should be written in the empty circles:

1. $(7) \xrightarrow{\times 3} \bigcirc \xrightarrow{\div 3} \bigcirc$

6. $\bigcirc \xrightarrow{+6} \bigcirc \xrightarrow{-6} (5)$

2. $(5) \xrightarrow{+8} \bigcirc \xrightarrow{-8} \bigcirc$

7. $\bigcirc \xrightarrow{-5} (12) \xrightarrow{+5} \bigcirc$

3. $\bigcirc \xrightarrow{-9} (4) \xrightarrow{+9} \bigcirc$

8. $(3) \xrightarrow{+1} \bigcirc \xrightarrow{-1} \bigcirc$

4. $\bigcirc \xrightarrow{\div 2} (8) \xrightarrow{\times 2} \bigcirc$

9. $\bigcirc \xrightarrow{\div 2} (11) \xrightarrow{\times 2} \bigcirc$

5. $\bigcirc \xrightarrow{\times 4} \bigcirc \xrightarrow{\div 4} (3)$

10. $\bigcirc \xrightarrow{\times 5} \bigcirc \xrightarrow{\div 5} (15)$

What do you notice about the numbers in the first and the last circles in each question?

Exercise 3

M

Find the numbers that should be written in the empty circles:

1. $(4) \xrightarrow{\times 2} \bigcirc \xrightarrow{+7} \bigcirc$

2. $(3) \xrightarrow{+5} \bigcirc \xrightarrow{\times 4} \bigcirc$

3. $\bigcirc \xrightarrow{\times 3} (12) \xrightarrow{-5} \bigcirc$

4. $\bigcirc \xrightarrow{-4} (5) \xrightarrow{\times 7} \bigcirc$

5. $\bigcirc \xrightarrow{\times 5} \bigcirc \xrightarrow{-8} (7)$

6. $\bigcirc \xrightarrow{-7} (5) \xrightarrow{\times 2} \bigcirc \xrightarrow{+1} \bigcirc$

7. $\bigcirc \xrightarrow{\div 3} \bigcirc \xrightarrow{+2} (8)$

8. $\bigcirc \xrightarrow{-5} \bigcirc \xrightarrow{\times 2} (12) \xrightarrow{+7} \bigcirc$

9. $\bigcirc \xrightarrow{\div 2} \bigcirc \xrightarrow{-3} \bigcirc \xrightarrow{\times 3} (15)$

10. $\bigcirc \xrightarrow{\times 4} \bigcirc \xrightarrow{-6} \bigcirc \xrightarrow{+8} (18)$

Exercise 4

Write the following as algebraic expressions (i.e. use letters instead of words).

e.g. Multiply the number by 3 then subtract $5 = 3n - 5$.

1. Double the number.

2. Add 7 to the number.

3. Subtract 8 from the number.

4. Halve the number.

5. Divide the number by 8.

6. Multiply the number by 4 then add 9.

7. Find one-third of the number then subtract 8.

8. Multiply the number by 5 then subtract 1.

9. Subtract 7 from 3 times the number.

10. Add 6 to the number then multiply the result by 4.

Exercise 5

Write the following algebraic expressions using words.

e.g. $4n + 7 =$ Multiply the number by 4 then add 7.

1. $n + 6$

2. $x - 5$

3. $6x$

4. $\frac{1}{3}p$

5. $2t + 4$

6. $4m - 2$

7. $\dfrac{u}{4} + 9$

8. $3k + 5$

9. $8 - 4h$

10. $5(c - 3)$

Exercise 6

e.g.

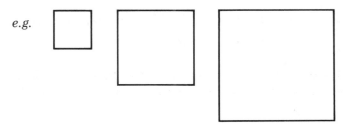

A square of side 1 cm has a perimeter of 4 cm.
A square of side 2 cm has a perimeter of 8 cm.
A square of side 3 cm has a perimeter of 12 cm.
etc.

If l cm = the length of the side of the square and P cm = the perimeter, then

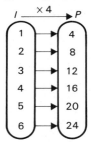

the perimeter = 4 × the length
i.e. $\qquad$ $P = 4 \times l$
or $\qquad$ $P = 4l$
(we can miss out the × sign)

1. If l cm = the length of the side of an equilateral triangle, and if P cm = the perimeter of the triangle, then write down a formula for P in terms of l.

2. Referring to the squares in the figure, if the length of the sides is l cm and n is the number of dots on the perimeter, find a formula for n in terms of l. (Note that when $l = 3$, $n = 12$.)

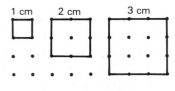

3. Ann and Marie share 16 jelly babies. If Marie has m jelly babies when Ann has a jelly babies,
   (a) make a mapping diagram for a and m. Choose your own values for a.
   (b) write down a formula giving m in terms of a.

Exercise 7

1.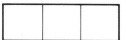

The rectangles above are made up of squares (1 cm squares). If n stands for the number of squares and P cm for the perimeter of each rectangle, then copy and complete the following mapping diagram and table:

No. of squares, n	1	2	3	4	5	6	7	8
Perimeter, P cm	4	6				14		

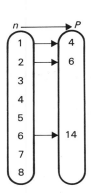

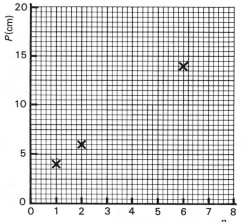

Now plot a graph. Try to write a formula for P in terms of n.

2. If each of the given rectangles measures 3 cm by 2 cm, and if n stands for the number of rectangles in each figure, and P cm stands for the perimeter, then:

(a) Make out a mapping diagram for rectangles up to $n = 8$.

(b) Make out a table showing n and P.

(c) Plot a graph of P against n. Let n be along the horizontal axis (2 cm to 1 unit) and P along the vertical axis (1 cm to 2 units).

(d) Try to find a formula for P in terms of n.

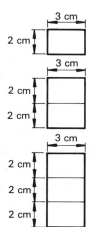

385

Exercise 8

Find the missing numbers:

1. $x \xrightarrow{\;\times 3,\ +4\;} y$

5 ———————→ ?
7 ———————→ ?
12 ———————→ ?
? ———————→ 13
? ———————→ 28

3. $t \xrightarrow{\;-9,\ \times 5\;} f(t)$

12 ———————→ ?
28 ———————→ ?
? ———————→ 30
? ———————→ 55
? ———————→ 0

2. $x \xrightarrow{\;\times 5,\ -7\;} f(x)$

4 ———————→ ?
9 ———————→ ?
? ———————→ 28
? ———————→ 43
? ———————→ 3

4. $x \xrightarrow{\;+7,\ \times 2,\ -4\;} y$

5 ———————→ ?
13 ———————→ ?
? ———————→ 16
? ———————→ 34
? ———————→ 12

Exercise 9

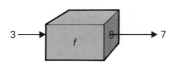

3 → f → 7

Here is a 'function machine'. This machine adds 4 to any number that is input.
For this machine, we say that function f is 'add 4'.

When we *input* 3 the *output* is 7.
When we *input* 8 the *output* is 12. This is shown below, using a front view of the machine:

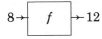

8→ f →12

For each of the following questions, work out what each machine does, then copy the question and fill in the missing numbers.

Note Function f does not always have to be 'add 4'; however, if it is 'add 4' in a certain question, then it will be 'add 4' throughout that question.

1.

$7 \rightarrow \boxed{f} \rightarrow 14 \rightarrow \boxed{g} \rightarrow 8 \rightarrow \boxed{h} \rightarrow 4 \rightarrow \boxed{k} \rightarrow 13$

$4 \rightarrow \boxed{f} \rightarrow 8 \rightarrow \boxed{g} \rightarrow 2 \rightarrow \boxed{h} \rightarrow 1 \rightarrow \boxed{k} \rightarrow 10$

$9 \rightarrow \boxed{f} \rightarrow \boxed{?} \rightarrow \boxed{g} \rightarrow \boxed{?} \rightarrow \boxed{h} \rightarrow \boxed{?} \rightarrow \boxed{k} \rightarrow \boxed{?}$

$5 \rightarrow \boxed{f} \rightarrow \boxed{?} \rightarrow \boxed{g} \rightarrow \boxed{?} \rightarrow \boxed{h} \rightarrow \boxed{?} \rightarrow \boxed{k} \rightarrow \boxed{?}$

2.

$2 \rightarrow \boxed{p} \rightarrow 11 \rightarrow \boxed{q} \rightarrow 22 \rightarrow \boxed{r} \rightarrow 18 \rightarrow \boxed{s} \rightarrow 9$

$6 \rightarrow \boxed{p} \rightarrow 15 \rightarrow \boxed{q} \rightarrow 30 \rightarrow \boxed{r} \rightarrow 26 \rightarrow \boxed{s} \rightarrow 13$

$8 \rightarrow \boxed{p} \rightarrow \boxed{?} \rightarrow \boxed{q} \rightarrow \boxed{?} \rightarrow \boxed{r} \rightarrow \boxed{?} \rightarrow \boxed{s} \rightarrow \boxed{?}$

$4 \rightarrow \boxed{p} \rightarrow \boxed{?} \rightarrow \boxed{q} \rightarrow \boxed{?} \rightarrow \boxed{r} \rightarrow \boxed{?} \rightarrow \boxed{s} \rightarrow \boxed{?}$

3.

$5 \rightarrow \boxed{s} \rightarrow 15 \rightarrow \boxed{t} \rightarrow 10 \rightarrow \boxed{u} \rightarrow 20 \rightarrow \boxed{v} \rightarrow 21$

$9 \rightarrow \boxed{s} \rightarrow 27 \rightarrow \boxed{t} \rightarrow 22 \rightarrow \boxed{u} \rightarrow 44 \rightarrow \boxed{v} \rightarrow 45$

$2 \rightarrow \boxed{s} \rightarrow \boxed{?} \rightarrow \boxed{t} \rightarrow \boxed{?} \rightarrow \boxed{u} \rightarrow \boxed{?} \rightarrow \boxed{v} \rightarrow \boxed{?}$

$7 \rightarrow \boxed{s} \rightarrow \boxed{?} \rightarrow \boxed{t} \rightarrow \boxed{?} \rightarrow \boxed{u} \rightarrow \boxed{?} \rightarrow \boxed{v} \rightarrow \boxed{?}$

4.

$3 \rightarrow \boxed{f} \rightarrow 12 \rightarrow \boxed{j} \rightarrow 3 \rightarrow \boxed{l} \rightarrow 6 \rightarrow \boxed{m} \rightarrow 3$

$8 \rightarrow \boxed{f} \rightarrow 32 \rightarrow \boxed{j} \rightarrow 23 \rightarrow \boxed{l} \rightarrow 26 \rightarrow \boxed{m} \rightarrow 13$

$5 \rightarrow \boxed{f} \rightarrow \boxed{?} \rightarrow \boxed{j} \rightarrow \boxed{?} \rightarrow \boxed{l} \rightarrow \boxed{?} \rightarrow \boxed{m} \rightarrow \boxed{?}$

$9 \rightarrow \boxed{f} \rightarrow \boxed{?} \rightarrow \boxed{j} \rightarrow \boxed{?} \rightarrow \boxed{l} \rightarrow \boxed{?} \rightarrow \boxed{m} \rightarrow \boxed{?}$

5.

$9 \rightarrow \boxed{d} \rightarrow 54 \rightarrow \boxed{e} \rightarrow 42 \rightarrow \boxed{f} \rightarrow 14 \rightarrow \boxed{g} \rightarrow 23$

$4 \rightarrow \boxed{d} \rightarrow 24 \rightarrow \boxed{e} \rightarrow 12 \rightarrow \boxed{f} \rightarrow 4 \rightarrow \boxed{g} \rightarrow 13$

$7 \rightarrow \boxed{d} \rightarrow \boxed{?} \rightarrow \boxed{e} \rightarrow \boxed{?} \rightarrow \boxed{f} \rightarrow \boxed{?} \rightarrow \boxed{g} \rightarrow \boxed{?}$

$3 \rightarrow \boxed{d} \rightarrow \boxed{?} \rightarrow \boxed{e} \rightarrow \boxed{?} \rightarrow \boxed{f} \rightarrow \boxed{?} \rightarrow \boxed{g} \rightarrow \boxed{?}$

6.

$12 \rightarrow \boxed{f} \rightarrow 6 \rightarrow \boxed{g} \rightarrow 11 \rightarrow \boxed{h} \rightarrow 33 \rightarrow \boxed{i} \rightarrow 22$

$18 \rightarrow \boxed{f} \rightarrow 9 \rightarrow \boxed{g} \rightarrow 14 \rightarrow \boxed{h} \rightarrow 42 \rightarrow \boxed{i} \rightarrow 31$

$4 \rightarrow \boxed{f} \rightarrow \boxed{?} \rightarrow \boxed{g} \rightarrow \boxed{?} \rightarrow \boxed{h} \rightarrow \boxed{?} \rightarrow \boxed{i} \rightarrow \boxed{?}$

$16 \rightarrow \boxed{f} \rightarrow \boxed{?} \rightarrow \boxed{g} \rightarrow \boxed{?} \rightarrow \boxed{h} \rightarrow \boxed{?} \rightarrow \boxed{i} \rightarrow \boxed{?}$

7. 9 → [g] → 27 → [p] → 32 → [k] → 16 → [s] → 12

3 → [g] → 9 → [p] → 14 → [k] → 7 → [s] → 3

11 → [g] → [?] → [p] → [?] → [k] → [?] → [s] → [?]

[?] → [g] → [?] → [p] → [?] → [k] → [?] → [s] → 9

8. 9 → [h] → 13 → [j] → 26 → [t] → 21 → [d] → 7

3 → [h] → 7 → [j] → 14 → [t] → 9 → [d] → 3

12 → [h] → [?] → [j] → [?] → [t] → [?] → [d] → [?]

[?] → [h] → [?] → [j] → [?] → [t] → [?] → [d] → 5

Exercise 10

A Think of a number.
Double it.
Now add 3.

   1. Copy and complete this
   mapping diagram.

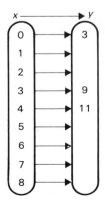

2. Make out a table from the mapping diagram:

3. Complete the table.

x	y
0	3
1	
2	
3	9
4	11
5	
6	
7	
8	

4. Plot a graph of y against x as shown. (Use a scale of 2 cm to 1 unit on the x-axis and 1 cm to 1 unit on the y-axis.) Join the points.

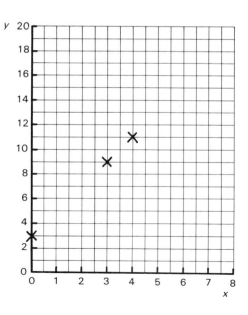

B Think of a number.
Multiply it by 3.
Subtract 2.

1. Make out and complete a mapping diagram. Let the set of x-values used be $\{1, 2, 3, 4, 5, 6, 7\}$.

2. Make out a table from the mapping diagram.

3. Plot a graph of y against x.

Exercise 11

1. Given that $f(x) = 7x$, find:
   (a) $f(3)$ (c) $f(0)$ (e) x, when $f(x) = 14$
   (b) $f(6)$ (d) $f(8)$ (f) x, when $f(x) = 63$

2. Given that $g(t) = t - 8$, find:
   (a) $g(12)$ (c) $g(17)$ (e) t, when $g(t) = 6$
   (b) $g(20)$ (d) $g(9)$ (f) t, when $g(t) = 0$

3. If $u(a) = 2a + 5$, find:
   (a) $u(7)$ (c) $u(4)$ (e) a, when $u(a) = 9$
   (b) $u(0)$ (d) $u(9)$ (f) a, when $u(a) = 7$

4. If $p(m) = 3m - 18$, find:
   (a) $p(10)$ (c) $p(11)$ (e) m, when $p(m) = 9$
   (b) $p(8)$ (d) $p(7)$ (f) m, when $p(m) = 0$

5. Given that $k(x) = 60 - 4x$, find:
   (a) $k(10)$ (c) $k(1)$ (e) x, when $k(x) = 0$
   (b) $k(3)$ (d) $k(7)$ (f) x, when $k(x) = 28$

Exercise 12   **M**

Find the missing numbers:

1. $x \xrightarrow{\times 3} y$ 2. $x \xrightarrow{+7} y$
   (a)   3 $\longrightarrow$ $\boxed{?}$ (a)   2 $\longrightarrow$ $\boxed{?}$
   (b)   7 $\longrightarrow$ $\boxed{?}$ (b)   9 $\longrightarrow$ $\boxed{?}$
   (c) $\boxed{?}$ $\longrightarrow$ 12   (c) $\boxed{?}$ $\longrightarrow$ 13
   (d) $\boxed{?}$ $\longrightarrow$ 27   (d) $\boxed{?}$ $\longrightarrow$ 28

3. $x \xrightarrow{\;-9\;} f(x)$

(a) $15 \longrightarrow \boxed{?}$

(b) $38 \longrightarrow \boxed{?}$

(c) $\boxed{?} \longrightarrow 29$

(d) $\boxed{?} \longrightarrow 9$

7. $x \xrightarrow{\;\times 7\;} y \xrightarrow{\;-8\;} z$

(a) $2 \longrightarrow \boxed{?} \longrightarrow \boxed{?}$

(b) $\boxed{?} \longrightarrow 42 \longrightarrow \boxed{?}$

(c) $\boxed{?} \longrightarrow \boxed{?} \longrightarrow 13$

(d) $8 \longrightarrow \boxed{?} \longrightarrow \boxed{?}$

(e) $\boxed{?} \longrightarrow \boxed{?} \longrightarrow 55$

4. $x \xrightarrow{\;\div 4\;} g(x)$

(a) $36 \longrightarrow \boxed{?}$

(b) $\boxed{?} \longrightarrow 9$

(c) $28 \longrightarrow \boxed{?}$

(d) $\boxed{?} \longrightarrow 12$

8. $x \xrightarrow{\;\times 5\;} y \xrightarrow{\;\times 5\;} z$

(a) $4 \longrightarrow \boxed{?} \longrightarrow \boxed{?}$

(b) $7 \longrightarrow \boxed{?} \longrightarrow \boxed{?}$

(c) $\boxed{?} \longrightarrow 15 \longrightarrow \boxed{?}$

(d) $\boxed{?} \longrightarrow \boxed{?} \longrightarrow 200$

(e) $\boxed{?} \longrightarrow \boxed{?} \longrightarrow 275$

5. $t \xrightarrow{\;\times 7\;} f(t)$

(a) $3 \longrightarrow \boxed{?}$

(b) $8 \longrightarrow \boxed{?}$

(c) $\boxed{?} \longrightarrow 49$

(d) $\boxed{?} \longrightarrow 63$

9. $t \xrightarrow{\;+7\;} u \xrightarrow{\;\times 3\;} v$

(a) $1 \longrightarrow \boxed{?} \longrightarrow \boxed{?}$

(b) $9 \longrightarrow \boxed{?} \longrightarrow \boxed{?}$

(c) $\boxed{?} \longrightarrow \boxed{?} \longrightarrow 39$

(d) $\boxed{?} \longrightarrow \boxed{?} \longrightarrow 57$

(e) $\boxed{?} \longrightarrow 11 \longrightarrow \boxed{?}$

6. $x \xrightarrow{\;\times 2\;} y \xrightarrow{\;+5\;} z$

(a) $3 \longrightarrow \boxed{?} \longrightarrow \boxed{?}$

(b) $8 \longrightarrow \boxed{?} \longrightarrow \boxed{?}$

(c) $\boxed{?} \longrightarrow 10 \longrightarrow \boxed{?}$

(d) $\boxed{?} \longrightarrow 14 \longrightarrow \boxed{?}$

(e) $\boxed{?} \longrightarrow \boxed{?} \longrightarrow 17$

10. $p \xrightarrow{\;\div 4\;} q \xrightarrow{\;+11\;} r$

(a) $8 \longrightarrow \boxed{?} \longrightarrow \boxed{?}$

(b) $\boxed{?} \longrightarrow 7 \longrightarrow \boxed{?}$

(c) $\boxed{?} \longrightarrow \boxed{?} \longrightarrow 20$

(d) $52 \longrightarrow \boxed{?} \longrightarrow \boxed{?}$

(e) $\boxed{?} \longrightarrow \boxed{?} \longrightarrow 23$

18 Symmetry

We can see symmetry in many things.

Symmetry occurs in nature (in leaves, berries, wheat, fruit, butterflies, birds, snowflakes, crystals, the human face, etc.) although it may not be perfect. It occurs in architecture (in buildings throughout the world – both ancient and modern), in painting, sculpture, and design (carvings, furniture, wallpaper and fabric designs), in music, and even in the letters of our alphabet.

After you have tried some of the following work, look back at the above list and make a scrapbook using some of the ideas. Collect photographs, newspaper articles, drawings, etc., that show some sort of symmetry.

Exercise 1

The pattern (or picture) below was made as follows:

1. Fold a piece of paper once.

2. Open it out.

3. Make a few small ink blots on the paper. (Paint could be used.)

4. Fold the paper along the first fold and gently rub the back. (The ink will spread, so this step must be carried out very carefully indeed.)

5. Open the paper again and let the ink dry.

Now make your own pattern. Be very careful at step 4.

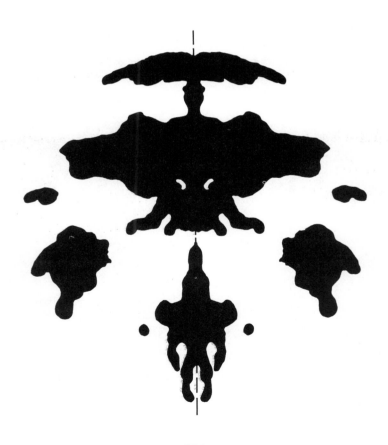

Exercise 2

1. Get a piece of paper. Fold it once. Cut out any shape, as shown, using scissors. Put the other piece down out of the way. Unfold the shape you have cut out.

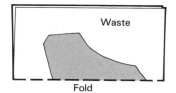

What do you notice about the shape of the piece of paper that you have unfolded?

How many axes of symmetry has it got?

2. Fold another piece of paper as before. This time, cut out a shape which, when unfolded, will give a man, or a woman.

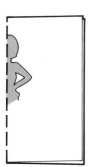

3. Fold another piece of paper.

Now fold it again in the other direction. Keep the folded edges together when you fold the paper this second time.

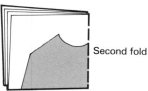

Cut out any shape. Unfold the piece of paper with the shape you have cut out.

What do you notice about the shape you have cut out?

How many axes of symmetry has it got?

Exercise 3

1. Make *one fold* in a piece of paper. With one straight cut, make a shape which, when unfolded, will be an *isosceles triangle*.

2. Make *one fold* in another piece of paper. With one straight cut, make a shape which, when unfolded, will be a *right-angled isosceles triangle*. (You are allowed to use a ruler for measuring to help you with this triangle.)

3. Make *one fold* in another piece of paper. Using two straight cuts, make a shape which, when unfolded, will give you a *kite*.

4. The outline pattern in fig. 1 was obtained by folding a piece of paper in half, then folding it a second time (fig. 2). Pieces were then cut from the folded piece of paper to give the final shape in fig. 1.

Fig. 1

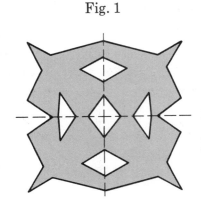

Make your own symmetrical pattern in this way. (Note that the pattern has two axes of symmetry.)

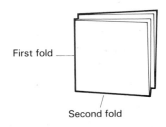

First fold

Second fold

Fig. 2

Exercise 4

For each of these problems, fold a piece of paper twice.

By cutting then unfolding, try to make:

1. A rectangle
2. A square (use 2 straight cuts)
3. A square (use 1 straight cut)

4. A parallelogram
5. A rhombus

Exercise 5

For these, make *three folds* as shown:

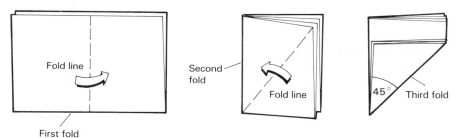

1. Make some single straight cuts.
There are five different ways you can do this:

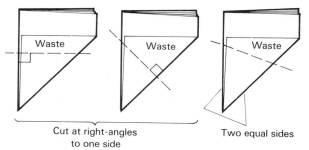

Cut at right-angles
to one side

Two equal sides

Try these cuts after three folds.
How many axes of symmetry
does each pattern have?

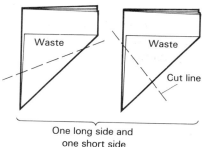

One long side and
one short side

2. Make three folds.
Now try two straight cuts as shown. (The cuts may be at any angle.) Note the number of axes of symmetry each time.

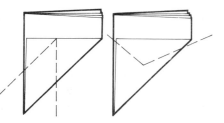

Exercise 6

Draw a straight line 67 mm in length.

Bisect the line using a pair of compasses.

Note that the perpendicular bisector is an axis of symmetry.

Exercise 7 M

A A printer wanted to print some tickets. This is how he saw the printing just before he started to make the tickets:

Some letters have not been turned around. Why not?
Write what is on the tickets.

B List the letters of the alphabet and mark on them any lines of symmetry.

e.g.   **A**   **-B-**   **-H-**

1. List the set of letters that have a horizontal axis of symmetry.

2. List the set of letters that have a vertical axis of symmetry.

3. List the set of letters that have both a horizontal and a vertical axis of symmetry.

4. List the set of letters that have more than two axes of symmetry.

c Write these words as a printer might see them:

1. PRINT
2. HURT
3. VAN
4. WHO
5. MAT

6. YOU
7. MEAT
8. CLOSED
9. HANNAH
10. BASKET

11. FLAG
12. ZERO
13. JUMP
14. QUICKLY
15. FINISH

Exercise 8 M

Copy the following on a sheet of paper. Complete each letter so that the broken lines are axes of symmetry.

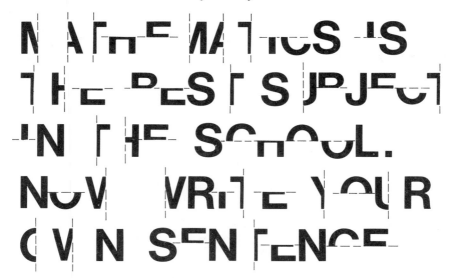

Exercise 9

Some letters of the alphabet can be made by folding a piece of paper, cutting out, then unfolding again.

Which letters of the alphabet can be made in this way?

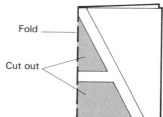

Fold

Cut out

Exercise 10

Copy these.
Where possible, draw the line of symmetry for each shape.
Some figures have one axis, some have more than one, some have none.

1.

2.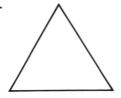

3.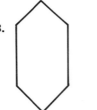

4.

5.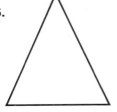

6.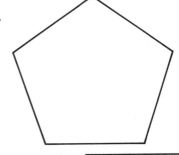

7.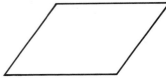

8.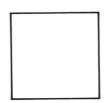

9.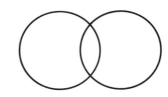

10.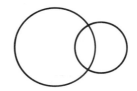

In each of the following sketches, the line of symmetry and half of the pattern have been drawn. Copy and complete each pattern.

1.

2.

3.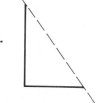

4.

5.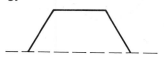

6.

7.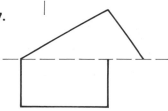

8.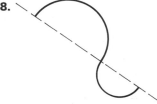

9.

10.

11.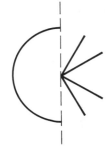

Exercise 12

Try to make a symmetrical mask.

Exercise 13 M

Copy these shapes on to squared paper.
Complete each one so that the broken line is a line of symmetry.

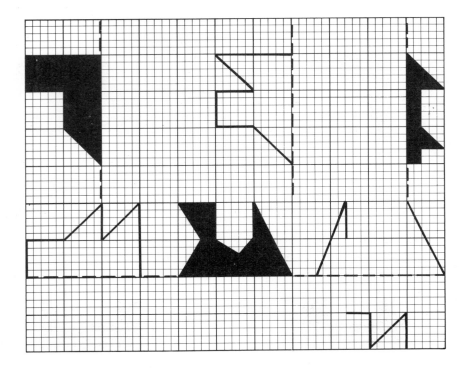

Exercise 14

Copy these shapes on to squared paper.
Complete each one so that the broken lines are axes of symmetry.

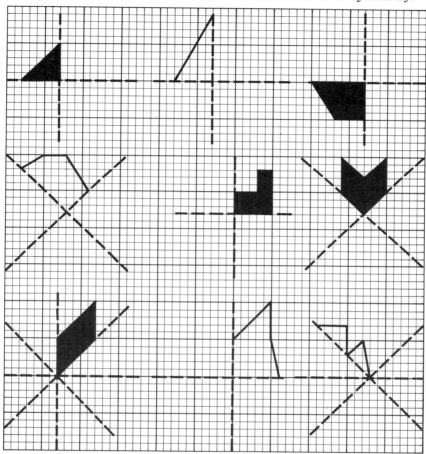

Exercise 15

Use a mirror on this shape to
make all the given shapes:

e.g. Question 1.

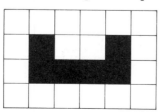

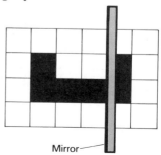

Mirror

403

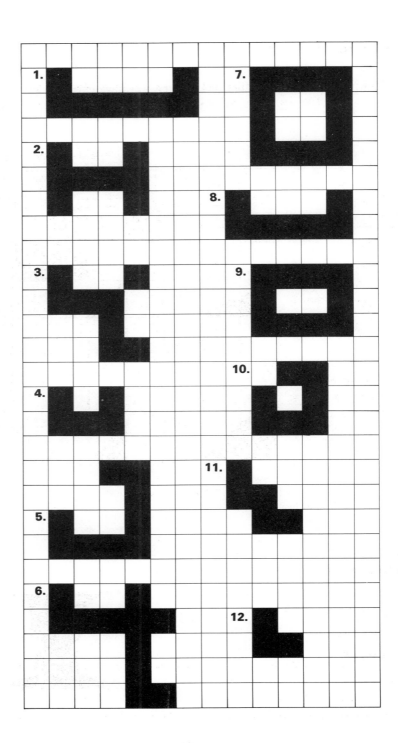

Exercise 16

The pattern in this square has two axes of symmetry, as shown.

Only part of the 'colouring' has been done.

Copy the pattern.

Complete the colouring on your patterns.

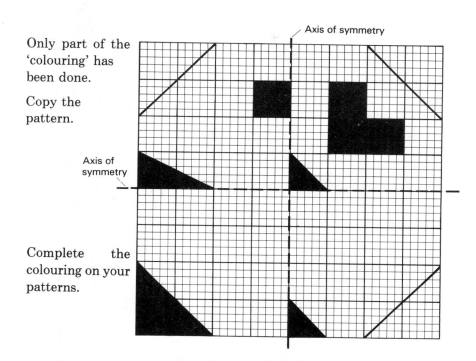

Axis of symmetry

Axis of symmetry

Exercise 17

What can you see?

Two faces?

A vase?

Try to draw your own symmetrical optical illusion.

Copy the semi-detached house and its ground-floor plan.
Draw in the right-hand house.

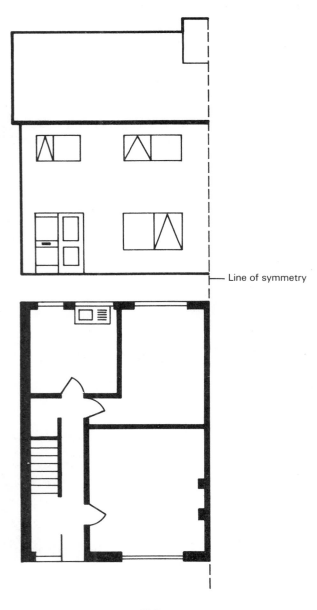

— Line of symmetry

Exercise 19

Quadrilaterals = {rectangle, square, parallelogram, rhombus, kite, isosceles trapezium}

Choose your answers to these questions from the given set of quadrilaterals.

Which quadrilaterals, if any, have:

1. no axis or axes of bilateral symmetry?
2. exactly one axis of bilateral symmetry?
3. exactly two axes of bilateral symmetry?
4. exactly three axes of bilateral symmetry?
5. exactly four axes of bilateral symmetry?

Exercise 20

Music can sometimes be written symmetrically.

This tune is symmetrical (ignore the bar lines).

Axis of symmetry ⎯⎯|

Write your own symmetrical tune.

19 Using a Calculator

Exercise 1

Which of these are true? (Use a calculator.)

1. $87 + 69 = 69 + 87$
2. $87 - 69 = 69 - 87$
3. $87 \times 69 = 69 \times 87$
4. $87 \div 69 = 69 \div 87$
5. $549 + 1 = 549$
6. $549 - 1 = 549$
7. $549 \times 1 = 549$
8. $549 \div 1 = 549$
9. $1 \div 549 = 549$
10. $275 + 0 = 275$
11. $275 - 0 = 275$
12. $0 - 275 = 275$
13. $0 \times 275 = 275$
14. $0 \div 275 = 275$
15. $0 + 275 = 275$
16. $427 + 591 - 591 = 427$
17. $684 - 156 + 156 = 684$
18. $708 \times 358 \div 358 = 708$
19. $5966 \div 157 \times 157 = 5966$
20. $462 \times 71 - 71 = 462$
21. $507 + 39 \div 39 = 507$
22. $507 \div 39 + 39 = 507$
23. $310 \times 85 \div 85 = 310$
24. $624 + 18 \times 18 = 624$
25. $9165 - 1099 + 1099 = 9165$
26. $19 \times 8 \times 14 = 19 \times 14 \times 8$
27. $236 - 108 - 39 = 236 - 39 - 108$
28. $145 - 33 - 69 = 69 - 33 - 145$
29. $358 - 209 + 157 = 157 - 209 + 358$
30. $15\,295 \div 35 \div 23 = 15\,295 \div 23 \div 35$

Exercise 2

WITHOUT using a calculator, write which of these are true:

1. $763 + 849 = 849 + 763$
2. $582 - 198 = 198 - 582$
3. $4613 + 0 = 4613$
4. $632 - 491 + 491 = 632$
5. $209 - 1 = 209 \div 1$
6. $298 \times 721 \div 721 = 298$
7. $4613 \div 1 = 1 \div 4613$
8. $0 \times 32 \times 41 = 41 \times 32 \times 0$
9. $683 \div 357 = 357 \div 683$
10. $4872 \div 56 + 56 = 4872$
11. $63 \div 29 \times 0 = 0 \times 63 \div 29$
12. $4365 \div 97 \times 97 = 4365$
13. $79 - 34 + 61 = 34 + 61 - 79$
14. $386 \times 201 = 201 \times 386$
15. $74 - 27 + 35 = 74 + 35 - 27$
16. $9226 \times 1 = 9226$
17. $7 \times 4 \times 12 = 7 \times 12 \times 4$
18. $0 \times 3197 = 3197$
19. $4066 + 987 - 987 = 4066$
20. $89 - 12 - 48 = 89 - (12 + 48)$

Exercise 3

A *Find a factor* (A game for 2 players and 2 calculators). The object of the game is to keep a whole number in the display.

1. Both players key in the first number given below (i.e. 35).

2. Both should work out *in their heads* a factor of that number. Factors used should be less than or equal to 10. The factor 1 should not be used.

3. Both should then use their calculators to divide the numbers on the display by the factors they thought of.

4. When both players have pressed $\boxed{=}$ on their calculators, they should show the numbers on the displays to each other.

5. If the display is a whole number, a point is scored. If it is a decimal no points are scored.

6. The steps above should be repeated for each given number.

The person with the most points wins.

Note   The teacher can time the game by allowing a certain number of seconds to find a factor of each number.

(a) 35	(e) 39	(i) 84	(m) 378	(q) 748
(b) 60	(f) 130	(j) 111	(n) 822	(r) 595
(c) 24	(g) 63	(k) 119	(o) 582	(s) 243
(d) 26	(h) 156	(l) 258	(p) 672	(t) 728

B Play the game above again, but this time, the player who has the smaller whole number on the display after dividing by the factor gets a point. The other player gets no points. If the same number is on each display, both players get a point.

Note that the factors used should again be less than or equal to 10. Again, the factor 1 is not allowed.

C (For 2 players and 1 calculator.)

1. The first player thinks of a number.

2. The second player keys that number into the calculator.

3. The second player works out *in his or her head* a factor of that number. Factors used should be less than or equal to 10. The factor 1 should not be used.

4. The second player then uses the calculator to divide the displayed number by the factor thought of.

5. On pressing $\boxed{=}$, if the display is a whole number, the second player gets a point. If the display is a decimal, the first player suggests a factor. The original displayed number is now divided by this new factor. If the result is a whole number, the first player gets a point, but if the display is a decimal, neither gets a point.

6. The game is repeated with the players changing places.

7. Play several games.

The winner is the player who gets most points.

Exercise 4

In each question, two numbers are given.

Key in the first number on a calculator.

Try to obtain the second number on the display by depressing *no more than 3 keys*.

e.g. 72, 12

72 $\boxed{\div}$ $\boxed{6}$ $\boxed{=}$ 12

1. 18, 3	**6.** 11, 5	**11.** 196, 204	**16.** 72, 8
2. 6, 15	**7.** 9, 63	**12.** 8, 64	**17.** 215, 43
3. 81, 75	**8.** 21, 27	**13.** 52, 13	**18.** 17, 102
4. 48, 8	**9.** 54, 6	**14.** 7, 56	**19.** 23, 161
5. 15, 5	**10.** 44, 36	**15.** 18, 54	**20.** 192, 24

20 Simple Equations

Write whether these sentences are true or false:

1. $16 + 12 = 28$
2. $14 + 13 = 29$
3. $17 + 14 > 30$
4. $12 + 15 < 30$
5. $40 \div 5 \leqslant 8$

6. $12 + 24 < 35$
7. $41 + 12 \geqslant 60$
8. $9 \times 8 \geqslant 72$
9. $4 \times 7 = 28$
10. $3 \times 9 = 36$

11. $84 \div 6 = 14$
12. $14 \times 7 = 96$
13. $6 \times 13 < 78$
14. $5 \times 17 > 80$
15. $35 \times 41 = 1520$

Exercise 2

Find the missing numbers to make these sentences true:

1. $\boxed{?} + 6 = 11$
2. $\boxed{?} - 4 = 9$
3. $3 + \boxed{?} = 8$
4. $10 - \boxed{?} = 7$
5. $\boxed{?} - 7 = 5$

6. $\boxed{?} - 9 = 6$
7. $\boxed{?} + 8 = 21$
8. $11 + \boxed{?} = 20$
9. $\boxed{?} - 12 = 11$
10. $20 - \boxed{?} = 7$

11. $\boxed{?} + 25 = 34$
12. $34 + \boxed{?} = 52$
13. $\boxed{?} - 18 = 31$
14. $\boxed{?} + 29 = 50$
15. $60 - \boxed{?} = 25$

Exercise 3

Find the missing numbers to make these sentences true:

1. $3 \times \boxed{?} = 24$
2. $\boxed{?} \times 5 = 20$
3. $\boxed{?} \times 4 = 16$
4. $\boxed{?} \div 2 = 6$
5. $28 \div \boxed{?} = 4$
6. $\dfrac{\boxed{?}}{3} = 7$

7. $\dfrac{30}{\boxed{?}} = 5$
8. $\boxed{?} \times 6 = 42$
9. $7 \times \boxed{?} = 56$
10. $\boxed{?} \div 5 = 9$
11. $\dfrac{36}{\boxed{?}} = 6$

12. $\boxed{?} \times 2 = 30$
13. $\dfrac{36}{\boxed{?}} = 4$
14. $14 \times \boxed{?} = 42$
15. $\boxed{?} \div 4 = 16$
16. $\boxed{?} \times 9 = 117$

411

Exercise 4

Solve these equations:

1. $a + 6 = 11$
2. $x + 11 = 20$
3. $8 + t = 17$
4. $p + 7 = 12$
5. $f - 9 = 11$
6. $m - 6 = 5$
7. $13 - k = 8$
8. $g + 8 = 19$
9. $u - 13 = 20$
10. $25 - w = 17$
11. $4e = 12$

12. $5n = 35$
13. $v \div 2 = 8$
14. $l \div 3 = 27$
15. $6d = 48$
16. $b \times 3 = 21$
17. $\dfrac{c}{6} = 9$
18. $9x = 72$
19. $7h = 42$
20. $8y = 32$
21. $q \div 9 = 5$

22. $z + 12 = 30$
23. $9d = 54$
24. $7g = 63$
25. $a \times 6 = 66$
26. $\dfrac{w}{7} = 5$
27. $45 - f = 29$
28. $c - 19 = 23$
29. $e + 24 = 30$
30. $48 \div h = 8$

Exercise 5

Answer 'yes' or 'no':

1. Does $t + 8 = 13$ when $t = 7$?
2. Does $p - 7 = 12$ when $p = 19$?
3. Does $4x = 28$ when $x = 7$?
4. Does $9 + a = 17$ when $a = 6$?
5. Does $14 - y = 8$ when $y = 6$?
6. Does $12 \div h = 2$ when $h = 6$?
7. Does $f \div 3 = 36$ when $f = 12$?
8. Does $m + 11 = 15$ when $m = 26$?
9. Does $u + 9 = 14$ when $u = 6$?
10. Does $5c = 35$ when $c = 7$?
11. Does $d + 15 = 31$ when $d = 46$?
12. Does $g - 12 = 18$ when $g = 30$?
13. Does $42 \div n = 11$ when $n = 4$?
14. Does $19 + v = 38$ when $v = 19$?
15. Does $7e = 77$ when $e = 11$?
16. Does $40 - k = 13$ when $k = 27$?
17. Does $l \div 3 = 39$ when $l = 116$?
18. Does $z + 23 = 52$ when $z = 29$?
19. Does $6p = 78$ when $p = 13$?
20. Does $100 - w = 57$ when $w = 33$?

Exercise 6

Form an equation, then solve it:

1. I added 8 to a number, x, and my answer was 15. Find x.

2. I subtracted 6 from a number, n. My answer was 7. Find n.

3. Julie had y marbles. She was given 9 more marbles. She now had 13 marbles. How many marbles did she start with? (i.e. find y.)

4. Steve had p pencils. If he lost 5 and had 12 left, how many did he start with?

5. When a number, k, is multiplied by 3, the answer is 18. Find k.

6. Alan is 14 years old and Paula is t years old. If their ages total 26 years, how old is Paula?

7. Andrew is 13 years old. If the sum of Andrew's and Pat's ages is 28 years, how old is Pat?

8. There are 31 pupils in a class. If there are 18 boys, how many girls are there?

Exercise 7

Solve these equations:

1. $3x + x = 28$

2. $c + c + c = 21$

3. $2m + 2m = 36$

4. $2y + 3y = 45$

5. $5e - 2e = 33$

6. $7v + 3v = 70$

7. $9q - 7q = 40$

8. $14t - 11t = 75$

9. $2d + 5d = 77$

10. $15w - 7w = 40$

11. $h + 6h + 2h = 81$

12. $9z - 2z + 3z = 80$

13. $12f + 7f - 13f = 54$

14. $8n - 3n + 7n = 108$

15. $11u + 8u - u - 3u = 75$

Exercise 8

Solve for x:

1. (a) $2x = 8$
(b) $2x + 3 = 11$

2. (a) $2x = 12$
(b) $2x - 5 = 7$

3. (a) $3x = 15$
(b) $3x + 4 = 19$

4. (a) $4x = 20$
(b) $4x + 5 = 25$

5. (a) $5x = 30$
(b) $5x - 4 = 26$

6. (a) $10x = 90$
(b) $10x - 12 = 78$

7. (a) $4x = 36$
(b) $4x - 7 = 29$

8. (a) $3x = 42$
(b) $3x - 6 = 36$

9. (a) $2x = 52$
(b) $4 + 2x = 56$

10. (a) $6x = 72$
(b) $6x - 9 = 63$

11. $2x + 9 = 19$

12. $4x - 3 = 29$

13. $10 + 2x = 28$

14. $3x - 8 = 10$

15. $5x + 10 = 50$

16. $5x - 10 = 50$

17. $9x + 8 = 71$

18. $2x - 11 = 15$

19. $3x - 14 = 13$

20. $2x + 25 = 63$

Exercise 9

Solve these equations:

1. $2x + 5 - x = 9$

2. $3t + 7 - t = 17$

3. $7m - 8 - 3m = 20$

4. $8w + 9 - 5w = 18$

5. $2z + 5 + 3z = 60$

6. $9k + 10 - 3k = 64$

7. $6y - 9 + 2y = 47$

8. $12 + 9w - 2w = 61$

9. $13f - 3f + 25 = 85$

10. $4l - 12 + 5l = 33$

11. $2a - 9 + 4a + 11 = 32$

12. $5g + 7 + 3g - 12 = 67$

13. $2c + 5c + 9 + c = 57$

14. $7n - 3n + 8 - 2n - 11 = 65$

15. $4x + 15 + 29 = 180$

16. $2v + 48 + v = 180$

17. $3s + 56 - s + 12 = 180$

18. $13d + 9 - 4d - 5 = 40$

19. $7e - 12 - e - 21 - 2e = 35$

20. $3p - 86 + 9p - 5p + 38 = 71$

Exercise 10

Form an equation from each of these diagrams.
Solve each equation for x.

e.g. 1

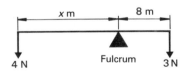

$4x = 24$

$\underline{\underline{x = 6}}$

Both sides must balance each other. The forces (given in newtons) and their distances (in metres) from the fulcrum (the point of balance) cause both sides to have the same turning effect (called its 'moment').

The moment of the left-hand side is $4 \times x$.

The moment of the right-hand side is 3×8.

Hence $4 \times x = 3 \times 8$

e.g. 2

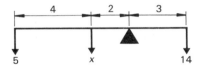

$2x + 5 \times 6 = 3 \times 14$

$2x + 30 \quad\ = 42$

$2x = 12$

$\underline{\underline{x =\ \ 6}}$

414

1.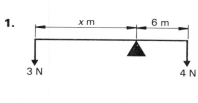

8.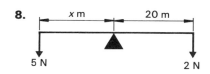

2.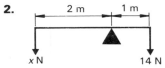

9.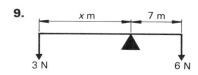

3.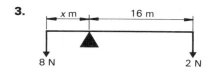

10.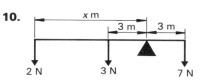

4.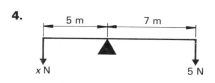

11.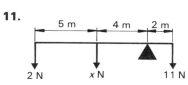

5.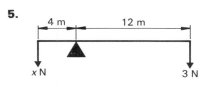

12.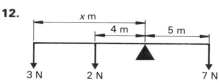

6.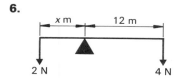

13.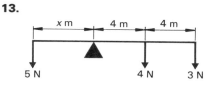

7.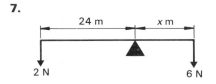

14.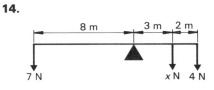

15.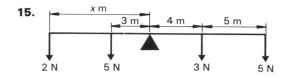

415

Exercise 11

Find *x* WITHOUT measuring:

1.

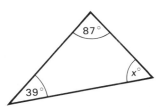

2.

3.

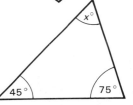

4.

5.

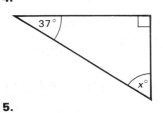

6.

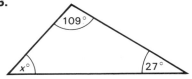

7.

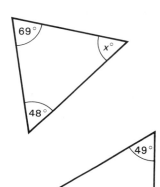

8.

9.

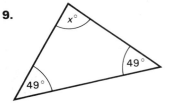

10.

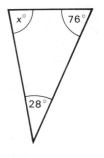

11.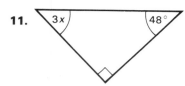

13.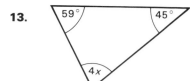

12.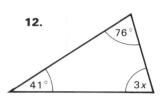

14.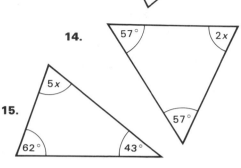

15.

Exercise 12 ▐ M

Copy and complete this crossnumber puzzle:

Across
2. $9x = 54$
4. $859 - x = 717$
6. $6x = 90 + 24$
7. $x + 4 = 28$
9. $3 + x = 7$
10. $46 + 23 = x$
12. $2x = 28$
14. $895 - x = 120$
16. $58 + x = 141$
19. $432 \div 6 = x$
21. $10 \times 71 = x$
22. $139 - x = 117$
23. $157 - 149 = x$
25. $257 + x = 606$
27. $468 \div 13 = x$
29. $7x = 441$
30. $127 - 54 = x$
31. $x + 5 = 8$
32. $543 + 354 = x$

Down
1. $13 \times 9 = x$
2. As 2 across
3. $128 \div x = 4$
5. $x \div 7 = 58$
8. $11 \times 37 = x$
9. As 9 across
11. $179 - x = 81$
13. $x \div 2 = 242$
15. $17 + 34 = x$
17. $15 \times 24 = x$
18. $x - 37 = 791$
20. $642 \div 3 = x$
21. $19 + 58 = x$
23. As 23 across
24. $3x = 39$
25. $111 \div 3 = x$
26. $348 + 651 = x$
28. $911 - 248 = x$
29. $x \div 3 = 21$
31. As 31 across

417

21 Co-ordinates

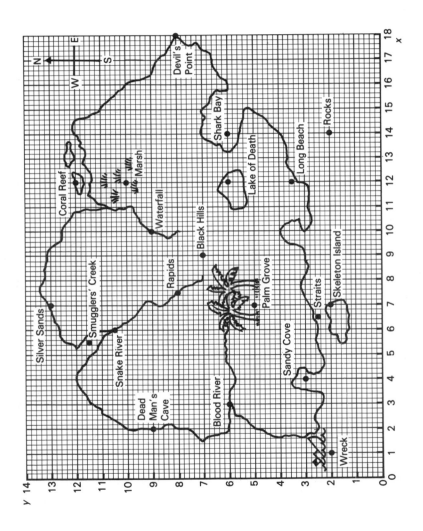

Exercise 1

Which places on the map opposite are given by the following pairs of co-ordinates?

1. (4, 3)?

2. (9, 7)?

3. (14, 6)?

4. (12, 12)?

5. (2, 9)?

6. (12, 6)?

7. (7, 2)?

8. (12, $3\frac{1}{2}$)?

9. ($7\frac{1}{2}$, 8)?

10. ($6\frac{1}{2}$, $2\frac{1}{2}$)?

Exercise 2

Give the pair of co-ordinates for each of the following places:

1. Wreck

2. Rocks

3. Palm grove

4. Silver sands

5. Devil's point

6. Waterfall

7. Marsh

8. Blood river

9. Snake river

10. Smugglers' creek

History of Co-ordinates

The method of plotting points using x- and y-axes and pairs of co-ordinates is due to René Descartes (1596–1650) who was born in France. His method was called co-ordinate geometry (or 'analytical geometry' or 'cartesian geometry').

A few days after René was born, his mother died. He was a pale, sickly child. At the age of eight he was sent to a Jesuit school. Due to his ill-health he was allowed to spend each morning in bed. He spent most of that time thinking.

After leaving school he became a soldier. He travelled and continued to study. At the age of thirty-two he went to live in Holland. In 1637, his work was first published.

Queen Christina, the nineteen-year-old queen of Sweden, persuaded Descartes, in 1649, to go to Sweden to teach her. Unfortunately for Descartes he was unable to stay in bed each morning – the queen insisted on having her lessons in a cold library at 5 a.m. It was too much for him – he died of pneumonia in February 1650.

Exercise 3   Quinco

This is a game for 2 players but it can easily be adapted for 4 players.

One playing surface of squared paper is needed per game. All players use the same playing surface.

Axes should be marked and numbered as shown. (Do not use less than 8 squares. You may use more than 8 or even more than 10.)

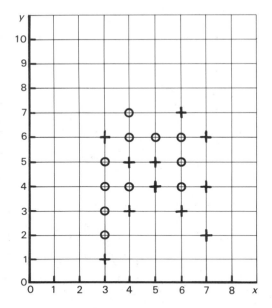

1. The first player calls out a pair of co-ordinates, *e.g.* (4, 5), and the second player marks the first player's position with a cross.

2. The second player now calls out a pair of co-ordinates, *e.g.* (5, 6), and the first player marks the second player's position with a circle.

3. Play continues until one of the players gets 5 marks in a straight line (vertically, horizontally or diagonally).

In the game above, the first player (the crosses) won, using a diagonal line. (3, 6) (4, 5) (5, 4) (6, 3) (7, 2) gave the winning line.

Notes:
1. Any player who calls out a point that has already been marked, loses that turn. (It is counted as a turn, but no point is marked.)

2. If a player marks the wrong point then he or she must, when told, mark the correct point, i.e. the other player has got a free point: *e.g.* if player 2 calls (4, 6) and player 1 marks (6, 4), then player 2 is allowed both positions and is given (4, 6) and (6, 4).

Exercise 4

Which places on the map are given by the following pairs of co-ordinates:

1. (03, 03)?
2. (09, 07)?
3. (14, 11.5)?
4. (05, 12)?
5. (12, 04.5)?

Exercise 5

Which places on the map are given by the following map references:

1. 150110?
2. 080035?
3. 020050?
4. 086115?
5. 112056?

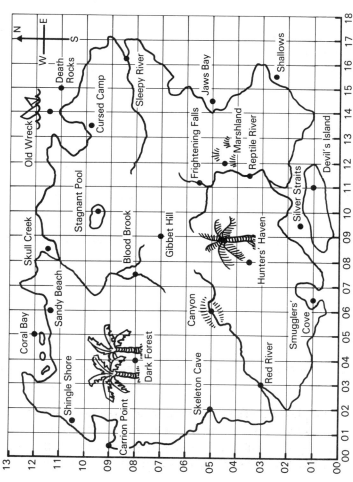

421

Exercise 6

Use the map on p. 421. Give the map reference and the pair of co-ordinates for each of the following places:

1. Dark Forest
2. Devil's Island
3. Canyon
4. Smugglers' Cove
5. Blood Brook

6. Silver Straits
7. Jaws Bay
8. Sleepy River
9. Sandy Beach
10. Shingle Shore

11. Carrion Point
12. Shallows
13. Cursed Camp
14. Reptile River
15. Stagnant Pool

Exercise 7

Draw a pair of axes as shown.

Use a scale of 1 cm to 1 unit on both axes.

Label the x-axis from 0 to 12.

Label the y-axis from 0 to 16.

Answer all the questions on the same piece of graph paper, using the same pair of axes.

For each question, plot the points and join them in the given order.

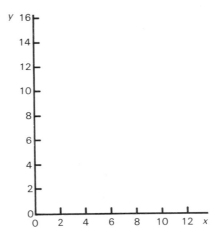

Inside each shape, write its name. Choose the correct name from this set: {square, rectangle, parallelogram, rhombus, trapezium, kite, right-angled triangle, isosceles triangle}.

1. (4, 2) (4, 5) (1, 5) (1, 2) (4, 2)
2. (12, 16) (8, 16) (8, 14) (12, 14) (12, 16)
3. (1, 10) (1, 13) (5, 10) (1, 10)
4. (11, 2) (10, 0) (6, 0) (7, 2) (11, 2)
5. (0, 15) (3, 16) (4, 15) (3, 14) (0, 15)
6. (10, 10) (9, 12) (11, 13) (12, 11) (10, 10)
7. (6, 15) (5, 12) (7, 12) (6, 15)
8. (1, 9) (0, 7) (6, 7) (4, 9) (1, 9)
9. (8, 3) (6, 4.5) (8, 6) (10, 4.5) (8, 3)
10. (8, 9) (8, 7) (12, 7.5) (12, 9.5) (8, 9)

422

Exercise 8

Draw a pair of axes as shown.

Use a scale of 1 cm to 1 unit on both axes.

Label the x-axis from $^-7$ to 7.

Label the y-axis from $^-7$ to 11.

Answer all the questions on the same piece of graph paper, using the same pair of axes.

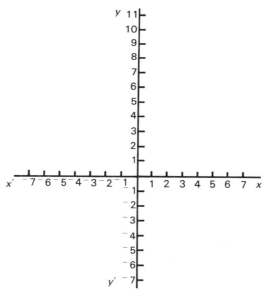

For each question, plot the points and join them in the given order.

Inside each shape, write its name.

1. $(4, 3)$ $(7, 4)$ $(6, 6)$ $(3, 5)$ $(4, 3)$
2. $(6, ^-5)$ $(6, ^-7)$ $(4, ^-7)$ $(4, ^-5)$ $(6, ^-5)$
3. $(^-7, 4)$ $(^-7, 6)$ $(^-4, 6)$ $(^-7, 4)$
4. $(3, 7)$ $(2, 9)$ $(6, 11)$ $(7, 9)$ $(3, 7)$
5. $(^-4, 7)$ $(^-3, 9)$ $(^-4, 11)$ $(^-6, 11)$ $(^-7, 9)$ $(^-6, 7)$ $(^-4, 7)$
6. $(^-1, 10)$ $(1, 6)$ $(^-1, 5)$ $(^-3, 6)$ $(^-1, 10)$
7. $(^-6, 0)$ $(^-3, ^-1)$ $(^-4, 2)$ $(^-7, 3)$ $(^-6, 0)$
8. $(0, 1)$ $(4, 1)$ $(3, ^-1)$ $(^-1, ^-1)$ $(0, 1)$
9. $(^-5, ^-2)$ $(^-1, ^-3)$ $(^-7, ^-6)$ $(^-7, ^-3)$ $(^-5, ^-2)$
10. $(^-1, ^-4)$ $(3, ^-5.5)$ $(^-1, ^-7)$ $(^-1, ^-4)$

423

Exercise 9

On graph paper, mark your axes as shown; x from 0 to 60, y from 0 to 60. Use 1 cm to represent 5 units on each axis.

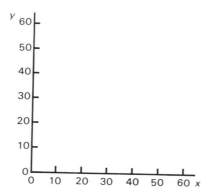

Plot the following points all on one graph and join them in the given order with a *smooth curve*. At the end of each question, lift your pencil and start again at the next question.

1. (50, 59) (48, 56) (46, 55) (45, 55) (42, 53) (39, 50) (35, 45) (33, 43) (30, 41) (29, 40.5) (16, 41) (14, 41) (12, 40) (10, 38) (8.5, 35) (8, 32.5) (8.5, 30) (9, 27) (10, 25) (10.5, 23.5) (10, 22) (9.5, 19) (8.5, 16) (7.5, 15) (7.5, 14) (8, 12) (7.5, 10) (8, 6) (8, 4) (8.5, 3) (9, 2.5) (8.5, 1) (10, 0.5) (13, 1) (12, 2.5) (11, 3) (10, 5) (10, 9) (11, 12) (12, 15) (15, 20) (18, 25) (19, 25.5) (20, 27) (21, 29) (21.5, 31) (22, 34)
2. (17, 23) (19.5, 25) (21.5, 24.5) (25, 23) (30, 22.5) (35, 23)
3. (11, 12) (12, 5.5) (12.5, 4.5) (13.5, 4) (13.5, 2) (15, 2) (17, 2.5) (16, 4) (15, 5) (15, 6) (14, 8) (14, 11) (15, 15) (17, 18) (18, 20) (20, 24) (21.5, 24.5)
4. (9, 1) (10, 2) (12, 2.5)
5. (13.5, 2) (15, 4) (16, 4)
6. (10, 16) (8, 14) (8.5, 12.5)
7. (21, 26) (26, 24) (31, 23.5) (34, 24)
8. (36, 28) (35, 26.5) (36, 25) (35, 23) (36.5, 21) (36.5, 15) (36, 12) (37, 11) (37, 5) (36.5, 4) (37.5, 3.5) (37.5, 1) (40, 0.5) (42.5, 1) (40, 4) (39, 7) (39, 11) (40, 13) (40, 18) (41, 23) (42, 25) (43, 28) (42.5, 30)
9. (38, 1) (39, 2) (41, 3)
10. (42, 2) (43, 2) (42, 4) (40.5, 6) (40, 10) (41, 13) (41, 15) (42, 20) (43, 25)

424

11. $(41, 3)$ $(42, 4)$
12. $(41, 23)$ $(43, 25)$ $(45, 28)$ $(45.5, 30)$ $(45, 32)$ $(44, 35)$ $(42, 38)$ $(40, 39.5)$ $(37, 41)$
13. $(15, 39.5)$ $(12.5, 38)$ $(10, 35)$ $(9.5, 30)$ $(10, 28)$ $(11, 26)$
14. $(11, 39.5)$ $(7, 39)$ $(5, 37.5)$ $(4, 36)$ $(3, 32)$ $(3, 25)$ $(4, 20)$ $(5, 16)$
15. $(5, 16)$ $(6, 19.5)$
16. $(6, 19.5)$ $(7, 18)$
17. $(7, 18)$ $(7, 22)$ $(7.5, 25)$ $(6.5, 28)$ $(7, 32)$ $(9, 36.5)$
18. $(50, 59)$ $(49, 54)$
19. $(51.5, 58)$ $(50, 55.5)$
20. $(51.5, 58)$ $(51.5, 54)$
21. $(50, 55.5)$ $(51.5, 54)$ $(53, 52)$ $(53.5, 50)$ $(54, 49)$ $(55, 47)$ $(56, 45.5)$ $(56, 43.5)$ $(55, 42.5)$ $(53.5, 42.5)$ $(53, 43.5)$ $(52, 44.5)$
22. $(45.5, 51)$ $(45, 48)$ $(46, 46)$ $(47.5, 45.5)$ $(48.5, 45.5)$ $(50, 44.5)$ $(52, 43.5)$ $(52, 42.5)$ $(54, 42)$ $(55, 42.5)$
23. $(47.5, 45.5)$ $(47, 40)$ $(46, 36)$ $(45, 33)$
24. $(45, 54)$ $(41, 50)$ $(39, 47)$ $(36, 43)$
25. $(46.5, 45)$ $(46.5, 43)$ $(46, 40)$ $(45, 37)$ $(44.5, 36)$
26. $(54.5, 45)$ $(54, 44)$ $(55, 43.5)$ $(55, 44)$ $(54, 44.5)$
27. $(51, 51)$ $(50.5, 52)$ $(49.5, 51)$ $(50.5, 50.5)$ $(51, 51)$

Exercise 10

On the same pair of axes, plot the given pairs of points and join them with straight lines. For each question, write down the co-ordinates of the point of intersection of the two lines.
(Use 1 cm to represent 1 unit on both axes.)

1. (a) $(1, 7)$ and $(4, 1)$
   (b) $(2, 2)$ and $(5, 5)$

2. (a) $(9, 10)$ and $(12, 16)$
   (b) $(9, 15)$ and $(13, 13)$

3. (a) $(10, 9)$ and $(14, 11)$
   (b) $(11, 11)$ and $(14, 8)$

4. (a) $(6, 10)$ and $(6, 15)$
   (b) $(10, 13)$ and $(2, 9)$

5. (a) $(0, 12)$ and $(4, 14)$
   (b) $(3, 10)$ and $(1, 16)$

6. (a) $(11, 6)$ and $(13, 0)$
   (b) $(11, 1)$ and $(14, 7)$

7. (a) $(8, 18)$ and $(14, 16)$
   (b) $(13, 18)$ and $(8, 15.5)$

8. (a) $(5, 15)$ and $(2, 18)$
   (b) $(1.5, 17)$ and $(7, 17)$

9. (a) $(6, 5)$ and $(10, 0)$
   (b) $(10, 5)$ and $(6, 0)$

10. (a) $(2, 8)$ and $(11, 7)$
    (b) $(5, 3)$ and $(7, 9)$

Exercise 11

Find the co-ordinates of the mid-point of the straight line that joins each pair of points. (Plot the points if you need to do so.)

1. (2, 4) (2, 10)

2. (8, 5) (8, 13)

3. (3, 9) (9, 9)

4. (1, 8) (1, 5)

5. (4, 6) (11, 6)

6. (3, 3) (7, 7)

7. (5, 0) (0, 8)

8. (6, 1) (7, 3)

9. (2, 4) (0, 4)

10. (7, 1) (1, 7)

11. (6, 3) (2, 10)

12. (1, 11) (13, 3)

13. (4, $^-$2) (4, 6)

14. ($^-$3, 1) (7, 1)

15. ($^-$8, 12) ($^-$4, 12)

16. (1, $^-$6) (5, $^-$2)

17. ($^-$2, 0) (10, $^-$8)

18. ($^-$4, $^-$9) (8, $^-$3)

19. (5, 7) ($^-$5, $^-$3)

20. (0, $^-$8) ($^-$2, $^-$2)

Exercise 12

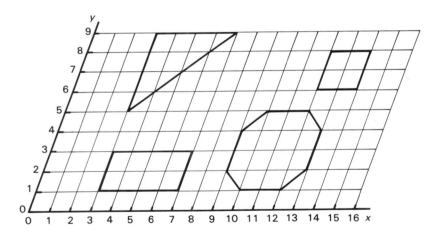

Give the co-ordinates of the vertices of:

1. the parallelogram
2. the rhombus
3. the isosceles triangle
4. the octagon

Exercise 13

Plot the following points on a square grid (ordinary graph paper) *and* on a grid of rhombuses. Join the points in the given order, using straight lines, to form a closed shape. For each question write the name of the shape drawn on each grid. All the questions can be drawn on the same square grid and the same grid of rhombuses.

1. (2, 2) (4, 2) (4, 4) (2, 4) (2, 2)
2. (8, 3) (9, 5) (13, 5) (12, 3) (8, 3)
3. (1, 17) (1, 15) (4, 15) (4, 17) (1, 17)
4. (11, 6) (8, 9) (9, 10) (12, 7) (11, 6)
5. (7, 11) (9, 11) (7, 15) (7, 11)
6. (4, 6) (7, 6) (7, 9) (4, 6)
7. (2, 9) (3, 5) (1, 5) (2, 9)
8. (3, 13) (2, 11) (4, 10) (5, 12) (3, 13)
9. (9, 15) (10, 18) (12, 16) (9, 15)
10. (13, 12) (12, 14) (9, 13) (10, 11) (13, 12)

Exercise 14

Draw a pair of axes taking values of x from 0 to 20 (i.e. $0 \leqslant x \leqslant 20$) and values of y from 0 to 16 (i.e. $0 \leqslant y \leqslant 16$).

1. Plot the points (19, 1) (15, 1) (15, 3) (19, 3) and join them to obtain a rectangle. What are the co-ordinates of the point of intersection of the diagonals?

2. Join the points (17, 16) (20, 14) (18, 11) (15, 13) (17, 16) in that order. What shape have you obtained? What are the co-ordinates of the point of intersection of the diagonals?

3. If the points (0, 15) (4, 16) ($\boxed{?}$, $\boxed{?}$) and (1, 11) are the vertices of a square, find the missing point.

4. BC is the base of triangle ABC where A, B and C are the points (14, 9) (14, 4) and (20, 7) respectively. What are the co-ordinates of the base of the altitude?

427

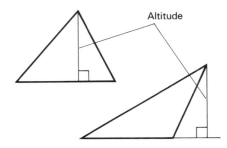

Altitude

An altitude (or 'perpendicular height') of a triangle is a line segment drawn at right-angles to a side of a triangle, or that side produced, to meet the opposite vertex. Every triangle has three altitudes.

5. The points (7, 8) (8, 5) and (11, 4), when joined in that order, are three vertices of a rhombus. Find the co-ordinates of the fourth vertex and also the point of intersection of the diagonals.

6. Find the co-ordinates of the point of intersection of the medians of triangle A(6, 11) B(8, 15) C(10, 10).

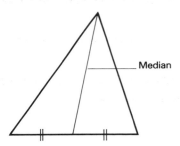

Median

A median of a triangle is a line segment that joins a vertex to the mid-point of the opposite side. Every triangle has three medians.

7. (5, 3) is one vertex of a square. If the diagonals intersect at (3, 4), find the other three vertices.

8. PQR is an isosceles triangle where QR is parallel to the x-axis. If P and Q are the points (12, 10) and (10, 15) respectively, find the co-ordinates of R if PQ = PR.

9. Trapezium JKLM is right-angled at L(5, 6). MK is parallel to the x-axis and M is the point (1, 8). If JK is parallel to ML and if ML = 2JK, find the co-ordinates of J and of K.

10. U is the point (6, 4) and V is (12, 3). Find the co-ordinates of W and of X where UVWX is a parallelogram and where (9.5, 2) is the mid-point of diagonal VX.

Four people tried to find some hidden treasure.

They were given 3 pairs of co-ordinates each:

John was given (7, 3), (8, 8), (5, 6)
Ann was given (0, 10), (1, 4), (4, 5)
Susan was given (3, 9), (4, 5), (8, 8)
Alan was given (1, 8), (6, 2), (7, 3)

The co-ordinates of all four people had to be plotted and then joined to give the path to the treasure.

Straight lines had to be used.

Each person's part of the journey had to be followed, one after the other.

At the point at which one person's part of the journey ends, the next person's part of the journey begins.

After all of the journey has been drawn, no lines should cross each other.

Neither the given order of the names, nor the order of the pairs of co-ordinates are in the correct order for the journey.

Draw a pair of axes and label them as shown. (Use 1 cm to represent 1 km on both axes.)

Plot the points and sort out the correct order.

Show the whole journey, and find *two* possible places for the treasure.

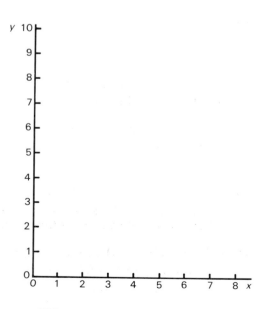

Exercise 16

1. A certain article costs £6 to buy. This table shows the cost of buying up to 8 of these articles:

Number of articles, n	0	1	2	3	4	5	6	7	8
Cost in £, C	0	6	12	18	24	30	36	42	48

Now plot a graph of C against n using this table.

Put C on the vertical axis; let 2 cm represent £5.

Put n on the horizontal axis; let 2 cm represent 1 article.

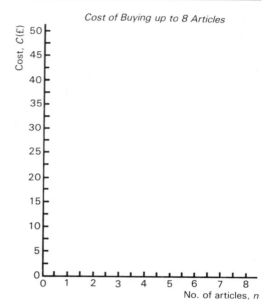

Cost of Buying up to 8 Articles

2. If I travel 14 km on each litre of petrol I use, this table shows the distances I can travel on a given number of litres of petrol:

Number of litres used, l	0	1	2	3	4	5	6	7
Distance travelled, D km	0	14	28	42	56	70	84	98

Plot a graph of distance travelled against petrol used (D against l). Distance (D km) should be on the vertical axis. Use a scale of 1 cm to 5 km.

Number of litres used (l litres) should be on the horizontal axis. Use a scale of 2 cm to 1 litre.

3. This table shows how fast I am travelling (v kilometres per hour) as I begin to slow down on a car journey (time, t, is in seconds):

Time, t s	0	2	4	6	8	10
Velocity (how fast), v km/h	40	32	24	16	8	0

Now plot a graph.

Use your graph paper in the way suggested by the sketch.

Use a scale of: 2 cm to 1 s for time (on the horizontal axis) and 2 cm to 5 km/h on the vertical axis.

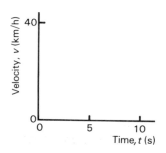

(a) How fast am I travelling after 3 s?
(Use your graph to help you to find the answer.)
(b) How fast am I travelling after 7 s?

4. In a science experiment, I heat some water until it boils. I then leave the water to cool, but write down its temperature every 30 s. This is a table of my results:

Time, t s	0	30	60	90	120	150	180	210	240	270	300	330
Temperature, T °C	100	77	62	50	41	35	30	27	25	23	21	20

Plot a graph of these results. Use 1 cm to 25 s on the horizontal axis, and 1 cm to 10 °C on the vertical axis.

This curve is called a 'COOLING CURVE'.

Use your graph to find:
(a) the temperature of the water after 75 s
(b) the time taken for the water to cool to 45 °C
(c) the temperature of the water after 250 s

22 Indices

The square has an area of 9 cm^2 and the dot pattern shows the square number 9.

There are 3 rows of 3 dots ($3 \times 3 = 9$).

There are 3 rows of 3 squares ($3 \times 3 = 9$).

We can write this as $3^2 = 9$.

3^2 means 3×3 and is read as '3 squared'.

Exercise 1

Find the value of:

1. 5^2 **3.** 7^2 **5.** 1^2 **7.** 9^2 **9.** 10^2

2. 2^2 **4.** 4^2 **6.** 6^2 **8.** 8^2 **10.** 0^2

Exercise 2

Rewrite using indices:

e.g. 1 $a \times a \times a \times a = \underline{\underline{a^4}}$ *e.g. 2* $3 \times 3 \times 3 \times 3 \times 3 = \underline{\underline{3^5}}$

1. $p \times p \times p$

2. $d \times d \times d \times d \times d \times d$

3. $x \times x \times x \times x \times x$

4. $m \times m$

5. $c \times c \times c \times c \times c \times c \times c \times c \times c$

6. $4 \times 4 \times 4$

7. 5×5

8. $10 \times 10 \times 10 \times 10$

9. $7 \times 7 \times 7 \times 7 \times 7 \times 7 \times 7 \times 7 \times 7$

10. $8 \times 8 \times 8 \times 8 \times 8 \times 8$

11. $12 \times 12 \times 12 \times 12 \times 12 \times 12 \times 12$

12. $2 \times 2 \times 2 \times 2 \times 2 \times 2 \times 2 \times 2 \times 2 \times 2 \times 2 \times 2$

Exercise 3

Find the value of:

e.g. $2^5 = 2 \times 2 \times 2 \times 2 \times 2$
so $2^5 = \underline{\underline{32}}$

1. 3^2	**5.** 7^3	**9.** 3^3	**13.** 4^4	**17.** 10^9
2. 2^3	**6.** 4^3	**10.** 5^4	**14.** 3^6	**18.** 100^2
3. 3^4	**7.** 10^5	**11.** 2^7	**15.** 6^3	**19.** 2^{10}
4. 5^3	**8.** 2^4	**12.** 10^3	**16.** 6^4	**20.** 12^2

Exercise 4

Use a calculator to find the value of:

1. 8^4	**5.** 6^7	**9.** 13^5	**13.** 6^9	**17.** 15^4
2. 3^{12}	**6.** 9^6	**10.** 4^9	**14.** 5^{10}	**18.** 9^8
3. 5^8	**7.** 12^5	**11.** 8^5	**15.** 2^{20}	**19.** 3^{14}
4. 7^6	**8.** 11^5	**12.** 7^8	**16.** 4^{11}	**20.** 24^3

Exercise 5

Find the value of:

1. (*a*) $3^2 \times 3^3$	(*b*) 3^5	**5.** (*a*) $3^2 \times 3^4$ (*b*) 3^6
2. (*a*) $2^4 \times 2^2$	(*b*) 2^6	**6.** (*a*) $10^2 \times 10^5$ (*b*) 10^7
3. (*a*) $4^2 \times 4^3$	(*b*) 4^5	**7.** (*a*) $5^3 \times 5^2$ (*b*) 5^5
4. (*a*) $2^5 \times 2^4$	(*b*) 2^9	**8.** (*a*) $3^4 \times 3^3$ (*b*) 3^7

Exercise 6

Simplify, where possible, leaving answers in index form:

e.g. $4^3 \times 4^6 = \underline{\underline{4^9}}$

1. $2^6 \times 2^2$ **9.** $9^6 \times 9^5$ **17.** $a^6 \times a^7$

2. $5^4 \times 5^8$ **10.** $3^4 \times 3^4$ **18.** $d^4 \times d$

3. $7^2 \times 7^7$ **11.** $2^6 \times 2^8$ **19.** $z^7 \times z^7$

4. $9^4 \times 9^6$ **12.** $7^6 \times 2^8$ **20.** $t^{12} \times t^5$

5. $10^2 \times 10^4$ **13.** $12^2 \times 12^3$ **21.** $u^4 \times u^{10}$

6. $6^5 \times 6^7$ **14.** 6×6^9 **22.** $y^9 \times y^{12}$

7. $5^9 \times 5^4$ **15.** $15^3 \times 15^5$

8. $8^3 \times 8^{10}$ **16.** $x^3 \times x^5$

Exercise 7

Simplify, leaving answers in index form:

1. $x^4 \times x^2 \times x^7$ **5.** $m \times m^3 \times m^9$ **9.** $t^2 \times t^9 \times t$

2. $y^3 \times y^4 \times y^5$ **6.** $n^{10} \times n^4 \times n^4$ **10.** $d^4 \times d^7 \times d^2 \times d^3$

3. $a^7 \times a^2 \times a^6$ **7.** $f^6 \times f^7 \times f^4$

4. $c^8 \times c \times c^7$ **8.** $g^6 \times g^2 \times g^{12}$

Exercise 8

Find the value of:

1. (*a*) $\dfrac{4^4}{4^2}$ (*b*) 4^2 **4.** (*a*) $\dfrac{10^9}{10^5}$ (*b*) 10^4

2. (*a*) $\dfrac{2^9}{2^4}$ (*b*) 2^5 **5.** (*a*) $\dfrac{3^7}{3^3}$ (*b*) 3^4

3. (*a*) $5^4 \div 5^2$ (*b*) 5^2

Exercise 9

Simplify, leaving answers in index form:

1. $\dfrac{7^4}{7^2}$

2. $6^5 \div 6^3$

3. $\dfrac{9^5}{9^2}$

4. $2^{12} \div 2^7$

5. $\dfrac{3^7}{3^3}$

6. $5^6 \div 5^3$

7. $d^7 \div d^2$

8. $\dfrac{e^9}{e^3}$

9. $\dfrac{a^7}{a^4}$

10. $m^{11} \div m^5$

11. $t^{10} \div t$

12. $d^{12} \div d^3$

13. $x^{14} \div x^8$

14. $u^{17} \div u^9$

15. $\dfrac{n^{19}}{n^{11}}$

Exercise 10

Write in index form:

1. $a \times a \times a \times a \times a \times a \times a$

2. $c \times c \times c \times c \times c \times d \times d$

3. $l \times l \times m \times m \times m$

4. $m \times n \times n \times n \times n \times n \times m$

5. $b \times a \times a \times a \times b \times b \times c \times c \times c$

6. $x \times y \times x \times y \times x$

7. $t \times t \times u \times t \times u \times t \times t$

8. $g \times g \times g \times g \times g \times g \times g \times g \times h$

9. $w \times w \times w \times z \times z \times z \times w$

10. $p \times q \times q \times p \times t \times p \times t \times q$

Exercise 11

Simplify, leaving answers in index form:

1. $a^4 \times c^5 \times a^3 \times a^2$

2. $d^7 \times e^3 \times e^4 \times d^2$

3. $x^7 \times x^3 \times y^4 \times y^8$

4. $t^5 \times u^9 \times t \times u^7$

5. $f^9 \times g \times f^7 \times g^7$

6. $z^4 \times h^4 \times z^7 \times h^3$

7. $l^7 \times m^9 \times m^{10} \times l^8$

8. $n^{10} \times k^2 \times n^7 \times n^7$

9. $w^{12} \times p^3 \times p^9 \times p^5$

10. $q \times v^{11} \times q^{11} \times v$

Exercise 12

1. The area, A cm², of a square is given by $A = l^2$.
   Find the value of A if the length, l cm, of each side of the square is 8 cm.

2. If $V = x^3$, find V when $x = 6$.

3. $A = 4b^2$. Find A when $b = 3$.

4. If $t = 7$, find P where $P = 3 \times t^2$.

5. $T = 2 \times m^3$. Find T when $m = 5$.

6. Given that $S = 6 \times l^2$, find S when $l = 6$.

7. If $R = a^4$, find R when $a = 3$.

8. Given that $y = 4$, find the value of V where $V = 3 \times y^3$.

9. $W = 5 \times n^4$. Find W when $n = 4$.

10. If $p = 2$, find the value of C where $C = 4 \times p^6$.

Exercise 13

1. $\sqrt{9}$
2. $\sqrt{100}$
3. $\sqrt{81}$
4. $\sqrt{144}$
5. $\sqrt{36}$

6. $\sqrt{16}$
7. $\sqrt{49}$
8. $\sqrt{25}$
9. $\sqrt{169}$
10. $\sqrt{64}$

11. $\sqrt{121}$
12. $\sqrt{225}$
13. $\sqrt{400}$
14. $\sqrt{900}$
15. $\sqrt{4900}$

23 Statistics

1. Make several copies of this flag.

   Colour the two parts of each flag as follows.
   (Each flag should be different.)

   (*a*) Use exactly two colours to colour the two parts.
   How many different flags can be made with
   the same two colours?

   (*b*) Select three different colours. Now using two of these three
   colours at a time, make as many different flags as you can.
   How many different flags can be made?

   (*c*) Now select four different colours. Using two of these four
   colours at a time, make as many different flags as you can.
   How many different flags can be made?

   (*d*) Select five different colours. Using two of these five colours at
   a time, make as many different flags as you can.
   How many different flags can be made?

2. Make several copies of this flag.

   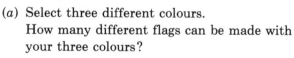

   Colour the three parts of each flag as follows.
   (Each flag should be different.)

   (*a*) Select three different colours.
   How many different flags can be made with
   your three colours?

   (*b*) Select four different colours. Using three of these colours at a
   time, make as many different flags as you can.
   How many different flags can be made?

3. Make several copies of this flag.

   Use four different colours to make as many
   different flags as you can.
   How many different flags can be made?

Exercise 2

1. Here is a domino:

1	3

This is the same domino:

3	1

(changing the numbers around does not make a different domino.)
If the full set of dominoes only uses the figures 0, 1, 2 and 3, draw
a full set on squared paper.
How many different dominoes are there in your set?

2. Draw, on squared paper, a full set of dominoes that uses the figures
0, 1, 2, 3, 4, 5, 6 and 7.
How many different dominoes are there in your set?

Exercise 3

1. This *pictogram* (sometimes called a pictograph or ideograph) shows
the average number of hours of sunshine each day during September
in different parts of the world:

Number of Hours of Sunshine each Day in September

(a) How many daily hours of sunshine are there in Greece?

(b) How many more daily hours of sunshine are there in Egypt
compared with London?

(c) What is the total number of hours of sunshine for September
in Yugoslavia?

(d) Greece and Yugoslavia have about the same number of hours
of sunshine each day.
Now write down a sentence of your own about this pictogram.

(e) Why should some holidaymakers find this pictogram useful?

(f) Why do some countries get more daily sunshine than others?

2. Use this table to draw a pictogram:

Number of Houses Sold by an Estate Agent in a Week

Day	Number Sold
Sun	12
Mon	3
Tues	5
Wed	8
Thurs	9
Fri	6
Sat	10

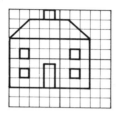

Diagram can stand for 2 houses

Do not forget to give your pictogram a *title* and a *key*.

Write two sentences about house sales. Use your pictogram to help you.

Exercise 4

Colours of cars in the car park

Write two ways in which this pictogram is misleading.

Exercise 5

1. *Data* was collected to show the numbers of children in families. A *tally chart* was used to collect the data:

Number of children in each family	Tally	Frequency
1	ⅣⅣ ⅣⅣ |||	13
2	ⅣⅣ ⅣⅣ ⅣⅣ ⅣⅣ ⅣⅣ		26
3	ⅣⅣ ⅣⅣ ⅣⅣ ⅣⅣ	20
4	ⅣⅣ ⅣⅣ ⅣⅣ		
5	ⅣⅣ ⅣⅣ ||	
6						4
7	ⅣⅣ		6
8				2
9		0
10			1

(a) How many families had 4 children in them?

(b) How many families had 5 children in them?

(c) What was the total number of families questioned in this survey?

2. Make out a tally chart to find the number of children in each family for the pupils in your class.

3. Make a tally chart to show the ages of the pupils in a school party that went ice-skating.

The ages are listed here:

14	13	16	11	13	14	12	12	15	14	13	12
13	16	15	15	16	12	11	14	14	13	16	15
15	12	14	15	14	14	13	15	13	12	15	14
14	13	12	13	14	13	16	11	14	13	15	12
12	14	15	13	15	14	14	13	15	14	13	14
13	15	15	14	13	15	13	16	14	14	14	13

Exercise 6

1. Here are the goals scored in each match by a certain football team:

1	0	2	1	1
2	0	3	1	2
2	1	1	2	4
3	2	2	0	2
3	2	2	1	2
1	1	0	2	4
3	5	1	2	0
3	2	2	0	1
2	1	2	4	2
1	2	0	2	3

(*a*) Make a tally chart for this data.

(*b*) Draw a pictogram (use a football or a footballer).

(*c*) Use the results shown in your pictogram to help you to write a sentence about goals scored.

Carry out the following *surveys*. For some of them you will need to make a tally chart.
Draw a pictogram for each one.
Write a sentence about the results of each survey.

2. Use a travel brochure to find the hours of sunshine per day for each month of the year (or for part of the year) at any place you choose.

3. Find the favourite TV channel for all the pupils in your class.

4. Carry out a survey of the musical instruments played by pupils in your class.

5. Find the favourite pop group of pupils in your class (or in your year at school). You may need to list six or seven pop groups and let people choose a group from your list.

6. Carry out a survey of the number of bags of crisps (or drinks, or chocolate bars) sold in your school tuck shop.

Here are two *bar charts* (sometimes called block graphs or column graphs). Both graphs show the same information. The only difference between them is that the first graph has a space between each column.

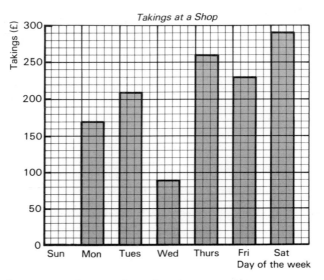

Answer these questions using the given graphs.

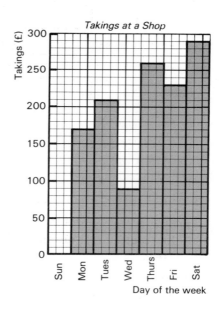

1. How much did the shop take on Tuesday?

2. How much more were Saturday's takings than Monday's?

3. What were the total takings for the week?

4. Why did the shop take nothing on Sunday?

5. Give a reason for the poor takings on Wednesday?

6. On which day were the takings £60 more than Monday's takings?

Exercise 8

This table shows the force of the wind at sea. It is measured on the Beaufort scale.

A graph can be drawn using the results in the table.

Scale No.	Wind force	Wind velocity
0	calm	0 km/h
3	gentle breeze	15 km/h
5	fresh breeze	35 km/h
6	strong breeze	45 km/h
7	near gale	55 km/h
8	gale	70 km/h
10	storm	95 km/h
11	violent storm	110 km/h

This type of graph is called a *horizontal bar chart.*

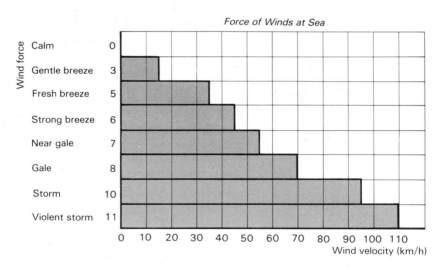

Force of Winds at Sea

1. How many km/h is a gale?
2. What wind velocity is twice that of a fresh breeze?
3. How many km/h difference is there between a storm and a gentle breeze?
4. How many km/h difference is there between a storm and a near gale?

443

Draw bar charts from these tables.

Write a sentence about each bar chart.

1. Kings of England 1154–1399 (The Plantagenets)

King	Length of reign
Henry II	35 years
Richard I	10 years
John	17 years
Henry III	56 years
Edward I	35 years
Edward II	20 years
Edward III	50 years
Richard II	22 years

2. Number of calories per 100 g of each food

Food	No. of calories
apples	45
butter beans	90
peas (raw)	65
new potatoes	75
chips	240
milk	65
steamed cod	80
grilled lamb	320

Exercise 10

1. Copy this tally chart:

Day of Birthday this Year

Day	Tally	Frequency
Mon		
Tues		
Wed		
Thurs		
Fri		
Sat		
Sun		

2. Complete your tally chart for the pupils in your class (or for the pupils in your year group).

3. Draw a neat table of your results.

4. Draw a bar chart of your results (see below for an idea of how to do this). You must decide how big your bar chart will be.

Do not forget to give your bar chart a title.

Both axes on your bar chart must be labelled.

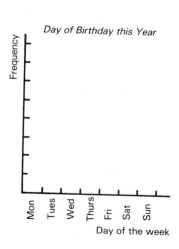

445

Carry out at least two of the following surveys.

Draw a tally chart, a table and a bar chart for each survey.

1. The month in which pupils in your class (or year group) were born. The tally chart should have the headings:

Month	Tally	Frequency

2. The number of pupils absent each day in your class.
   (Use a register to collect the information.)
   Headings:
   Day   Tally   Frequency

3. The number of pupils absent during a certain week for several classes.
   Headings:
   Class   Tally   Frequency

4. The most popular sport to watch.
   Headings:
   Sport   Tally   Frequency
   (A prepared list of sports can be used and people should then choose one from that list.)

5. The most popular sport to play.
   Headings:
   Sport   Tally   Frequency

6. How pupils travel to school.
   Headings:
   Method of travel   Tally   Frequency
   (Method of travel can include: walk, cycle, bus, car, other.)

Exercise 12

1. Draw a horizontal bar chart from this table:

Lengths of Rivers

River	Length
Nile	6700 km
Amazon	6500 km
Missouri–Mississippi	6000 km
Yangtse	5500 km
Colorado	3200 km
Danube	2800 km
Zambezi	2600 km
Murray	2600 km

Write a sentence about your bar chart.

2. Here are the heights of several volcanoes correct to the nearest 100 m:

Heights of Volcanoes

Volcano	Country	Height
Cotopaxi	Ecuador	5900 m
Popocatépetl	Mexico	5500 m
Mount Etna	Sicily	3300 m
Vesuvius	Italy	1300 m
Mauna Loa	United States	4200 m
Hekla	Iceland	1500 m
Tambora	Indonesia	2900 m

Draw a bar chart using this table.

3. Draw a bar chart to show the heights of some of the highest mountains in the world. (Find the heights correct to the nearest 100 m.)

Exercise 13

This bar chart shows the attendance each day at a cinema:

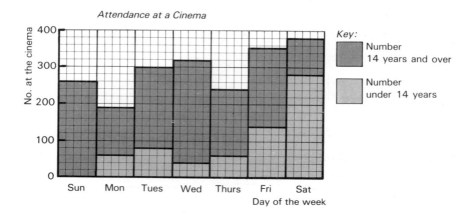

Attendance at a Cinema

1. How many 'under-14's' attended on Friday?

2. How many people aged 14 years or over went to the cinema on Monday?

3. How many more people aged 14 years or over, compared with under-14's, were at the cinema on Thursday?

4. If, at this cinema, those aged 14 years or over paid £3 a ticket while the under-14's paid £2 each, what were Tuesday's takings?

5. How many under-14's attended the cinema throughout the whole week?

6. What was the total weekly attendance at the cinema?

7. Calculate the total weekly takings if tickets for under-14's cost £2 while everyone else paid £3.

8. Give one possible reason why there were no under-14's at the cinema on Sunday.

9. Write a sentence about cinema attendance using the results on this graph.

Exercise 14

The table below shows the stopping distances for cars, under perfect conditions. (The calculation was based on values in imperial units quoted in the UK Highway Code; braking distances have been rounded up to the nearest whole metre.) At each given velocity, the stopping distance is split into 'thinking distance' and 'braking distance'.

Draw a horizontal bar chart to show this information.

By shading, let each block show both the thinking and braking distances.

Stopping Distances of Cars

Velocity	Thinking distance	Braking distance	Total stopping distance
32 km/h	6 m	6 m	12 m
48 km/h	9 m	14 m	23 m
64 km/h	12 m	24 m	36 m
80 km/h	15 m	38 m	53 m
96 km/h	18 m	54 m	72 m
112 km/h	21 m	74 m	95 m

Exercise 15

1. For some dice games you need to throw a six to start.
Alan and Ken play a game. Ken said that he would throw a three to start and not a six.
Alan tried to throw a six.
Who is likely to start playing first?

2. (a) Is it easier to throw a three than a six?
(b) Is it easier to throw a one than a three?

3. Try this experiment.

(a) Copy this tally chart first:

Number on the die	Tally	Frequency
1		
2		
3		
4		
5		
6		

(b) Throw a die about 100 times.
Show your results on the tally chart.

(c) Draw a bar chart of your results.

(d) Which number turned up the most?

(e) Copy the given frequency table:

Throwing a Die

Number on the die	Frequency
1	
2	
3	
4	
5	
6	

(f) Collect data from the class to find the frequency for each number.

(g) Draw a bar chart of the class's result.

(h) Which number turned up the most for the whole class?

4. Does it matter which number you need to get to start a game?

Exercise 16

1. I tossed a coin four times.
   The *outcome* was heads, heads, heads, $\boxed{?}$.
   What do you think the fourth outcome was, heads or tails?

2. Are you certain that your answer to question 1 is correct?

3. Try an experiment.
   Toss a coin 100 times. Collect your results in a tally chart:

Tossing a Coin

Outcome	Tally	Frequency
head		
tail		

4. Draw a bar chart to show your results.

5. Write a sentence about your results.

6. Total the number of heads obtained by the whole class.
   Total the number of tails.

7. Draw a bar chart of the class's results.

8. Write a sentence about the class's results.

Exercise 17

In hospitals, jagged line graphs are drawn for each patient. The graph below shows temperature, pulse rate, and respiration. Normally, a graph showing blood pressure is also plotted.

The readings for the graphs shown were taken every 4 hours.

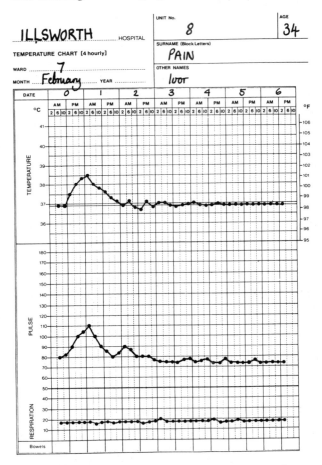

1. On which day (0, 1, 2, 3, 4, 5 or 6) and at what time was the temperature at its highest?

2. What was the highest temperature (in °C)?

3. What was the highest pulse rate?

4. What was the pulse rate on day 2 at 2 a.m.?

5. What was the temperature on day 2 at 6 p.m.?

6. What was the difference between the highest and the lowest temperatures?

7. What is 'normal' temperature?

8. What is the 'normal' rate of respiration?

9. The graphs are for a patient who has just had an operation (a 'post-op' patient). Drugs were used to help to lower the temperature. Give the time and day when the drugs began to have an effect.

10. What was the difference between the highest and the lowest pulse rates?

Exercise 18

Draw jagged line graphs for each of these tables of data or surveys (the vertical axis is normally numbered from zero).

1. *Average Temperature each Month in Athens*

Month	Jan	Feb	Mar	Apr	May	June	July	Aug	Sept	Oct	Nov	Dec
Temperature (°C)	9	10	12	15	19	23	26	26	22	18	14	11

2. Find the monthly temperatures at any place in the world (use an atlas).

3. *Mass of a Baby during the First 16 Weeks of its Life*

Age (weeks)	0	1	2	3	4	5	6	7	8	9	10	11	12	13	14	15	16
Mass (kg)	3.2	3	3.2	3.5	3.6	3.8	4	4.2	4.3	4.5	4.7	4.9	5.2	5.3	5.5	5.8	6

4. Find the total school attendance each week (or each month or each day).

5. Find the temperature in your classroom (or in your home) at the same time each day throughout the week.

Exercise 19

1. Here is a drawing of a pie. Draw your own pie at a larger size.

   By drawing lines on your copy and by labelling, show how you would share the pie between four people so that Ann gets $\frac{1}{2}$, Bob gets $\frac{1}{4}$ and Chris and Dave get $\frac{1}{8}$ each.

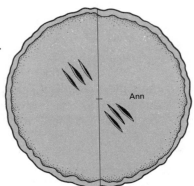

2. Draw another pie, the same size as before. Share this pie so that Edward gets $\frac{1}{2}$, Fiona gets $\frac{1}{4}$, George gets $\frac{1}{6}$ and Heather gets $\frac{1}{12}$.

3. Here is another circle. This time, it is not a pie.

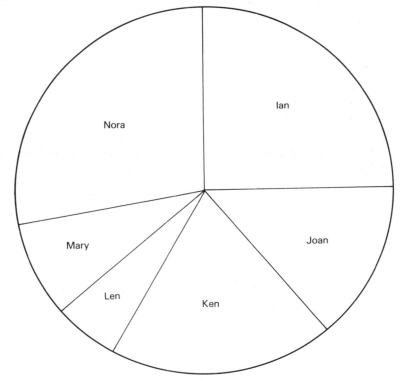

The diagram is called a *pie chart*.

Suppose the whole circle stands for 36 sweets. The circle is cut into parts to show how the sweets are shared.

There are 360° in a full turn. The circle stands for 36 sweets.
Since 360° stands for 36 sweets,
          10° stands for 1 sweet.
In this pie chart, Ken gets 7 sweets (an angle of 70°).
List the names of all who shared the sweets.
Next to each name, write the number of sweets that person was given.

Exercise 20

1. The pie chart shows the weather during February of a certain year that was not a leap year.

   Weather in February

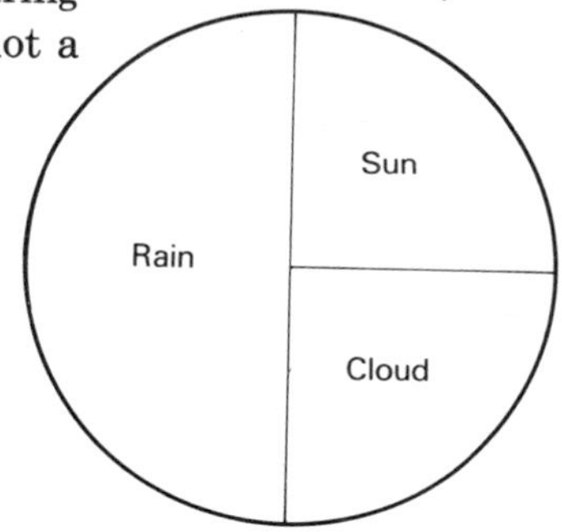

   (a) What fraction of the month was sunny?
   (b) How many degrees in the pie chart stand for sunny weather?
   (c) What fraction of the month was wet?
   (d) How many degrees in the pie chart stand for rainy weather?
   (e) How many days were wet?
   (f) How many days were cloudy?
   (g) How many days were sunny?
   (h) Copy and complete this table to show how the number of degrees and the number of days can be worked out:

Number of days	Number of degrees
28	360°
14	
	90°

2. A survey was carried out where 30 people were asked what type of heating they had at home. Here are the results:

   Coal   7
   Electric 9
   Gas   11
   Oil   3

Copy and complete the table.

Draw a pie chart to show the different types of heating. Use the table to help you.

Number of people	Number of degrees
30	360°
15	
5	
10	
2	
1	
	36°
7	
	132°

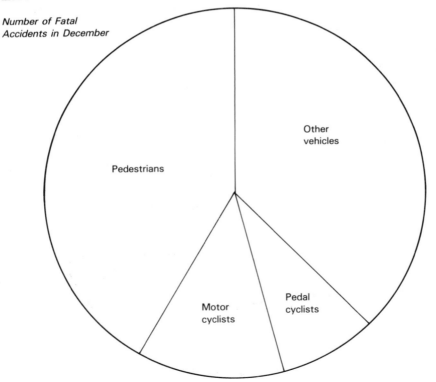

Number of Fatal Accidents in December

Pedestrians

Other vehicles

Motor cyclists

Pedal cyclists

1. The pie chart opposite shows the number of fatal accidents in a certain town in December last year. If there were 24 fatal accidents altogether, find:

   (a) the number of pedal cyclists killed

   (b) the number of motor cyclists killed

   (c) the number of pedestrians killed

   (d) how many deaths involved other vehicles

2. The pie chart below shows the hobbies of several people (each person chose one hobby). Twelve people chose stamp collecting.

   (a) How many people were there altogether in this survey?

   (b) How many chose photography?

   (c) How many more chose model-making than embroidery?

   (d) Which two hobbies attracted the same number of people?

Hobbies

3. Draw a pie chart to show how you spent yesterday. List what you did throughout the day. Include sleeping. (Your day should show 24 hours.)

Write, in your list, the number of degrees you use in your pie chart.

4. During two hours in a restaurant, the following number of meals were served:

beef 7, steak 22, lamb chops 5, chicken 18, duckling 2, scampi 14, plaice 4.

Draw a pie chart to show these meals.

5. In a certain school, the number of periods per subject were: maths 6, English 6, music 2, science 4, French 4, geography 3, history 3, RE 2, art 2, technical 2, games 4, PE 2.

Draw a subject pie chart.

6. Draw a pie chart to show the subjects you take in one week at your school.

7. List five sports. Ask 20 (or 30) people which sport on your list they prefer to watch on TV. Show the results of your survey on a pie chart.